DOUBLE-
Helix
WATER™

DOUBLE-
Helix
WATER™

David L. Gann and
Shui-yin Lo, PhD

D AND Y PUBLISHING | LAS VEGAS

D and Y Publishing
3651 Lindell Road, Suite D-210
Las Vegas, NV 89103

Double-Helix Water
© 2009 by D and Y Publishing
All rights reserved. Published 2009

DOUBLE-HELIX WATER is a trademark of D and Y Laboratories, Inc.

The authors wish to thank World Scientific Publishing Co. Pte. Ltd. for their permission to reprint certain research documents presented in part two.

Cover design: John Barksdale, HiTops, Inc., www.hitopsdesign.com
Cover Photoshop: Samantha Levi, www.samanthalevi.com
Atomic force microscope photography: John Cardarella, D and Y Laboratories, Inc.
Editing: Rosemary Delderfield, www.expertcopyeditor.com
Design and typesetting: Rigney Graphics, www.rigneygraphics.com
Printed by James Printing Company, www.jamesprinting.com
www.doublehelixwater.com for more information
ISBN: 978-0-578-04252-7

Printed in the United States of America

Contents

Part One

Contents

Part Two
Research Documents and Published Scientific Papers

Disclaimer

One would think that a book encompassing a body of research on the subject of *water* would make a strange bedfellow for a medical disclaimer. Unfortunately, we as a society have allowed our freedoms of discovery to become somewhat tainted with the control of the almighty dollar. In less than two hundred years, our western society has regrettably lost sight of its hard-fought origins, which granted us not only a freedom to speak but an even deeper freedom to think, to know and to discover.

It is with somewhat of a sad heart that I must now, in 2009, state: This book contains only the *opinions* of myself, David L. Gann, the opinions of my research partner, Shui-yin Lo, and the opinions of the authors who have contributed to this line of research. If you, as the reader, so choose to act upon any information contained herein in any manner that applies to your own or the care of another's health, **please do so by first seeking the advice and supervision of a licensed healthcare professional.** The publisher, authors and others who contributed to the content, the distributors and bookstores are presenting this book and the information contained herein **for educational purposes only. Neither I nor any of the previously listed individuals are attempting to prescribe any medical** treatment or suggesting that the information contained herein is for use within the field of the medical arts.

Nothing in this book or work of research is presented here as an effort to offer or render medical advice or opinions or otherwise engage in some type of medical practice.

The information pertaining in any way to biological processes is, at best, of a general nature and based upon our current findings and cannot and should not be substituted for the advice of a medical professional. As stated in this book, neither David Gann nor Shui-yin Lo are medical doctors.

None of the individual contributors or their associated sponsors or the distributors of this book can take any responsibility whatsoever for the results or consequences of any attempt to use or adopt any of the information presented in this book for the purposes of biological healing and/or medical practice.

The statements in this book have not been evaluated by the Food and Drug Administration and none of the information contained herein is intended to diagnose, treat, cure or prevent any disease.

Any references to companies, individuals, governments, political situations, banking or educational institutions or religious organizations are based solely on my personal opinions and personal observations and are not the opinions or observations of D and Y Laboratories, the contributors, the publisher, distributor, bookseller or any other person or persons connected with this book.

DAVID L. GANN

Foreword

C. Norman Shealy, MD, PhD

President, Holos Institutes of Health, Inc.
Professor Emeritus of Energy Medicine,
Holos University Graduate Seminary
Founding President,
American Holistic Medical Association

The Secret of Life has been the foundation of philosophy and medicine throughout history. The Chinese called it *qi*; the Japanese, *ki*; the Indians, *prana*; and Wilhelm Reich, *orgone.* Much of medicine before 1940 was rather pragmatic empirical practice with many errors. Since 1940 the bulk of modern medicine has been a takeover by the PharmacoMafia—my title for the pharmaceutical industry. Today modern medicine is at least the third leading cause of death in the United States (*JAMA*, July 2000). Drugs that have little justification and serious risks, called side effects, are added almost daily to the stream of offerings. Numerous brave souls question the current system, and yet it is THE SYSTEM rejecting and attacking viciously virtually every alternative.

Homeopathy was introduced by Hahnemann when the mainstay of the medical profession was bloodletting, purging and leeches. Even then homeopathy was rejected by those who snobbishly considered themselves intellectually superior. Despite this rejection, homeopathy remains a major force in Europe and England. In the United States, early in the twentieth century, the American Medical Association, in collaboration with the Rockefeller Foundation, conspired to have Abraham Flexner produce his report attacking everything except allopathic medicine, with its drugs and surgery. Half of all medical schools and hospitals were closed. Acupuncture, used in the U.S. since at least the 1850s, was abandoned. Homeopathy was excommunicated. Osteopathy was vigorously attacked, and chiropractic was even more viciously attacked until the AMA was finally defeated by the chiropractors in 1966. The remarkable pleomorphism theories and practices of Royal Rife were destroyed by the czar of the AMA, Morris Fishbein, setting back for over sixty years the potential cure of cancer.

The work of Georges Lakhovsky, George Crile and Harold Saxton Burr on the electrical foundation of life remains ignored. These three proved beyond any reasonable scientific doubt that the essence of life is indeed electrical. The chemistry and even the physical aspect of life are dependent upon the electrical matrix. But medicine has looked almost exclusively at the physical and chemical. Although life expectancy has increased over 50 percent in the past century, Dr. Thomas McKeown (*The Role of Medicine*) has emphasized that this increase is the result of pasteurization of milk, chlorination of water, proper disposal of sewage and adequate protein and calories.

David and Yin have taken the concept of homeopathy into the twenty-first century with the most elegant experiments to date. Their demonstration of microscopic clusters in water is groundbreaking and revolutionary! Their purification of water, with the atmospheric purity described, places homeopathy on a scientifically valid foundation that is equal at least to the discovery of atomic energy. I had the privilege of testing some of the earliest clustered water and found statistically significant improvement in basic immune function. Their further refined products are even more exciting. Obviously additional research is needed, as it has been with radiation for the past century. But we now have an equally exciting New Frontier of Science, infinitely safer and potentially radically more effective in redefining *life* and *healing*. Kudos, David and Yin! The world awaits the next step in the development of electrically and chemically pure homeopathy. Hahnemann would be as excited as I am to see the results of your work. You have made a great step forward in understanding the Secret of Life.

Introduction

C. Norman Shealy, MD, PhD

Your current daily U.S. lifestyle, hand in hand with the colossal giant known as modern medicine, is killing you.

Quite a dramatic statement coming from someone who spent his entire life practicing medicine, wouldn't you agree? But I should know; I have seen and lived the change within my profession for more than fifty years, through treating over forty thousand patients, and I can say with all honesty the above is a factual statement.

For years I needed to be careful of what I said. Oh, I have been considered somewhat of a rebel within the medical community, especially in my long investigative research into Alternative Medicine; but because of my background as a neurosurgeon and the results that I have been known for, I was able to speak . . . well, *most* of my mind. There was still a line that one did not cross—certain words that were not to be uttered; *cure*, for instance, was not part of polite vocabulary at medical conventions. Yet I loved my profession and have always felt a deep kindred belonging to an alliance of the best minds and, on the whole, the most dedicated individuals alive.

I knew as a young child that I would become a physician and quest to cure all ills, and I must say that I still have that same enthusiasm. But along the way I discovered, as in any group—be it engineers, scientists or whoever—that there is a political side to survival. Some things are better left unsaid.

Today, thankfully, I am retired. I have a very comfortable lifestyle. I live with a wonderful wife of nearly fifty years on our beautiful 256-acre horse ranch and no one owns me. I don't *have* to write; I'm not looking for my rent, not yearning for more accolades: bottom line, I can't be bought; but I can and will speak my mind—all of it. The medical politics of survival no longer apply to me.

But, digressing, it has not always been this easy to speak. Any good scientist (as I consider any good physician) at some point in his or her career begins to "feel" this element of hypocrisy. What do I mean by that? One should not fear discovery or fear researching an area because it is considered outside the current accepted "comfort zone" of knowledge. I am not going to start complaining, as my purpose is not to point a finger of fault but to demonstrate that if we can see this mechanism of hypocrisy for what it truly is, maybe we can get past it. For, in truth, it is a form of simple economics: whoever has the most dollars controls the evolution of a subject. Now, herein lies the problem, especially in the arena of science, where health and medicine rightly belong. Scientists are not so concerned with economics and should be, by their very nature, lousy marketers, as they are not captivated by the discovery process from the viewpoint of how this will appeal to the mass market. But there are those who are, and they have learned that he who controls *science* controls the cash register.

So let's look at who has controlled this evolution of my subject, medicine.

I was sixteen when I entered Duke University shortly after World War II as an undergraduate in 1949. During that generation, the family doctor was the pivotal point within the community for medical knowledge and, usually, was not that wealthy. He lived better than most but the machine that built today's empire was really not in full swing. A family doc was well respected and his (the *vast* majority were men) word was synonymous with truth and compassion. He was unquestioned in his actions—one did what the doctor said, period. It was a humanistic venture seeded with great minds seeking answers to help their fellow citizens.

So what happened? It still should be a humanistic venture but something has changed. I believe that medicine has been pulled away from its original goal.

If you read Robert O. Becker, MD, in his book *The Body Electric* (1985), he succinctly characterizes this shift in our profession, one that led the medical profession away from the objective of the patient's well-being to one of "balancing chemistry" (the current pharmaceutical industry's buzzword).

As a young medical student at the end of the war working in New York's Bellevue Hospital, Becker describes how lobar pneumonia (an infection that involves only a single lobe, or section, of a lung) was a prominent U.S. killer, crossing all social boundaries, killing rich or poor, old and young. Becker tells how, within a few days of a patient contracting the bacteria, a definitive prediction of the outcome of the disease would occur: *"The fever rose to 104 or 105 degrees Fahrenheit and delirium set in. At that point we had two signs to go by: If the skin remained hot and dry, the victim would die; sweating meant the patient would pull through."*

At the time, he correctly concluded that the outcome of the struggle between the bacteria and the victim was determined solely by the patient's own resistance—50 percent died and the half that walked out of the hospital did so because of a working immune system. Prior to this point in time, medicine was searching for this holy grail: a true understanding of one's own natural defenses.

> *The surgeon can cut, remove, or rearrange the tissues, and sew up the wound, but only the patient can do the healing. Surgeons must always be humble before this miracle. We must treat the tissues with sure, deft gentleness, and above all we must do no harm, for we are nothing more than nature's assistants.* —Dr. John Mulholland, from *The Body Electric* by Robert O. Becker, MD

In 1961 I was fortunate to be selected as a Research Fellow in Neurosurgery under the Nobel Laureate Sir John Eccles. As a young physician such an appointment tends to give one a bit of an air of confidence, and now, nearly fifty years after that event, I can admit that the appointment added a slight swagger to my gait. But the noble ingredient of this great profession of medicine is that the realities of life-threatening illness can soon humble one, and you would have to be a fairly insensitive soul not to be awed by the struggle faced by your patients. And *insensitive* would not be the correct adjective to describe one as a healer if these experiences did not appeal to one's intellect to *ask the correct question:* **What triggers the immune response?** And why did some individuals' innate immune systems fail? What are the secrets to the workings of that mechanism and how could medicine use this to truly heal (and here is this rather distasteful word), *cure*, people?

That—a person's own defenses—was *the* focal point in medicine's search for understanding until Sir Alexander Fleming's discovery of penicillin, around 1930. But penicillin was not readily available to the general public until after WWII, when it quickly became known as "the miracle drug." Not only could one survive pneumonia with the simple administering of a white powder, but the patient could face a host of other bacterial infections with complete immunity. However, its effect on medicine in the 1950s was so much more than the mere conquest of many bacterial infections.

With its vast deployment, penicillin created a complete shift in viewpoint toward treatment, not merely of bacterial infections, but in how one viewed a patient. It brought about the new awareness that a "magic bullet" existed. No longer did the physician need to stand in awe of the body's own defenses—"Just give me more bullets." So it was penicillin that was the double-edged sword of the twentieth century. It unquestionably changed the course of history and is properly held, along with its discoverer, as a crowning moment in modern medicine.

But now, follow this change in medicine further, as we are going to go from science to marketing. It was science that made the discovery of the antibiotic penicillin possible, but it was not the use and effectiveness of the antibiotic penicillin that caught the eye of numerous fledgling pharmaceutical companies after World War II; it was the potential to manufacture, sell and distribute "this new modern science" that truly spelled *miracle* in the form of financial success.

Here is where economics begins to take over the evolution of a subject. From the roots of the penicillin discovery, a marketing machine was built and the pursuit of a chemical approach to the treatment of all acute and chronic diseases alike was born. Today, not only does the pharmaceutical industry dominate healthcare within the U.S., it has turned into a worldwide machine. It has funneled billions in profit back into advertising to create a U.S. public mind-set that says: *Health issues are only manageable by taking drugs.*

This is not true. A vast number of chronic degenerative conditions do not respond to drugs, since, in most cases, the underlying condition is not addressed. Consequently, only stronger prescription drugs, many severely addictive, will mask or lessen the pain. Most health issues—**up to 85 percent**—are best addressed *without* drugs and surgery.

Now, I would love to blame these international conglomerates for all our problems, but, in truth, we as doctors have allowed an industry that produces billions of dollars of chemicals for the general public each year to take over our profession. So we can all put down our pitchforks and lanterns, at least for now, and look at what is at the bottom of this.

How did we get into this situation? Actually, it is too simple. We allowed Marketing and Science to sleep in the same bed. Only this incestuous relationship could ever describe such a union.

It should be obvious that the purpose of science (especially in medical research science) is to find cures, whereas the purpose of marketing is to create a want and a need for a product. If an industry is publicly traded and has stockholders demanding increased profits and market share, isn't there a conflict? One interest says, "Find a cure that makes no need for the product," and the other says, "Find a way to sell more product."

This is not new news. Look at the petroleum industry. Is it any wonder we have no clean, safe energies? Gee.

It comes down to dollars. People work for these industries and after a while a person really gets accustomed to his or her paycheck. In 2007 the federal government announced that the health industry would balloon to $4.1 trillion a year by 2017. It's growing out of control.

With that kind of an income stream, for the most part—at least from a capitalistic point of view—one could say, "What's the problem? How do I get some of those dollars? Put me on that gravy train." But here is the problem—and it's a serious one—your children and grandchildren will die at a much younger age and their lives will be unhealthy ones filled with medical trauma and stress unless we confront the madness that has become modern medicine.

You want evidence? It is a published statistic that 56 people die in the U.S. *each hour* from iatrogenic causes (death caused inadvertently by a physician or surgeon or by medical treatment [pharmaceutical drug] or diagnostic procedure); that's approximately 1,300 each day, 490,000 each year. Forget about cancer and heart disease. These are preventable deaths.

In illness, about 15 percent of the time, especially in the treatment of trauma and life-threatening situations, your life *depends* upon the near-miracles of modern medicine.

What you need to avoid like the plague is the *marketing-science form of medicine.*

However, up to 85 percent of illnesses are the result of unhealthy habits. My fifty years of medical practice have convinced me without a doubt that there is a better, simpler, cheaper and safer method of dealing with these types of illness, which 85 percent of my patients have responded to remarkably.

So, am I saying that the pharmaceutical industry is to blame for today's failing healthcare system? No—no more than any other single factor in this equation of what is wrong with our healthcare system. Then the marketers are the evil ones, right? That doesn't really fly either—no room filled with fat, old evil men in dark suits, sitting down at a bird's-eye-maple conference table in uptown Manhattan, devising how to do you in. If only it were so easy, we could just grab those pitchforks again.

Then what *is* the answer?

It is so simple. Knowledge, *real* knowledge—we need to know the truth! To ask the right question and research the right area without bias!

Why in heaven's name have we turned over our research to those who want to sell more drugs? What happened to real research? What happened to looking for the holy grail of medicine—the mechanics of the immune system?

And why on earth are we looking down a pharmaceutical aisle thinking one of those neatly packaged, superbly marketed petrochemical preparations is going to fix an organism that spent the last countless millions of years repairing its own ills without a single mistake? That's right! If you are reading this, your DNA is the summation of every right response to an illness for at least a billion years. Your genetic line has won every fight with every other organism that ever existed. Plus, that exact record, that code (DNA), is just as alive in you today as it was during the days of the dinosaurs.

If I were to tell you that I got my blue eyes from my dad, you would nod in agreement and that would be that—we would both agree that simple genetics pass down certain traits, generation to generation. But could there exist even more basic relationships, not just from our recent ancestors, but from the first biological beginnings of life? Could there be some sort of code within the code—something prior to DNA that is an integral part of our immune response?

As physicians we may sit back smugly and pat ourselves on the back, looking at all the strides medicine has made over the last hundred or so years, and it is true that much has been discovered; but in comparison to the volume of information stored in a single strand of DNA, it would be like comparing one glass of water to all of the oceans on Earth. And if anyone were to protest such a statement, let me remind him or her that although it is true that modern medicine has been burning the midnight oil for several hundred years, dedicating itself to the noble mission of conquering disease, the human form and all its ancestors have been doing the same for over a *billion* years—totally successfully. That's right—not ONE iatrogenic death; zero—and on top of that, the body has kept a perfect running record of each successful action. Compare that to the medical-chart-record mistakes found in any hospital on any single day!

You are sitting somewhere reading this introduction because your body and the body before it and the body before that, for millions and millions of years, healed itself. Your DNA is the exact record of your body fighting off every known infection, virus and predator in the history of Earth. It is as simple as that. Your body is the exact record of a perfect health score for more than a billion years!

I founded the American Holistic Medical Association back in the seventies because I felt, as did many others within my profession, that the Hippocratic oath of "Do no harm" was the cornerstone of healing. There are so many drugs being peddled by the pharmaceutical companies (I will use my coined word here)—peddled by the PharmacoMafia—that the American public does not need.

If medicine's primary purpose is to heal, then pushing drugs that do more harm than good is not moving toward the original goal.

Now, the key is—and the essence of the holistic medical movement was and still is—to get the body back on its own code and remove the barriers that current society has accumulated around it and in it and on it so that it can function as it has for eons.

And what I have been doing for the last thirty years, at least, is to understand which natural substances the body needs for the code to function. Interestingly enough, most are simple; but they should be— they are what the body has used for millions of years to build its own defenses. Yet this is counter to the current public's thinking: Modern is better; new, fantastic discoveries in medicine are happening every day; Dr. House is sure to save us all.* Where do these viewpoints come from? Modern media. Might there be some vested interest in getting you to have such a viewpoint?

In the last hundred years we have been chasing the bacteria and virus as the root or creators of illness, and we have been demanding that those pharmacy guys get their act together to find us some new magic bullets. But wait. . . . Wait a minute. Who was watching the store before that? Come to think of it, there were no pharmaceutical shops along Tyrannosaurus Avenue.

That's right, we survived without the pills. And how did we survive? We survived because of *the stored information in our DNA*. Nature likes to record our successes.

The pharmaceutical industry has made it "normal" to be on drugs for the rest of your life. If you are sad, take this; if you are shy, take that. If you sneeze, you must have an allergy and you need this. Can't sleep? . . . Don't worry.

Read *The Truth About the Drug Companies* by Marcia Angell, MD. Marcia is the former editor in chief of the *New England Journal of Medicine* and is currently a member of the Harvard Medical School's

---

* Dr. Gregory House is the central character of a popular FOX television medical drama series, *House, M.D.*

Department of Social Medicine. It's a good read and gives no quarter on this openly bizarre spectacle of the takeover of medical research by the pharmaceutical industry.

There are simple healthful things that will handle the day-to-day stress of living. Sure, they take some willpower and some commitment, but unfortunately most people do not include them in their lives until they have a heart attack or a stroke. It is as plain as that. I hate to say it but it takes a club to the forehead for most of us to wake up to this fact. Then we change our lives for the better and we do get well.

What I am preaching here is that medicine must be focused on the further understanding of the workings of the healing process. We need to get back to our roots. There is so much we can learn about our bodies if we look for real knowledge—not a great sales slogan.

Did you know that we share the same roots of DNA as those of a salamander? So why can't we regenerate an entire limb? A salamander can. Can we? Shouldn't we find out?

I wanted to write this introduction primarily to say that we must continue to seek knowledge in the right place. And I believe the following research is an excellent place to look—right from where we came: *water*. This is a huge missing link in our understanding of our past, and it is our most fundamental relationship to our beginnings.

Medicine, *real science*—not the sale of drugs for profit—needs to be pushed forward, and that is why this research should be supported. It is an important and detailed investigation of the most basic and abundant molecule in our bodies: water—H_2O. I believe when we fully understand this molecule's relationship to the body, it will be one of the most important discoveries since penicillin. And though, through the hands of the marketer, penicillin sort of derailed us from searching for the holy grail of healing, it is my hopeful prayer that this and other discoveries like it will soon lead us back to that quest.

DOUBLE-
Helix
WATER™

PART ONE

Chapter 1

The Adventure Begins

Some days it is easy to feel like Bilbo Baggins. There is a racket at the front of your house; Gandalf's standing there banging his cane across the door, shouting about dragons, doom and chaos, and your first thought is to . . . *just . . . keep . . . that . . . door . . . closed*. The world will survive without you for the day—it made it this far without your help; but then you realize, as you have countless times before, that your job as a researcher is simply to know, to find out, to discover the truth, and so you drag yourself out of bed and go back into the lab.

Most people have a grandiose idea of scientific research: sophisticated environments filled with the latest analytical equipment, bubbling flasks of multicolored liquids, House-like characters strolling sagely about ultraclean contraptions, taking long knowing glances into imposing microscopes, carefully noting the results into black-bound lab books.

Ah yes, the Hollywood image of laboratory research. For the most part, that image is as far from the truth as a hog farm filled with electron microscopes. Lab work is not about machines or bubbling liquids, and truth be told, it's not that interesting—downright boring. It is doing the same exact thing over and over, in the same surroundings, same place, same stuff, same stuff, same stuff. And the real discoveries don't come with brilliant flashes of light along with an "OMG!" No . . . normally they are merely, "What's that?" And it is about one of those "What's that?" moments that this book is written.

I and my good friend and colleague Yin Lo have been on a fifteen-year quest, which started with the same "What's that?" and we are still at it today. The human mind and spirit are quite amazing phenomena: one sees something that doesn't quite fit and the next thing you know, you are pulled down a research line purely to understand "why." And that really *is* the simplistic answer to the question, how did all this start?

Just to quell any suspicions that Yin and I began this adventure to prove the validity of homeopathy, neither of us had had any association with or any real understanding of the subject prior to beginning this research. It just popped its head up during the early years of investigation; and with complete confidence and conviction I can say that we have no certainty whether the *existing* practice and manufacture of homeopathic preparations have much relevance to this research. That area is not part of this fact-finding mission. On the contrary, this mission began as an investigation into a charged particle that could be useful in enhancing combustion. How more distant a form of research could it have been?

And to this day our purpose for compiling the work presented here is not to validate homeopathy or *any* particular current-day health practice; our purpose is to simply present our findings in a chronological history, coupled with the findings of fellow colleagues who have helped greatly along the way. We want to lay the groundwork so others can contribute— so others can potentially find an easier path toward what we hope will be a new age of environmentally friendly and workable chemical, industrial and *biological* processes and understanding. It would satisfy us greatly if indeed that simple question of "What *is* that?" led to a quantum step in man's understanding of his world.

But since this question of ultralow doses or homeopathy will undoubtedly come up—and it will, trust me—I asked Norman Shealy to write an introduction for this volume and to lend a hand in defining some terms. *Homeopathy* (or *homeopathic medicine*) he defines as an alternative, holistic method of treatment that has had prominence in many parts of the world since the late eighteenth century. Norm happens to have founded the American Holistic Medical Association, in 1978, and is considered to be one of the world's authorities on most of the alternative medical practices. The roots of this word *homeopathy* are from the Greek *omoios*, "like," and *pathos*, "suffering" or "disease." According to Norm, the treatment method is safe and, correctly done, a very effective treatment for a host of illnesses. The theory behind this two-hundred-plus-year treatment method is that substances which produce symptoms of a particular sickness in healthy people can have a beneficial effect when given in very minute quantities to those who are ill and displaying those specific symptoms; the idea being that the body's immune response is triggered—and, as Norm discussed in the introduction, the only real healing is self-healing.

From an intuitive viewpoint, I must absolutely agree with Norm that healing comes from what he calls "the code." It makes sense to me that a biological organism that has successfully come forward for billions of years and is alive today must have a stored record of successful actions on the survival line.

But again, the purpose of this book is not to tout prior treatment methods or to draw some new line in the sand between conventional medicine and alternative methods. As you will discover from reading, our research has been purely physical and has not intentionally walked into the province of healing. Our interest has been atomic structure and mechanics—simply chasing a puzzle that we found in water. Yet the subject of water is so intrinsically interconnected with the subject of biological organisms that our investigation could not help but step into the realm of human biology. Any honest attempt at discovery in this arena could only lead down the same path. And our hopes and prayers are that this new information does not open old wounds but brings about a basis for a future understanding of heretofore unexplored physical and biological realms, based upon sound and truthful research, which becomes germane and beneficial to the human experience.

Before I get too far into these discussions, let me first introduce ourselves. My name is David Gann and I consider myself more of an engineer than a scientist, although I have been fortunate to work with some great scientists over the last thirty or so years. I am more of a hands-on builder. I have been the guy who was given the task of constructing and keeping these ultraclean labs running for over thirty years. My father, who was a self-taught 1930s-era engineer, made the mistake of encouraging my first building attempts (I was five or six and was erecting my clubhouse on the family farm), and that validation was all it took for me to focus on a life of designing and constructing things. So my role has been creating the facilities and experimental devices and equipment to get the job done. The bonus of my labor has been to live and work around many of the great minds of the day, and my research partner is one of those rare birds. Yin received his PhD in theoretical particle physics, in 1962, as a member of the theory group led by Yoichiro Nambu at the University of Chicago. Nambu is considered one of the leading figures in the development of modern particle physics and was this past year's (2008) Physics Nobel Prize recipient. Daniel Tsui was Yin's college roommate; they both came to the U.S. on full scholarships to study physics and have remained dear friends to this day. Tsui received the Nobel Prize in Physics in 1998.

Yin has always been right there on the cutting edge of particle physics, having been invited to the First International Conference on High Energy Physics, in 1979, by Chairman Deng of China. He was invited together with T. D. Lee and C. N. Yang, both Physics Nobel Laureates, to help promote physics research in China. One of Yin's oldest friends and life-long math buddy is Shing-Tung Yau, the 1982 Fields Medalist in mathematics. (There is no Nobel Prize in mathematics, and the Fields Medal is regarded as the highest professional honor a mathematician can attain.) Yau is the current Distinguished Professor of Mathematics at Harvard.

So it becomes pretty apparent that particle physics has been Yin's passion. Labs around the world—Rutherford High Energy Laboratory, UK; the Institute of Theoretical Physics, Chinese Academy of Sciences, Beijing; the Stanford Linear Accelerator Center, Menlo Park, California; the Department of Physics, McGill University, Montreal, Quebec; the Department of Physics, National University of Singapore; the Institute of High Energy Physics, Beijing; the Institute of Theoretical Physics, Stony Brook, New York; the Institute of Theoretical Physics, Berlin; the Niels

Bohr Institute, Copenhagen; and the Department of Physics, University of Prince Edward Island—have invited Yin for research.

A good point that I want to make here—not belabor, but state emphatically—is that we are not medical researchers and did not come to our conclusions based upon biological assumptions or theories. We have strictly been following a physical particle path. We have no hidden agenda in proving or disproving alternative methods. But make no mistake: we are seasoned veterans, complete with "Purple Hearts," from being caught in open-ground crossfire whizzing from all directions as certain factions battle over nearly a trillion-dollar industry. I know of what I speak when I say I have heard Gandalf's cries warning of doom at my door. But—and here is our real disclaimer—just as part of the record, we are not funded by either faction. I have always had a high regard, almost reverence, for the subject of medicine and its practitioners; but as a researcher you must be guided by what the data reveals, no matter how popular or unpopular that avenue may be.

Additionally, over the years, I have found that physics research has a level of vigor all its own, very dissimilar to the medical arts. I recall sitting in the Athenaeum with Yin and several of his physics buddies (the Athenaeum is the Faculty Club at Caltech, probably one of the most prestigious hangouts for scientists on the West Coast; Stephen Hawking was seated at a table just to our right) when a friend of Yin's—a well-known medical researcher whom he had invited to lunch—mentioned that she was involved in testing a new cancer drug. "How exciting, Lynda. What is the exact action of the drug?" That was the question asked by one of Yin's physics buddies, truly interested in this new discovery. "What do you mean by exact action?" was her reply. He came back with a very precise technical question about the chemical interaction of the drug. He wanted to know on an exact level how the drug interacted with a particular body chemistry.

I was fascinated by the conversation, as Lynda looked totally surprised. She, the MD and a well-known medical researcher, went on to explain to the physicist that medicine did not base its research on the exact chemical action of a drug, saying that the human chemistry was far too complex to understand all the possible combinations that could ensue; it was much too complicated to analyze or follow. Instead, such research had to be based on statistics: the drug was compared to the use of a placebo in a long, arduous line of controlled studies—rodents, larger animals and eventually humans. She continued that the testing was done, first, to ensure the drug was not harmful (relatively so, compared to its benefit), and second, to demonstrate that there would be some statistically positive effect. In other words, would the tumor shrink or die?

There was a moment of uncomfortable silence at the table and then a look came across the physicist's face of *"How can this be?"* How could a revered science like medicine put a chemical into a person's body without really knowing the exact chemical reaction—and when one says *exact* from a theoretical physicist's viewpoint, one means exact.

It was a realization for me also, and even though I have a tremendous respect for the subject of medicine, we must understand that it is a far cry in exactness from the subject of particle physics.

But, OK, I realize you want to know how did this subject of homeopathy come up in our work in the first place and what is all this controversy? Well, let me tell you, you are in for an interesting story.

Chapter 2

Stumbling into the Water

met Yin Lo in a very unassuming warehouse lab a few blocks from the Caltech campus in Pasadena, California, around 1993. As I walked back through a long hallway, I began to get glimpses of massive stainless steel high-vacuum chambers, and I remember thinking, *Boy, somebody is doing some work that needs real containment*. Vacuum pumps, a mile of tubing, and compressed-gas bottles sat around the chambers and those were all surrounded by multiple tall racks of electronic power supplies—wiring everywhere. This was right out of a Boris Karloff movie; all that it lacked was some bubbling colored liquid rising in long-necked glass beakers. I instantly liked whoever had put all this together. Who was this guy?

Yin had been teaching at the University of Melbourne several years prior when he and the university jointly filed a patent on a revolutionary new type of particle beam. The patent was soon discovered to be outside the comfort zone of the university; consequently the university president handed it back to Yin. Rightfully so, as shortly after the filing, the Australian Secret Service told the patent attorney and Yin that all information about the invention had just become "Top Secret" and any disclosure would be a violation of the Australian Treason Act. Disclosure could result in their execution—actual true story.

The university, at that time, knew they had made the right decision and gave Yin a five-year leave of absence. Yin's friends could not believe he was giving up his tenure; jobs for particle physicists were mostly limited to making bombs for the government, and having tenure at a university was something one would *never* walk away from—but Yin did and to this day has not yearned for pure academics.

This patent, this particle beam, Yin had called Baser. It was potentially capable of extreme high-energy levels and was invented for the purpose of destroying nuclear waste while at the same time providing clean, pollution-free energy. Anything that is powerful enough to burn nuclear waste has also a great military potential—hence the Secret Service involvement and a visit from the U.S. State Department once the patents were filed in the United States. The Australian patent attorney was interested in getting it out of his hands as well; so he introduced Yin to a rather wild-west wealthy Australian entrepreneur and soon the project was moved to Pasadena to be near Caltech. As I mentioned, that is where I first met Yin—and he showed me around that very interesting first Baser lab in Pasadena.

Several years later, I helped form a publicly traded company around the project and we moved the first prototype chamber to Caltech. Caltech was selected because it was the top technical school on the West Coast, plus Caltech wanted to make Yin a visiting professor there. Many of the world's top physics and math community showed up to help on that project. Why? It was something that could change the world. This was a very interesting time; come to think of it, it would make a great book.

I had just come from catalyst research. I ran a small independent company that held a contract with a major oil giant to find a solution to one of their costly problems—pollution fines.

I had tackled the problem with known catalysts to reduce smoke and pollutants on equipment that was being used around the Santa Barbara area offshore drilling platforms. There is a host of large diesel engines that are employed in and around oil production, and I had become successful on one particular engine I had been assigned to fix. It is sort of an ironic story, as I fixed the smoke problem, dramatically reduced the particulates from the engine, but came under fire from the existing air-quality board for using a platinum-based solution. Not because of the cost (platinum is normally more expensive than gold), but because the catalytic metal had not been studied as an atmospheric particulate. I was commiserating one night, at some party my wife had dragged me to, with a gentleman whom I would describe as a backyard inventor (he openly stated he had no scientific background), who told me that he had a water-based catalyst that contained simply the "fields" of other catalysts and would work as well as my chemicals.

Well, I am originally from Missouri and I simply said, "Show me."

As I had numerous large test engines at my disposal, I began testing the water-based catalyst from this person but, for the most part, had no or limited success. Then I gave him my "chemical" solution, which he (as I discovered later) used a homeopathic dilution technique on and gave back to me.

That changed the results dramatically. I came in one morning with a new sample from the inventor and soon I was watching an engine in amazement. There was definitely a catalytic action to this water.

I asked for more. The second batch did not work and the third had some effect but was limited. I was snagged. What was it in that first batch that had performed so well? Fortunately there was still material left from the first test; I had it in a small blue bottle, so I knew what the next step would be—analyze it.

Yin and I had become friends after our original meeting (it would be hard to not like Yin), and so I showed him the sample and we began to investigate what was up with this particular water. When we looked at the contents from a chemical analysis, we saw only water—pure H_2O, basically distilled water. When we viewed the sample using magnetic resonance, employing a big machine that was the forerunner to MRI at your local hospital, there was a slight but definite difference—yet something was not right. It was the "What's that?" puzzle I mentioned earlier. It started to suck us down a long garden hose into a quagmire of mystery. What was going on in this particular water that created a catalytic action?

Yin's opening comment to me was he would first need to read all the existing literature on water—which he did. He read a mountain of material on water—physical properties, hydrogen bonding—paper after paper. It was while reading this initial ton of dissertations that he picked up Jacques Benveniste's work. Benveniste was not a physicist nor a chemist but a renowned research physician; he was credited with the discovery of platelet-activating factor (a landmark finding in the 1970s with broad applications within the understanding of the immune system) and had been published extensively throughout the world prior to the 1988 paper that had found its way into Yin's reading. Benveniste was considered during his day to be one of the "top guns" in medical research. That was surely the reason *Nature* considered publishing the particular paper that Yin was about to read (submitted in August 1987), as there is no question *Nature had to know* that publishing Benveniste's new work was going to ruffle some feathers. It was walking right down the path of the major no-no of the AMA—*homeopathy*.

This legendary paper, "Human basophil degranulation triggered by very dilute antiserum against IgE," *Nature*, Vol. 333, 30 June 1988, summarizes Benveniste's work that he began sometime in early '87 and in essence states that he had found valid evidence for ultralow doses, or homeopathy. It is a series of experiments to study the effects of antibodies on white blood cells—a simple experiment showing that when the blood cells were exposed to a particular antibody, the cell structure changed in a fashion that could be measured optically. Benveniste's research revealed that the same reaction would statistically occur as the solution of the antibody was diluted. To be specific, you could optically see the influence on the cell of a one-for-one dilution, but at one-for-ten dilutions you saw only one influence out of ten; at a hundred parts dilution, there was only one reaction in a hundred attempts, and so on. All is well, right? Not quite that easy, because—and this was what created worldwide debate and skepticism, and was the deciding factor for Benveniste's eventual out-casting from nearly all scientific associations (including losing his tenure at a prestigious university): *When the dilution reached a point where there was only one antibody per one million parts of water—BANG!—the original reaction reappeared and continued to reappear, not statistically proportionate, but every time.*

More mystery!

This part of the puzzle pulled us both further into the mire of intrigue. First, was Benveniste's result real or just some weird contamination (although originally it had been repeated in a host of other labs at *Nature's* request); but even more mysterious was this supposed magic number of dilution (one part per million). What the heck was that?

Yin, as most theoretical physicists, knows his math—it is the language of the subject; and recall that his classmate and old math buddy is one of the top mathematicians on Earth, Shing-Tung Yau. So his first interest was to see if there existed any possible mathematical model based upon what was already known about the relationship of the water molecule to substances that have been dissolved in it. In other words, what happens to particles as you dilute them in water and what could their possible relationship be if you diluted them down into this ethereal la-la land— the land beyond one part per million?

His first inclination was to look at the work of Peter Debye (Dutch physicist, chemist and Nobel Laureate) on dilute solutions. The Debye-Hückel set of equations is the definitive study of these relationships and later became the foundation of Yin's own mathematical model.

I am not going to put that math in this part of the book because most of us would go to sleep right about now if I did. If you want those exact equations, they are contained in the papers that follow in part two. You are welcome to sharpen your #2 pencil in that section. This section is for the rest of us. But simply, if you dilute, for instance, common table salt in water, what happens? The Debye-Hückel set of equations demonstrates that the salt separates into charged particles (ions). Table salt becomes sodium (a plus) and chloride (a minus)—water acts as a wedge and keeps pushing them apart. The atomic structure of water (H_2O) means that the big oxygen atom has a constant motion or a kind of continual hum to it as the much smaller hydrogen atoms move in and out. It is this constant motion that makes water a great separator. It just wants to get between things. It wants them pushed apart. Water is the greatest solvent around.

Yin had pretty much disappeared for several weeks during this time of reading. He had buried himself in his office, which was covered with blackboards (which were covered with equations) and stacks of scientific literature teetering across his desk. He was mostly out of touch with the rest of the world for those weeks as he churned through the literature. But that ended one morning when he ran into my office (really looking like a mad scientist) and yelled, "I know what's in the water! I CALCULATED IT!" His math model had predicted Benveniste's blood cell–antibody reaction at the exact dilutions found in Benveniste's work.

Aha! . . . But what did this mean exactly?

Benveniste had theorized in his paper that the original antibody acted somehow as a "template," and for some reason this template had altered the properties of the water. He went on to declare that this altered state was transferred to each succeeding dilution, so that the water in some fashion had a certain "memory" of the original molecule.

He later stated that it was probably a type of electronic effect but could not offer a real explanation.

Hard position to justify—no scientific model, no prior science, no math model, just a theory based upon some type of electronic effect that he had no explanation of, and all the while broadcasting this to a world where an existing industry (the pharmaceutical giants) watched carefully, surely imagining that their gargantuan market share was at risk.

It would have saved Benveniste a lot of grief if he had just painted a bull's-eye on his chest, as he quickly became one of the past fifty years' most controversial research figures.

There is a major problem with introducing new discoveries into our world if they threaten seated players. And the longer that seat has been held and the more money that seat is worth, the more difficult it becomes to add another chair in the room. The pharmaceutical sales game currently has no rival when it comes to size; it has been growing by leaps and bounds since the 1970s and will surpass petroleum on its current trend by 2020. So when we speak of selling drugs, we are speaking about the Super Bowl of marketing games: big offices overlooking the Manhattan skyline, salaries of senior marketing executives starting in the mid–six figures, and stock options worth fortunes when those drugs fly off the pharmacy shelves. This is not a game that is easily upset—we are talking major-league commerce. And if you are walking around Madison Avenue with one of these coveted jobs, you *know* that you are *somebody*. But I bet you know something else too, sitting behind that three-thousand-dollar Brazilian rosewood desk: if you don't continue to sell more drugs to more people, that cutthroat industry will chop your head off with not a whisper of regret.

This coldblooded, bottom-line, corporate kill-or-be-killed scenario does not and will not ever, *ever* work in the field of science. They are at opposite ends of any spectrum, no matter how you justify it. The future of our race depends upon scientific discovery. No one can or ever will commercialize discovery. It is there for all mankind regardless of what office one happens to own or rent. It is truly one of those *for the people, by the people* underlying principles that are part of the real fabric of existence. And when the two are mixed, we get what we have now: as Norman stated in the introduction, the biggest killer in the U.S. is the industry that is supposed to heal.

I said I was going to tell you the story of how Yin and I fell into the biological arena—the story of how this subject of homeopathy came up—right? To understand it better we need a little more background.

Samuel Hahnemann is probably a good place to start. He is considered to be the father of homeopathy, which as Norm pointed out to me derives from a combination of Greek words that mean "similar suffering."

The time frame is the late 1700s, early 1800s. History says that Hahnemann was very disturbed by the crude medical system of his time and believed that the use of strong drugs and invasive treatments did more harm than good. I would venture that iatrogenic deaths were as prominent back then as they are today (Samuel and Norman Shealy would have gotten along very well). Hahnemann performed experiments on himself using Peruvian bark, which contains quinine—used to treat malaria. His findings concluded that in a healthy person, quinine creates the same symptoms as malaria, including fevers and chills, suggesting to him that it would be useful as a remedy. He then began to analyze different substances found in nature and categorized them in large homeopathic references called *materia medica*, or materials of medicine.

Hahnemann founded his subject on the principles of the Law of Similars (like cures like), the Law of Infinitesimal Dose (the more dilute, the stronger the potency), and that illness was always specific to the individual.

Now, Hahnemann was not the first to isolate the idea of the Law of Similars, as it is first mentioned by Hippocrates in the fourth century BC; plus one finds the same reasoning behind vaccinations, created by Edward Jenner and Louis Pasteur. These vaccines provoke a reaction in the individual that protects against the actual disease. Allergy treatments today work in a similar fashion. By exposing a person to minute quantities of the allergen, the person's tolerance levels are elevated.

Thus, according to the literature, homeopathy has been around for some time and in the early 1900s was very popular in America, with over 15 percent of all doctors being homeopathic. There were twenty-two major homeopathic medical schools, including Boston University and the University of Michigan. But it and many other forms of the healing arts have not kept pace with what we would call conventional or *allopathic* (American Medical Association) medicine—interestingly enough, a term that also came from Hahnemann. *Allopathic medicine* is normally defined as a method of treating disease with remedies (drugs) that produce effects different from those caused by the disease.

Looking at it now as an outsider, as someone who is not a practicing homeopath nor a medical researcher, it is obvious that the difficulty with the subject lies in the absence of a model to suggest why it works, period. One must have an underlying physical principle to support the claims that have been published in reputable journals. Heaven knows, homeopathy has to be hundreds of times safer than pharmaceuticals, and there are hundreds, possibly thousands, of medical doctors around the world who do include it in their practices. After Yin published the first paper nearly fifteen years ago, there were numerous speaking requests received from practicing homeopaths and MDs alike. There was a stir of excitement—which did not last long—and I will get to that soon.

Returning to our *Nature* story, the journal finally folded to pressure and recanted a year after they had published the paper on Benveniste's work. This was quite an episode in their publishing history. Under inducement from the scientific community—and you have to know, the pharmaceutical industry—*Nature* disavowed the work and published an article saying that they were wrong and should not have presented the paper, as they now felt the work was "unscientific." This after the paper had been originally refereed by its editors and a group of fellow scientists and was then replicated in five laboratories in four countries, duplicating Benveniste's results.

Bottom line, I think that Benveniste got a bum rap. He was a casualty of that crossfire I referred to earlier. But his real problem was simple—*no explanation.* Consequently, the explanation that continued to raise its head was contamination. It had to be some kind of dirt or something similar that was creating the effect of Benveniste's solutions.

We wanted to repeat his work, but it would be cleaner and much simpler to begin with something less complex than antibodies; plus we wanted a catalyst—we had no interest in healing.

We began with known catalytic solutions similar to the one I had given the backyard inventor, and we also employed ultraclean laboratory conditions; this was something I was very accustomed to, as my entire career had been in the construction and maintenance of rooms that were cleaner than outer space. In addition—and this was most important—we had a model to follow. If Yin's model was correct, it would predict the exact dilution in which the particle would grow and it should also predict how to grow the particles in greater number; and given that certain conditions and certain procedures were exactly followed, the model should, if correct, be able to predict not only the existence of the particle at the right dilution but also how to manipulate it to form larger and larger particles.

The more we followed the model, the more catalytic action we saw on test engines. It was exciting, unbelievably exciting. The model predicted the magic number (below one part per million), and the magic catalytic action occurred at the exact dilution.

This all sounds very simple and in principle it is, but there are about a million or ten million things that can go wrong if you don't control all the variables; because as the dilution continues, the distance between the now separated particles becomes greater and greater, and if the water is ultrapure, it becomes more and more aggressive. It wants to reach out and grab things—ANYTHING! So contamination is a real issue. And if not controlled, you don't know what particle you will grow or if any will grow at all. Also, if you did grow a particle, would it be the right one to cause some type of catalytic action? It could have just the opposite effect.

Now, what about homeopathic solutions? If it is true that there are helpful effects (and I'll cover more on this later), then the control process of how the particle is made is absolutely critical.

I am trying to make this process (creating these little particles, in theory) easy to understand. So let's just stick with table salt. You pour a small, very small, amount of salt into clean, very clean, water. What will occur is the salt will begin to dissolve. In other words, the plus and the minus will begin to come apart. Think of the plus as a teenage cheerleader daughter, OK? And think of the minus as the captain of the basketball team. What do these guys like to do? Right—they want to hang; they want to get real close, and, left alone, they will get together. If you are a parent, you know what I am saying—they will get together! The same thing happens with these plus and minus charged particles of salt. They are slamming into one another, but then the water acts as Mom and Dad and pushes them apart. This is going on in a millionth of a second (fast kids)—slamming together and then the wedge action of the water (Mom and Dad) pushing them apart.

What happens as one continues to dilute—as you take the solution and pour out 90 percent of it and add more water? The solution will become more dilute; you just shoved a ton more moms and dads into the equation. Now there are heaps of new moms and dads all saying, "Stay apart, stay away, stay away," and fewer cheerleaders, fewer basketball players. (Remember you poured out 90 percent of the solution and filled it just with water—moms and dads.) So the distance between the two particles (the teenagers) becomes greater but they are STILL ATTRACTED to each other ("Damn, babe, you are soooo cool!" "Yeah, but you in that uniform—OMG! You're such a hunk!"). I have two gorgeous daughters—been there, done that.

If you continue to do this, there comes a point where there is enough distance between the plus and minus charged particles that there is no getting together. In actual fact, these particles are colliding and the water is constantly pushing them apart. When the distance reaches a certain point, the collisions begin to miss—the particles are attracted to each other but so many moms and dads push them this way and that, that they don't connect. The girl is racing toward her guy and he is racing toward his girl, but they just don't get together. Too many moms and dads. What happens then, just as would happen to the teens, is they sort of collapse back on themselves. That is to say, the teenagers would give up.

Now, this is where Yin's model goes beyond Debye's work (recall that Yin used Debye's equations to originally formulate his model). Debye stopped, and he did not theorize what would occur if you kept diluting—Yin did. He took his calculations further and then theorized what would happen if those two particles got so far away from one another that they could no longer find each other. That is, they no longer had any influence on each other—the only influence was their own and the water around them. Each one would be the only particle—isolated. And just like in real life, if this were to occur, that cheerleader would emotionally collapse inward, so does the particle. Yin looked at the forces that are present in a single charged particle. It is that same force that wants to constantly interact with another particle—the plus constantly looking for the minus. This force that surrounds each particle is called the Coulomb force, after Charles Coulomb, who was one of the true founders of the field of electricity and magnetism. There is a law here about charge that states that the magnitude of the force which exists between two charged particles is directly proportional to the amount of charge each particle has but is inversely proportional to how far they are apart. (*The electrical force between two charged objects is directly proportional to the product of the quantity of charge on the objects and inversely proportional to the square of the separation distance between the two objects.*)

Prior to this point in the evolution of the subject, physics has pretty much looked at this and stated *it doesn't know what happens when that force gets close to zero in water.*

It should go to zero, inversely proportional to the square of the separation distance. In other words, the more distance you put into the equation, the smaller the attraction charge becomes—but that does not say the charge goes away. It is still going to be there, and when it is stretched and stretched out, looking for the basketball player, and finally gives up . . . slam!—it collapses back on itself.

That calculation was what Yin added to his set of equations. He calculated what the generated force would be when that REACH-REACH-REACH outward slammed back. It is a big number. It actually would be equivalent to a hundred thousand pounds of pressure. Now, this is a bit of a misnomer, as you cannot have a hundred thousand pounds of pressure in water or atmosphere unless you put everything in a stainless steel chamber and close the door. But there is an analogy here because we are dealing with electrical pressure. And it is a *huge* electrical pressure that is generated. Again, I have purposely not put these mathematical equations in this first section of the book; but they are right there in the second part of the book, and they are there for anyone who wants to take an in-depth look at what we are saying here.

In the beginning, Yin and I were just working on the assumption that if we saw a catalytic response, it probably meant that the particles were there. We also were going on the assumption that if *that* was true, then the model should be able to predict a way that we could make more particles, and these assumptions should evidence themselves by yet a stronger catalytic action.

Both of those assumptions proved out. The next step was to actually find the particle and photograph it. It was *far* more than looking for a needle in a haystack.

Chapter 3

The First Attempts to Measure

A single strand of hair is approximately one hundred times wider than one of the largest particles. In other words, if it were possible to take one hair fiber and cut it into a hundred slivers sideways, you would have something that was equivalent to one of the "big" particles. The smaller ones would be a *thousand times smaller* than that. But regardless, if we were ever going to be able to sleep at night, Yin and I needed to *see* one of these guys.

Oh, we could have stopped there; we could have just manufactured the catalyst, sold it and made some money, but this puzzle was a long way from being solved. The mathematical model predicted that the particle should grow to as large as 1 micron in diameter by 3 microns in length. Using an electron microscope, I began the search. We had succeeded in creating what we *felt* were strong solutions and I had dehydrated those samples and had procured some time on an electron microscope at Caltech. I was pretty familiar with that microscope, having operated a similar one for several years in a former lab in Santa Monica, California.

An electron microscope uses a beam of (that's right) electrons to get its picture. Think of electrons as little charged bullets. If you heat a wire in a vacuum, these electrons fly off. They are too small to see, but they are there just the same.

The older TV sets before flat screens—remember the kind that used the big picture tube?—operated in a very similar fashion to an electron microscope (it is called an SEM, for *scanning electron microscope*). In the back of a big TV picture tube there is a gun (essentially a hot wire) that shoots out a stream of electrons to the front of the TV picture tube. The little charged bullets (electrons) excite the coating that is painted on the back of the face of the TV screen, and when they hit that coating, it lights up and you see a picture.

With an electron microscope (SEM), it is very similar.

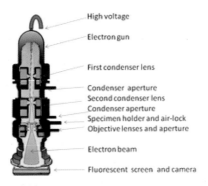

High voltage

Electron gun

First condenser lens

Condenser aperture
Second condenser lens
Condenser aperture
Specimen holder and air-lock
Objective lenses and aperture

Electron beam

Fluorescent screen and camera

Transmission Electron Microscope

You have a gun, in essence a coil of wire that heats up (shown above); next you have a series of lenses—not the kind in a camera, but they do the same thing: they focus the beam (actually they are made from magnets because the electrons can be affected by magnets); and finally you have a screen at the bottom, very much like the front of the old TV sets.

First, you create a beam with the hot wire; next you focus that beam with the magnets; and then you strike the sample.

The spray that comes off the target is called secondary electrons—basically it is stuff that is coming off the sample because it is being struck—and that stuff ends up hitting the screen (or detector) and you get a picture. SEMs have been around for a long time. Actually the first one was invented back in the thirties. I don't want this book to become an engineering manual—you can always read the papers in section two of this book if you want more technical detail; but when I was using this SEM, what I would see was a ghostlike image. It would be there for only a moment and then, as I would attempt to focus (hit it with more and more electrons), it would disappear. Frustrating—there, then gone; there, then gone.

There were hours of this aggravation, but I just had a feeling . . . *I was looking at the particle.* I didn't know enough about it at that juncture to get a photograph; as a result, those early photo attempts were a bust and I gave up on the SEM at that time. However, my hunch turned out later to be correct.

The next possible piece of equipment that we thought might work was a new microscope called the *atomic force microscope.* These particles are too small to see with a normal light microscope, the kind you would find in a doctor's office or chemistry department. Those microscopes are limited to magnifying something about a thousand times. An electron microscope can magnify up to a million times, although it is difficult to get a good picture at that power; they are better at 50,000 to 100,000 power—at least that is where I got my best images in the past.

But the atomic force microscope is currently the top of the line for looking at something small. It was not even invented until the 1980s and the two physicists who did so received the Nobel Prize; it was also not commercially available until the 1990s. Today the newest standard, sort of the crown jewel of AFMs (atomic force microscopes), is the Veeco Innova. (I've got one of those in my lab—pretty cool, huh?) The Innova can actually see atoms. Atoms are measured in units called angstroms; there are 10 billion angstroms in a meter—small, to say the least.

The Innova has resolutions down into the 1 to 2 angstrom range. So, since you find almost all atoms in combination with other atoms, you are going to be able to see them with an AFM.

Back then in the mid-nineties, Yin and I did not own an AFM; consequently we found ourselves, one early morning, traveling to Santa Barbara to a company called Digital (this was the company that was later bought by Veeco). We had only so much money in our pockets and the use of the microscope was by the hour, one rate for the equipment and an additional rate for the operator. We began the day in total exuberance, just knowing that we would quickly find this particle. Sure, it might take an hour or two, but certainly no more than that; there was the fact that the time was quite expensive and we did have our budget. . . . *Eight hours later*, we were way past our budget, our pockets were empty (now into our credit cards), and . . . nothing.

The problem is that you are not looking for a needle in the haystack; you are looking for a microscopic fragment of that needle.

We were soon confronting the end of the day and the end of our money; the operator wanted to go home (the rest of the staff had left hours before), and Yin and I were both about as glum as we could be. It was not only the fact that we had spent a lot of cash; even more, it was that sense of disappointment we had felt so many times before. There comes a point where you really start to question if what you are doing is right—were we in fact merely chasing a ghost?

Having a background with electron microscopes, I think the thing that lifted my spirits for a moment was that I wanted to see what this new world-class scope could do. I had seen photos that had been taken with this new invention, and the SEM could not come close to the resolution or the magnification; so I said to the operator, "Show me what this AFM can do—let's take her for a spin." We had been simply searching and paying no attention to occasional debris particles that we would see, as we knew we were not interested in just any random contaminant. But at that moment I wanted some kind of a ride for buying the ticket, and a very expensive ticket at that. I wanted a front-row show; so I asked the operator to find any piece of dirt or debris, a bug—something—and demonstrate the machine's ability.

Even the operator brightened up, as it took his attention off the fact that his dinner was long since cold at home; and to show off the machine—well, he was up for that; that was cool. So he began searching for whatever large piece of contamination he could find and then started to focus in more closely on the detail of a piece of junk he had spotted. He and his equipment were definitely impressing me, as more and more features came into focus while he adeptly manipulated the device. With an atomic force microscope you are not seeing the particle with light as you would with a regular microscope, and you are not seeing the image of the particle as you would if you were using an electron microscope. No, an atomic force microscope is actually *feeling* the particle. It is touching the particle with an infinitesimally gentle hand. It is like a blind man feeling his way around a room, except in this case the hand that is out there feeling is a small electric charge on the apex of a minuscule tip. It "feels," then it takes the delicate sensation it receives on the electrically charged tiny tip and translates that information through a computer, and then slowly, ever so slowly, the computer begins to draw a picture.

We were scanning along the side of the debris particle (probably a piece of carbon)—the operator adjusting, adjusting, so as to get a better image—when all of a sudden there was a change. The debris particle was sitting on something, something that looked rod shaped. "What's that?" I asked. The operator looked at me and said, "Don't know . . . never seen that before."

What do you know—another *"What's that?"* Perfect. I yelled for Yin, since he had stepped out of the room; and he surely saw the expression on my face as he ran back in, because at that moment he yelled, "Measure it!"

The math model had predicted that the largest of the particles should be 1 micron in diameter by 3 microns in length.

The operator used his software contained in the program of the microscope, then he turned to us and said, "It's 1 micron fat and 3 microns long."

Unbelievable. Unbelievable! We had just found, *by total chance,* our first particle. The odds of finding that particle, when you consider how long it takes to go only a few millionths of an inch with the tip of the AFM, would be akin to if there were only one rock on the entire surface of Mars that proved the existence of life and you traveled the fifty or so million miles to get there and your ship just happened to set down on that very specific rock, and then as you took your first step out of the spacecraft you tripped over it. That is what I mean by *unbelievable.*

The problem with doing one of these searches with the AFM is that there are so many parameters that have to be set just exactly right to see something, and then you are searching in the dark on unknown land. So if you have never found a sample of what you are looking for, you are missing all that necessary input data to tell the microscope how to feel. Is

23

it pushing too hard? Does it have too much pressure on the tip? Is the electrical charge set perfectly to be able to sort of talk to the particle? Is it the right tip and the right voltage on the tip? You almost have to have photographed the thing before you can photograph it—if that makes any sense to you. But it is true.

Now that the operator could see and feel the first particle, he quickly set all the parameters based upon that data and . . . BANG!—they were everywhere throughout the solution. We had suspected that this solution would have large numbers, as, based on his model, Yin had predicted a method that would make these guys grow. And grow they did. All of a sudden we forgot how broke we were.

It was a great drive back to Los Angeles from Santa Barbara. We had finally found our guy.

Now, you will see in the papers in the second part of the book many of those early photos. They look rather primitive, but they were the beginning. Today with top-of-the-line equipment they look more like this:

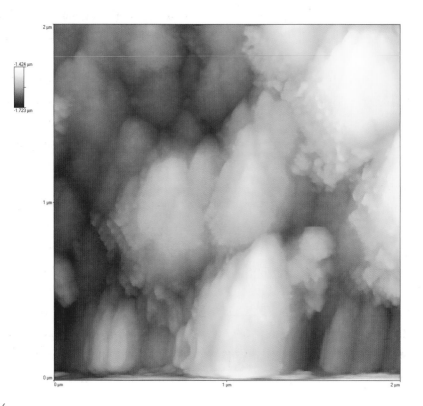

This is a very concentrated solution. Here the particles are stacked up like a snow drift. Those earlier photos have far fewer particles, but over the years we have learned a great deal about concentrating these guys.

But back to the story. A year or so later, we purchased our own first atomic force microscope and became quite proficient in looking at many different samples, including the original sample that had started the entire adventure.

That original sample definitely contained the same particle, but in very small amounts. This then led us into beginning to look at—yes, you guessed it—homeopathic solutions. That was an interesting adventure. We discovered that some solutions contain these particles and some don't. It is probably why there is a mixed result with many of the preparations.

What we found was that there is an exact procedure necessary to prepare a sample so it would actually contain what Yin would call in his first published paper, in 1996, I_E. This was *Ice* formed under an *Electric* field. That paper—"Anomalous State of Ice," *Modern Physics Letters B*, Vol. 10, No. 19 (1996), 909–919—is included in the second part of this volume: *Anomalous* (irregular, unusual) and *Ice* because there were numerous ice crystals known to form because of high pressure (not temperature). It was a bit of a misnomer and our first attacks came from this paper, mostly from individuals whom I like to call the Ice Guys. These were chemists and physicists who had spent their lives studying different forms of ice. And an ice that formed at room temperature without being inside a stainless steel chamber with thousands of pounds of pressure did not, and still doesn't, fit with what was known.

But Yin's extension of the Debye-Hückel equations suggested that an extreme electrical (not atmospheric) pressure was created around the single charged ion particle when the distance became great enough to where the "cheerleader" could not get together with the "basketball captain."

Boy, nothing fitted with what was known! This was not a little on the fence; this was totally outside the park, down the road and in the lake.

But we kept going—Yin theorizing, me building. Our purpose was to create an environmentally safe hydrogen-oxygen particle that would be as clean as water, was made from water, and would hold a big charge (like a little battery), which we could attach to a hydrocarbon (gasoline or diesel) and make it burn cleanly. It was a worthy venture.

We next steered ourselves to the chemical engineering department at UCLA. The chairman at that time was Selim Senkan, an excellent fellow and well respected in the hydrocarbon world. Chemical engineering is mostly about oil, as that is what drives the wheels on planet Earth. With Selim's help, we wanted to take this new catalyst and perfect it.

Selim suggested that the big concern was at refineries and a quick entrance into that arena would be to solve their coking problem. Now, coking is essentially carbon build-up—just like on your barbecue grill at home; there is lots of carbon there because everything does not completely burn. And that unburned carbon at the refinery level is a pain, as it costs money to clean it away.

Plastics come from petroleum; and try to find something today that is not made of the stuff—it is a huge, huge industry. Look around, what do you see—plastics, right? At a refinery you take natural gases, or something similar, and you put those gases through a process to make the basic ingredient in plastic. Without getting into detail (if you want detail, read Selim's paper in part two of this book), it is a dirty procedure and the big expense is this carbon build-up (coking) in the reactors where the operation is done. You run the process and within a month or so you have to stop and clean, clean, clean the equipment before you can start again.

Consequently it would be a good thing to slow down that build-up or even eliminate it altogether if possible.

So, working with Selim, an experiment was set up at UCLA to see if this new particle could create a difference in the rate of coke build-up. That work is presented in a paper in the second section of this book, called "Suppression of Coke Formation in the Steam Cracking of Alkanes: Ethane and Propane."

We set up a test reactor and first determined if this reactor would show a similar rate of coke build-up to what one would find within the industry. It did. And the results of the study showed that in the presence of the additive, we reduced coking by a factor of 4, first time without any modifications—an exciting result.

26

If you read Selim's paper ("The effects of an H_2PtCl_6 additive on the rate of formation of coke deposits . . ."), it is going to state that the additive was a minute solution of platinum chloride; but, of course, it was a stable-water-cluster solution.

Now, that test showed us that we could greatly reduce carbon build-up at the refinery level, and we had seen this same effect in trucks and buses for several years. We had engines that even after 200,000 to 300,000 miles were as clean as a spoon—no carbon, period.

But this was not the most interesting thing that occurred during this same time frame as I perfected a method of using the electron microscope to photograph the particle. Remember in the beginning I had tried but was unsuccessful due to the beam destroying the particle.

We had arrived at a better understanding of the particle and had modified the way we prepared the samples for the SEM. One afternoon I got a great photo but I also noticed there was a bug on the same sample—a bacteria. As I examined that bug, I realized the small particles had ruptured the protein sack surrounding the bacteria and thus his guts had spilled out across the sample slide—one dead bug. *This water appeared to demonstrate an antibacterial action.*

I had noticed something similar in the lab before this picture, which had given me an inkling that it was pretty difficult to grow bugs in this water. Normally that is a big problem with lab water, as it is very pure and bugs totally dig it—no chlorine; very pure water equals bug hotel. To keep lab water clean and pure, it must stay moving through a series of filters and strong ultraviolet light.

I had tested some water out of a production line that had been closed down for several months in a warm warehouse. This was stagnant water and I had told one of the engineers that he would need to flush the lines, use a ton of bleach, etc., and then begin flushing the lines with clean water until we got it free of all the bugs.

The engineer came back into my office with a sample of the water and said, "Smell this." It had no odor. The water was perfectly clean—no bugs. So when I saw this bacteria on the slide, I thought, *Interesting.* You could see that the particles had stuck all around the sides of the bug, and they were just the perfect size to create havoc in the bug's life—there was no way for him to grow.

The large oblong mass is the body of the bacteria and the small point-like structures are the stable water clusters.

I showed this photo to Selim, who in turn said I should take it to his friend who was head of the Department of Immunology at the UCLA Medical School. That was Benjamin Bonavida. Benjamin asked me about our work and wanted to know what this particle was. I told him that the particular one we were looking at was grown from a single charged platinum particle, although in truth you would not be able to find any particle of the metal in the solution but you would find a bunch of these ice-like particles. I went on to say it was possible that these ice-like particles might act as the original.

Benjamin became interested in the work, and he told me that platinum was one of the only true immunogens (something that would stimulate and trigger specific T-cell reactions), but the dilemma was that platinum had significant toxic effects in the body. It did not take a lot of platinum to create substantial problems.

We set up a series of experiments (controlled blind studies), and that work is represented in the paper by Bonavida "Induction and Regulation of Human Peripheral Blood TH1-TH2 Derived Cytokines by I_E Water Preparations and Synergy with Mitogens," B. Bonavida, X. H. Gan, Department of Microbiology and Immunology, UCLA School of Medicine.

The solutions used were a control (distilled water) and then our I_E water solution, which had in fact no platinum, just the particle that was formed from water, using platinum as a template. Possibly you might find one true metal particle in ten million ice crystals, but for the most part the metal would be gone.

Bonavida had seen actual platinum results previously and knew that such solutions would trigger a response, but our solutions compared to former results and the controls were *thousands* of times more active.

It was an exciting outcome, as it showed that the I_E we had made was extremely active in stimulating T-cells to secrete specific cytokines. (*Cytokines* are small secreted proteins that mediate and regulate immunity; the ones specific to the study were those which the body needs to fight cancer.) These blind studies really opened our eyes to the fact that we had stumbled onto something of significant importance. Even though it did not directly support Benveniste's earlier work, there was simply too much similarity to ignore. Now with the advent of a bona fide scientific model of why ultradilute preparations could work and the understanding of what this particle looked like, there just was no question: we were opening the door to some new key principle of healing, whether it be homeopathy or not. Truth be told, we were heading down a path that was going to make allopathic medicine take notice. This was not "Hey, we really don't understand the chemistry here but we will continue to run statistical studies." No, this was the first indication that maybe we could understand exactly, from a physics and chemistry point of view, why preparations work and, more specifically, how they actually get into the body. All chemical preparations pass into the body via the liver. Here was something that was already at the right size and basically a water particle that could instantly get to work directly on a cellular level. We were looking at the potential to develop safe revolutionary treatments for a host of serious illnesses.

Do you recall how I mentioned that Benveniste should have just painted a bull's-eye on this chest—remember that?

Well, we had just put a huge *X* on our heads like the ones the U.S. Air Force would use when they dropped an H-bomb on a Pacific test island.

My life and Yin's were about to change significantly for the worse.

Chapter 4

The Dangers of Discovery

So, what happened? What was it that caused Yin and me so much grief? Remember the visit from the Australian Secret Service, and the Baser, the high-energy beam—*the very high energy beam of enlarged particle clusters*? To give you some idea of *how much* energy, a laser would be to a Baser as a fly swatter would be to a Tomahawk cruise missile.

A *laser* is a coherent beam of light, and in physics, coherence is the principle of everything going in the same direction, at the same time. With light, this means that all the particles of light (called photons) are aligning and moving together. All the random motion is gone and therefore power and direction increases through the roof. Because of the property of coherence, you could take the same amount of energy that you use to light your bedroom (100 watts) and, focusing it with coherence, send a beam all the way to the moon and back.

Coherence is power. Hollywood likes to show lasers blowing things up; but, in truth, lasers actually generate only heat—not impact. *Force* (how hard something hits) is equal to *Mass* (how big something is, how much it weighs) multiplied by how fast it is going (*Acceleration*): (F=MA)—a very basic law of physics. But a photon (the actual particle of light) weighs nearly nothing—it is almost mass-less. Therefore, even if it is moving at tremendous speed (which it is; light is really cooking across the universe—it takes it only nine minutes to get here from the sun), when it strikes something, it creates little impact. Yin, years prior to meeting me, had been writing papers on the idea that it would be possible to get larger particles to display the property of coherence. Being a quantum physicist, he had been investigating for over twenty years the concept of applying this to something practical and useful.

The project at Caltech was that first big step to proving the existence of coherence with particles larger than light.

We were working with helium (the gas you put in a kid's balloon). We successfully cooled it down to approximately minus 450 degrees Fahrenheit, where Yin had predicted the atoms would lock into a coherent mass and could then be manipulated with an electric field.

That was 1996, and to further validate this work, Roy Glauber, a physicist from Harvard, in 2005 received the Nobel Prize for doing the theoretical calculations on the principle of coherence.

I truly believe that this was very likely one of the most important projects in physics since the splitting of the atom. An unprecedented team assembled: Alfred Wong, who had received the John Dawson Award for Excellence in Plasma Physics Research, was there; Yau, the Fields Medalist in mathematics was behind the scenes helping; plus a long list of the top guys, including scientists from the Berkeley fusion team.

So what brought all these great minds together? **Clean energy**. With the Baser, fusion—the dream energy—was not a dream; it was a real potential.

Fusion is what happens on the sun: atoms get squeezed together and energy is released. It is the ultimate clean, limitless energy machine. When planet Earth has fusion, we as a race—all humankind—will have a real shot at survival. With clean energy, the oil wars stop, the pollution stops, and a new age—a true renaissance on Earth—could begin.

Oh sure, there are those who will say, "No matter what, man is destined to fry himself." I don't believe it. With abundant energy, a peaceful planet could become a reality. The problem that has plagued mankind has been this idea that there is not enough to go around and consequently you must have the biggest club or the sharpest spear or the fastest missile to keep that pesky neighbor on the other side of the fence. Since there is always a shortage of food and fresh water, he is sure to sneak through the night and steal you blind.

But think of this: What if the world had all the energy it wanted? Could not that neighbor feed himself? In a drought, could he not pump water to his crops?

Well, stop right there. *Everybody knows* there is only so much fresh water on Earth, correct? Stop right there again, because those *everybody knows* statements are based upon the lie that there is not enough to go around. It is possible (actually easy) with fusion energy to turn the oceans into drinking water. That's right. It simply takes heat energy to pull the salt away, and the only reason we don't do it for cities like Santa Barbara or Los Angeles is the cost of making the electricity to do so. With fusion, fresh water becomes unlimited.

With clean, limitless energy, the cost of living goes down, down, down. Cost of production of goods is based on the cost of heat (energy). You need a tractor to sow your crops. You have to dig the iron ore out of the ground (energy); you have to manufacture the steel to make the tractor (energy); you have to form the steel into parts (energy); you have to run the factories to assemble the tractor (energy); and you have to pay the workmen a wage (their cost of living is also directly dependent upon the cost of energy). It comes down to the fact that you need a source of cheap HEAT. One must boil the water to make steam; the steam must turn the turbines at the electric plant, and then the energy must be distributed around the country.

With fusion, nothing in this chain of events would change except the cost—it would plummet.

The old rules of Earth would spin away into the cosmos and a totally new age would begin. Really take a look at this: What are the world's conflicts fought over? It's always *there is not enough to go around.* Pure survival is the bottom-line issue. It is easy to get a third-world country up in arms if the kids don't eat or there are no medical supplies for the pregnant moms. Sure, there are many who benefit from war, but in the end what do they want? They are always fighting over the idea that there is not enough to go around.

Now, we can't talk about energy without understanding the difference between *fission* and *fusion*.

Fission is splitting atoms, which is the kind of nuclear energy we have now. It is very dirty, very problematic, as you must use extremely heavy and unstable masses (uranium) in order to produce heat. You split an atom into smaller pieces and you release energy. This is the $E=mc^2$ equation we know from Einstein. With fission energy, you get very deadly byproducts—stuff that stays radioactive for thousands of years—and for all realistic reasoning, it is just an insane pain in the rear to try to handle the process and the byproducts. Heck, even the bomb makers said it was nuts and moved to fusion as a way to make a really big bomb. But we are not talking about making a bomb; we have more than enough of those. We are talking about producing *clean energy* with fusion. How much energy is possible with fusion? If you take a cup of gasoline, how far can you run your car? Well, depending on the particular car you are driving, it will vary; but somewhat of an average would probably be one to two miles (16 cups in a gallon). Now, what would happen if you released all of the *nuclear energy* in that same gasoline—same amount of mass, just release all of the energy stored in the tiny centers of the atoms? Would you believe that on the same cup of gasoline, you could drive your car a million miles? That is the power of fusion.

And that is the exact reason why this society and societies around the world have been convinced (on purpose) that fusion is *way, way, way* in the future; that basically anyone who even suggests it must be crazy.

Now, why would *anyone* want to perpetuate a lie like that? *Duh!* Who owns planet Earth? The oil industry. I am not saying that those guys are in some big conspiracy to stop science; but, in truth, fusion has been a household word in the hydrogen weapons industry for over fifty years! We have been manufacturing hydrogen (fusion) weapons in mass production style *since the late 1950s.* The equations and the math are known, the triggers are known—and the military has made tens of thousands of them! Yin and I were among the first civilians to be invited to the main nuclear weapons factory in the U.S. about fifteen years ago to determine how to clean up the mess that was left behind when the U.S. government decided to close Rocky Flats (one of our nation's nuke factories).

It is so easy to stop science; essentially, you tell the smart guys that if they do anything outside the doors of the secret military facilities, they are committing an act of treason and you will shoot them. That tends to keep them in line. So consequently the governments of the world have made talking about nuclear energy DANGEROUS. Just like Yin found out when he first brought up the idea in Melbourne: talk—get shot.

What the Baser team wanted to do was to take their *knowledge* of atomic physics and do something constructive—they wanted to make simple clean, cheap power.

Yin and his friends ran the calculations and found that the exact same impact energies that cause hydrogen weapons to explode were possible with a coherent beam of particles. That meant fusion was *real*. Sure, there was engineering to do, but the first atomic energy was produced with 1930 technology. What would happen if we ramped up the program with 2010 technology?

We were in the horse-and-buggy days when Marie Curie in 1898 discovered radioactive material. By 1905 Albert Einstein had whipped up his $E=mc^2$ equation. By 1919, the first true transmutation of one atom to another was done by Rutherford. In another fifteen years Fermi set up the first nuclear reaction, and a few years after that, in 1939, Einstein wrote a letter to FDR saying that Hitler would surely build a bomb and the U.S. better get off its butt and do something.

Do you see what happens when you simply let science roll? A society went from horse and buggy to a nuclear weapon in less than fifty years?

It happens when discovery is based upon observation and experimentation, with future predictions determined by mathematics.

In forty-one years, 1898 to 1939, there was an exponential explosion of knowledge, only to be sealed in an impregnable granite tomb with the advent of the Manhattan Project. The moment that project began, a lock and key was placed on any and all further development of nuclear energy (both fission and fusion). Nukes from that point forward were the property of the military.

So the hope of mankind, the promise of unlimited clean energy, energy that does not create greenhouse gases, energy that could be used to light, heat and power the world into the next millennium, was put under the absolute control of organizations whose purpose was to win wars.

It is not that I don't understand the rationale behind such a decision, but give me a break; it was not the sanest direction in which to point society. At the time, there was no real understanding of what burning carbon-based fossil fuels would do to the survival potential of the planet, plus you had cheap oil flowing out of every pore in Texas. Oil became power, and power was political and military might. But today, even if we had cheap oil, it is just not an option to keep burning it. Contrary to what you might hear in the news, there is absolutely no debate among legitimate scientists that we have the choice to burn it or not burn it. Get yourself a CO_2 meter and go outside and measure the carbon dioxide level. It is higher now than it has ever been in 300,000 years. Why? Because we burn around 3,000 pounds of carbon *per person*, per year. That means about 19.5 trillion pounds of carbon are going into a blanket around the earth every 365 days. It adds up and has been for nearly a hundred years. Yes, it is affecting and will continue to affect the climate, and yes, the earth's population is on an exponential growth curve and that means this number is rising faster than the national debt. And if we don't fix it soon, you can forget about the national debt, as well as all your credit card debt and all your kids and grandkids.

But wait a minute, you ask, how did we get into fusion from the water particle technology, and what happened to Yin and David having their lives turned upside down?

Sorry, but there is just no way to tell this tale without this background. You will see how it all fits together soon.

We formed a small public company to raise money to fund the Baser project at Caltech. Within a few years we had raised four or five million at a stock price of around one to three dollars. We had friends and family, anyone we personally knew, help. Our cry was, "Buy stock." It actually was not that difficult. People wanted to help; there is an innate deep interest in wanting to bring about a future for the earth where we would be pollution free.

We moved the Baser equipment from the lab that I described earlier (where I first met Yin) to Caltech and put the team together. It was not an overnight project, but for the first several years we were progressing fantastically. Then, out of the blue, we had a visit from a heavyweight technical team sent from Germany. Two young hands-on engineers, with strong physics backgrounds, came and spent a week with Yin and me at Caltech. They had been hired by a large industrial bank in Germany that had read an article about the Baser and consequently sent these guys to investigate and write a technical report on the promise and progress of the work.

Within several weeks we saw their report. It stated that the technology was absolutely real, progress was excellent and we should be a $50 stock. Whoever was behind that group—we suspected a bank—then began to purchase a large quantity of the available shares. There was little for sale; thus the company's stock in a matter of several months went from several dollars to nearly $20 a share.

Now, one would think that all would be grand with such a success story, right? High stock price, knowledgeable people validating the progress—all should be well, with the company safe and the project in high gear. But remember, in reality, a small penny-stock company, having a very high stock price and no actual sales or immediate products in sight, is in a very tricky spot. As long as the company has the continued support of the people who are driving the stock up, no problem; but . . . in this case . . . there was a problem.

Many of the original stock purchasers were delighted. It had been several years since their investment and it seemed like a perfect time to take some profit. The price was still rising, the group out of Germany was buying up the shares—what could be wrong with this?

Without anyone knowing it, a nuclear warhead was about to detonate.

A number of my friends who had originally purchased stock belonged to my church. There was nothing untoward about that. Church folk normally have a moral code that they adhere to, and creating a future for us all could definitely align with such.

The people I had introduced to the company had been very helpful from day one and some wanted to take advantage of the high stock price and donate a percentage of their shares. These were affluent people and rather than just selling their stock and buying a new car or a new watch, they donated their stock to their church, and consequently an account at a major stock house began to show up with these shares. Every week the donated shares went on the block. What could be wrong with that, you ask—donating money to one's church, a great market for them, a strong buyer out of Germany grabbing every available share?

It just so happens that my church is a very outspoken critic of many current social ills, one of the largest being the drugging of America via prescribed pharmaceuticals; and you might have guessed it by now, Scientology is my religion. During that particular time, there was an actual attempt in Germany to pass legislation to outlaw Scientology. Now, I am not here to tout my religion and we need only state the truth, and that is that the legislation was finally dropped due to public outcry. But somehow, and as much of a surprise to our little company and those who were a part of it, that group or bank was, I believe, tied by *some* means into the German attack on my church, probably not directly but via influence. So, whether they thought that they had just been taken by the church or that this had simply been bad planning on their part, it made no difference; what came about was, in my estimation, a significant short selling of the company's stock.

If you are unfamiliar with selling short, let me give you shorting 101. You sell stock that you don't own with the idea that the stock is going to fall and you can go out and buy it at a lower price to give it to the person you originally sold it to.

So, if you know it is going to go down, you borrow the stock and sell it; then you wait for the stock to fall. For instance, if you sold it at $15, you wait till it falls to $14; then you buy those shares and deliver them to the guys you sold them to and make a profit.

Now, here is where the illegal activities *may* come into play. Short sellers can be complete thugs. It is hard to find and convict them of their wrongdoing, but what they may sometimes do is start rumors or just post all-out lies on the Internet. They have been known to do whatever it takes to create a panic. Some short sellers have a motto: "Give NO quarter!"

To begin with, the company had *absolutely* **nothing** to do with my church; as a matter of fact, Yin Lo and all the scientists and the vast majority of the stockholders were not members or even supporters. The question, "What is your religion?" never came up.

But this was a sad, sad day. Here was a company that had technology that could help the world and it was caught in a vicious hate war.

Within days, the Internet was used to tell people that the entire company was crooked, that the technology was a scam, and that there were aliens and little green men running around the back rooms having cult rituals in every hallway of the company; therefore your investment is crap, as this bunch of devil worshippers is using it to make pornographic movies for convicted felons.

OK, I may be exaggerating. But if you were around then, well . . . Yet I am sure you will back me up on this: Once a short begins, especially with a company that has yet to sell its products and consequently has no earnings, there is not much one can do to stop it. There is a frantic effort for people to not lose their investment, so an avalanche of selling begins.

Now, what made matters worse was that the CEO (and controlling stockholder) came up with a plan to save the company, which in fact became the last nail in the coffin. He made a deal with what I believe was a fly-by-night multilevel group that was selling some scam laundry ball (and yes, in my opinion, it was a scam) to take a bunch of money from these guys to save the company. Yin and I both violently opposed getting involved with the multilevel group, but somehow they had gotten to the CEO and the promise of big dollars carried him into la-la land. A used-car-salesman type of a guy had put together a scheme to sell a plastic ball filled with what he called charged water (we tested the water and found no such charge). They had sold a lot of them based on the fact that this product was going to save the environment, but in truth it had little to no workability.

They came to us because they were already being investigated by several attorney generals in different states, and the bright idea of our CEO was that our scientists would make their laundry balls work.

Well, we quickly discovered that the concept was not workable and told them to add a surfactant (the thing that is in detergents to wash your clothes).

But it was too late; the little bit of money that was brought in by the CEO was insufficient to buy enough stock to hurt the short sellers.

Other salvage attempts were to bring in a number of heavyweight government people—one former Under Secretary of Energy, one former Assistant Secretary of Commerce, and even a former head of the NSA—but no one could put Humpty Dumpty back together again.

At this same time we were doing our first International Symposium on the Stable Water Clusters at UCLA and we presented Bonavida's results, which only strengthened Benveniste's findings and which I believe opened the door for still more attacks. It was a good time to kill this attempt at some real science in the world.

The real catastrophe was that this large group of world-class scientists, the people who had helped on the Baser and those you will see in the next section of this book—competent and admirable researchers who had openly given their names and support to the projects—were dragged through the mud, just by association.

And for what? A hate crime.

I, because of my association with my church, was asked to leave, and it was not long after that, that Yin left on his own accord.

But, there is always another door opening as one closes. This is true if you have the right attitude. And it was true for us, as there have been nothing but advancements for the water technology (as you will soon see in the next chapters), and also Yin never stopped his theoretical research into the Baser. He disclosed to me about six months ago an entirely new concept of how to make fusion occur with coherent particles (the principle behind the original Baser concept but with a totally new, easy approach). When he told me about it, I didn't sleep for a week. I still wake up at night and think, "We have to move quickly; the earth clock is ticking, and this will work."

However, I want to stay focused here on the water technology. I will write more later on the Baser.

The attacks that finished the company off were directed at the "magic water." Actually almost all of the attacks were focused on the water. It was just too difficult to attack the Baser. How do you attack Caltech? Plus the people on the project were the best of the best, and no one except a real physicist could understand it anyway to write something against it. So the attackers went for the water. They linked it all the way back to Benveniste's work in *Nature*, called the entire episode a scam to sell laundry balls, and dragged Yin into some insane attorney-general witch hunt. It was evil, absolute pure evil—and what was behind it? It started and continued as a hate crime, and it was directed toward a church that had become an outspoken critic of several German-based pharmaceutical giants.

But enough; what did occur was that Yin and I went sort of underground for years. We licked our wounds but continued. Yin's life changed for the worse; his wonderful wife and close friend of mine became very ill and passed away, I believe from all the insanity of those years. Yet out of senseless sadness came another door: Yin in the years that followed met someone who is a joy, and with focus on science, he is doing some of his best work ever.

A number of years ago we built a lab in the Midwest and have continued day and night to complete our mission. So what has happened in these last fifteen years with this water? I think you will find this interesting.

Chapter 5

A Summary of Research Thus Far

Let us take a moment and summarize the information I have given you so far on the water research. Getting sidetracked into the development of the Baser may have confused the issue a bit, so let's get back on track with the research we are most focused on—water, water . . . water!

To recap, Yin and I had stumbled across a catalytic effect within a water *sample* that had been given to me by a backyard inventor. He, the inventor, claimed it was a *water-based* catalyst. When Yin and I analyzed it chemically, it came back as distilled water; but when I used it in several large diesel test engines, it had a definite catalytic effect, just as if I were using a known chemical catalyst.

This puzzle drew Yin and me into a two-year search to find out how in the world an analyzed pure-water sample could have such a strong catalytic effect when added into a combustion cycle. Ordinary water had no such effect, so what was it about this particular water that created this action?

Yin theorized that the person who had given this to me had simply diluted the platinum chloride I had given him; but if that were true, why couldn't we detect it? And if it was diluted to the point that we could not find it with the sophisticated equipment we were employing, then how in the dickens was it causing this strong catalytic effect?

To add to the mystery, the person who had handed me the sample had given me the data that the water contained the "fields" from the metal catalyst I had supplied and suggested that some sort of electronic equipment had been used to imprint the water. That piece of false information certainly didn't help the research along.

Within those first several years we did learn that Yin had been correct in his assumption that the platinum had merely been diluted, and we eventually discovered that the person was using a simple homeopathic routine with a slight twist. That slight twist had indeed helped to concentrate the strong effect I was seeing with my test engines.

But even here, it was a fickle effect; some solutions we were given from the same inventor were not workable. So, why was there such an inconsistency in result? That part of the puzzle was pretty simple—there was no real understanding of the underlying mechanism by the inventor and therefore little or no way to predict what was going to happen.

Yin took Debye's mathematical model for dilute solutions and pushed it way past Debye's own work. He extended Debye's equations further into lower and lower dilutions. No one had attempted to construct the mathematical model that would go into this ethereal land of dissolved ions below parts per million. Yin did. Remember him running into my office yelling, "I know what's in the water! I CALCULATED it"? Well, that was his math predicting the existence of a new particle—one that would form from water itself.

Now, the right question to ask is, what happened to the original contamination—or whatever you want to call it—that you were diluting? We used salt in our earlier example, and the sodium part was the cheerleader while the chloride part was the basketball captain.

To dilute means you simply retain a small portion of the original solution and add more water. Recall our analogy was that the cheerleader and the captain want to get together, but if you put enough water between them, their plus and minus charges lose contact with each other. Let's envision here (keeping in mind this is just an analogy; please read the papers in the back of the book if you want exactness) that the cheerleader and the captain are good people and they each have a halo around them. This halo (analogy to the electric force around the single charged particle) normally goes outward and reaches for the opposite halo. When the cheerleader extends her halo as far as she can to see if any captain of the team is out there looking for her but gets no response, she gives up and lets go. When that outward reach—that outward concentric circle of charge—is extended . . . but does not connect . . . it then comes back in, creating an intense pressure.

That pressure grabs eight water molecules and squeeeeeeezes.

This collapsing squeeze is the pressure that Yin calculated would cause what he originally thought was an ice particle. He thought this because there is a known ice that forms as a result of extreme pressure—it is called *ice VI* and it forms at 100,000 pounds per square inch at room temperature. The reason he used this analogy was that the calculated pressure existing in close proximity to a single charged ion would definitely be of similar magnitude. But the analogy sort of stops short, as these are *electrical* pressures, not *atmospheric* pressures from which the ice VI forms.

The more Yin and I understood about the particle through the research, the more we realized that it was not an ice particle and we needed a new name for it.

I am not saying this will be the last name, since this is still an evolving science; but we then named the particle C_E for a water Cluster formed under an Electric field.

Now, another question to ask here is, why can't one detect this ion that would be in the center of all these water particles? What happened to the original cheerleader or captain and why can't you find either of them in a chemical analysis? Good question, but there is an answer.

Once that first particle forms, once the cheerleader or captain collapses and the eight water molecules entomb the single ion in a solid water cluster, it has a big charge to it. And it is this charge that begins to beget other clusters, except the others have no cheerleaders or captains in them; they are just water. Then if certain conditions are kept in effect, these clusters grow like the most uninhibited rabbits on the planet—they multiply into extreme numbers.

If one looks back to homeopathy for a moment, the adage that more dilute means stronger could actually be true *if*—and this is the big *if*—certain conditions are held. Contamination is the real killer of the process, and I mean all forms of contamination. Additionally, the axiom in homeopathy that you must shake the solution can also fit here because these particles will attach themselves to their neighbors, but if you shake hard, they break apart making more places to grow more particles.

So this is where we are currently: *If one dilutes in water a material that will separate into ions, at dilutions near one part per million a new particle can form under very controlled conditions and that particle will beget and continue to beget itself IF the original conditions are maintained.*

Now let's look at recent developments and what Yin and I believe could be the future of this C_E.

The Fuel Catalyst

I want to start with the fuel catalyst, as this has been our main focus and is still one of Yin's and my long-term goals. So bear with me for a few pages; then I will get back to the biological and homeopathic path of this work.

Recently we have advanced by leaps and bounds toward a cleaner planet with this simple clean-water particle.

Remember water is made of oxygen and hydrogen; hydrogen is a very clean gas and oxygen is the stuff you need to breathe. When they are combined they create the substance we call water, which covers four-fifths of the earth. Plus—and there is not much debate to this point—it is where life began on Earth (again I am talking about biological life, not trying to make a statement of spirituality here).

On a practical side, we see routine results of 20 percent improved fuel economy by adding this simple water-based solid particle (our C_E) into diesel. We have focused more on diesel, although it works very well with gasoline too, but diesel is an easy place to create a big effect.

Diesel used to be much cheaper than gasoline and the majority of trucks on the road are of a design that has been around for forty or more years. You can still see the black smoke puffing from them as they're going up hills, but not as much in the U.S. recently, as federal and state

46

mandates are requiring cleaner fuels and higher maintenance. However, there is plenty of black smoke around; just head down to Mexico if you haven't seen any lately. This smoke is simply unburned fuel and it is caused by the engine deteriorating with the build-up of carbon. Diesels lose a small percentage of their fuel economy with each passing year of use because carbon continues to build within the working parts of the engine. Without going into a great amount of detail, engines have parts in them that need to be kept free of carbon to hold particular tolerances, and when those parts get coated with carbon, a process starts and continues that brings about the lessening of the fuel economy.

A common place for this to occur is with buses within any number of school districts in the U.S. Here you have a bus (diesel) that does a ton of stop-and-go driving, and school districts normally have little or no money for proper long-term maintenance of their vehicles. Oil and filter changes are usually all that can be afforded, as dollars do not exist to do major items like injector cleaning and extensive overhauls, which can slow this deterioration process.

A short while ago, to prove this point, we took a number of buses in a small school district in south Texas as a test. The school district had seen their buses deteriorate from 9 miles per gallon to between 4.5 and 5 mpg over a period of five to six years, which is typical.

With half of their economy gone, you would think the school would institute long-term maintenance and overhauls to regain the mileage, but in truth the school district has no cash to do so; consequently, the buses run until they break.

Within three months of adding this little C_E into their fuel, the buses were back to 9 miles per gallon and then increased to 9.5 mpg. We have seen this for fifteen years. This little hydrogen-oxygen particle (C_E) increases the fuel burn to a point where virtually no carbon builds in the engine. In the beginning it cleans away the existing carbon; then nothing builds—always. It is startling to see if you have a background in mechanics, as that level of clean just does not happen in an engine. When I say *virtually no carbon*, I mean virtually no carbon, period. The only times that I ever found something contrary to this statement (a "fail" test) were when someone "failed" to pour the C_E into the fuel—it has happened more than once; we discover the unopened container in the garage!

It takes no more than 10 percent of the mileage or hours on an engine to completely clean the carbon away—actually quite a bit less now with the latest preparations. And I mean *clean*—even the exhaust manifold will be spotless. Engines perform at their peak, the way they were designed to, and stay that way, literally, for their entire life (which can be two to three times their former life span). Plus the C_E particle creates an enhanced combustion, which equates to an additional 4 to 5 percent increase in the overall performance of the engine.

This typically is equivalent to more than 20 percent better mileage with diesel, because 90 percent of these vehicles on the road are NOT clean. This means that today, not tomorrow or after ten more years of testing or development—today—we could reduce the carbon load by 20 percent across the board with diesel. I actually would go out on a limb here and predict that we could do that across the board on all carbon-based fuels; that includes cars, ships, airplanes, boilers, etc.

If a fuel is carbon based, you can get it to burn cleaner with this C_E particle, which means you are going to burn less, and that means less carbon into the skies. And remember it is WATER. With sunlight it breaks back down to the liquid state once it gets into the atmosphere.

So, this fits completely with Yin's and my long-term goal of reducing carbon emissions to zero in the NEAR future. We are a fifth of the way there if we can just get some implementation of this simple technology.

While we are in the industrial area of this book and before we get back to the biological side, let's look at a few of the other potential uses of this clean little guy. As mentioned earlier, you can find a paper on the suppression of coking in part two. Coking is a major problem at the refinery level and this C_E has shown substantial reduction in that problem by as much as a factor of 4.

Using this process at the refinery could also reduce carbon into the atmosphere by 5 to 10 percent, potentially more. In addition, this same little charged water particle can prohibit the formation of calcium deposits; so there could be an increase in heat transfer in boilers, thus reducing the use of whatever heat source is needed to generate electricity—and yes, that will be a carbon-based fuel, normally coal.

There are literally hundreds, potentially thousands, of ways that a simple, clean water particle, which carries a very strong polar charge, could be used to help clean up our planet. Right now it appears that the focus of the U.S. is to get people to be more economical with their energy uses, which is a good idea *but*, if you noticed, does not work so well—especially if you consider that we share the same atmosphere as third-world countries. We need to come up with ways to be more efficient at the points where the energy is produced and consumed worldwide. And it must make economic sense to all parties involved. Fortunately, this one works.

Basically, Yin and I strongly believe that this is a core technological discovery. The discovery of a *highly charged polar particle* that is made from the most fundamental substance on Earth—water—should change the fabric of chemistry as transistors changed electronics.

Now let us look at more recent work; most of the things we have talked about happened ten to twelve years ago. The latest research is the most exciting, as we are convinced that what we have stumbled into is not necessarily a new *particle* of water but a new *phase* of water—quite honestly, something that has been around since the beginning of life on Earth. Yin and I believe that this is an undiscovered molecular phase of water. So let's get to that part of the story. I think it is the most fascinating because all life could have some roots with this particular phase of water.

Chapter 6

The First
Double-Helix Photos

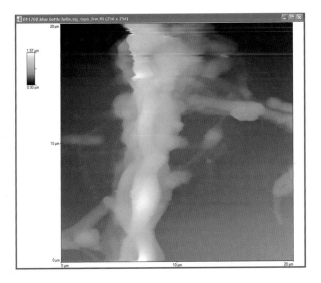

Sure looks like a double helix to me too. When we took that photo several years ago, it was a pretty exciting day. This was a solution which contained stable water clusters that had aged like wine for over ten years and became highly concentrated. It was a very similar solution to that which had been successful in stimulating T-cells in the first experiments with Benjamin Bonavida at UCLA and later with Norman Shealy (specifically, heightened interferon-γ—a protein produced by T-cells that goes after viruses, parasites and tumor cells). More recently, in the last few years, we have devised ways to concentrate these water clusters to very strong solutions, so that the above pictured helixes are easier to find, without the aging process. So, what do these new atomic force microscope photos mean? Why the double helix? And what does this structure have to do with water?

To begin, it *is* water, plain and simple; what we are viewing is a stable water cluster, but there is a slight difference—and we believe that change to be a different "phase." Remember we have talked about ice, liquid and steam being different phases of the same thing, water. We feel there is another phase, and that is because there is a slight alteration in the molecular structure.

In physics there is a principle known as *scaling*. Scaling is seen where the first structure replicates itself in a pattern, and that pattern will scale upward with multiple imitations to produce an overall composition that is—you got it—based upon the foundation. In simple terms, if you have a bunch of bricks laid in a circle and you continue to place the bricks on top of each other, you are going to end up with a smoke stack or silo, not a square chimney. Likewise with nature; consistent duplications of basic form that continue to carry through the entire whole are called scaling, and in this case scale up to be a double helix.

Now, scaling is not new news, but a double helix made out of water is. Let's go out on a limb again (sorry, there are no papers to back this up; so these assumptions are made here to spur on someone else to take a look in the lab). Let's take a guess that we are looking at something that could be somehow linked with the most known double helix, DNA.

Let's suppose that prior to biological life on Earth, the planet was covered with water—a very prominent theory. Now, we do know that these stable water clusters are pure H_2O, and I think it would also be an easy assumption that back billions of years ago on Earth there were no laboratories producing the same purity of water that I am pumping out of my labs. But here again, nature is seldom outdone and Mother Nature can produce a pure water molecule even in the dirtiest of places. How? At the moment of evaporation.

When water goes through the phase change from a liquid to a vapor, such as that which occurs as the sun evaporates water from the oceans and so forth, there is a fleeting moment when the water molecule is uncontaminated—a perfect H_2O molecule. Now, it is true that it would not last long in that state, as it would be surrounded by all sorts of contaminates in the air, and those other particles would be attracted to this pristine pure water. But there is no reason not to assume that in the abundance of nature during a period of vast evaporation some of the pure stuff would sneak through the dirty stuff unscathed long enough to create a stable water cluster.

How?

At that moment of evaporation, *if* a sharp change in electrical pressure, say, a lightning bolt or even, on a molecular level, a single charged particle, just happened to be uniquely present—bingo!—you would have one of these basic, basic stable water clusters. It is when those conditions align—pure water molecule and change in electrical pressure—that one has liquid water changing into a *solid state*. We are not talking temperature here, not talking ice; we are discussing the instant of the birth of a molecular solid state of water, or what we keep referring to as a *stable water cluster*.

And once the first one forms, it begets others. It replicates itself, not by some biological method, but by charge.

The charge present on the *solid state water molecule* pulls other water particles inward, and more of the solid state water molecules form, then break away; those, too, pull others inward to replicate, and one has— once you have seen this in the lab—a sort of bridging between the inanimate and animate.

This makes it even more interesting to take notice of the photo above; for as these particles continue to concentrate, their charge arrangement sets the basic foundation of a double helix.

Now, when and where does our most known helix, DNA, become something more than just matter?

From a biologist's point of view, it must be not only when an OH group (oxygen and hydrogen bond) is present but when nitrogen drops by; and once you have added carbon—*eureka*—it's alive!!! I realize I am being a bit dramatic and very simplistic, but when you add those ingredients, you have the basis of amino acids. From amino acids, you are staring right down the path of single-cell organisms.

Getting back to scaling for a moment: Understand that a helix is formed simply because the stable water cluster can bond or join with another stable water cluster, where its charges lie sort of like a facet on a stone foundation block—or better still, like the facets on the face of a cut diamond. Atoms combine because of the arrangement of their charge (plus or minus). Physics doesn't think that there are actual labels on the sides of the particle describing whether the charge is a plus or a minus, but merely that all matter has a tendency to pull inward or push outward because of a direction of its internal flow (that's right, all matter is in motion); and when certain flows get together, they want to attract or push away.

The key, I believe, to unlocking many of these mysteries is to look at the physical universe from a more simplistic viewpoint (again, the very skilled and learned people with chemistry and physics backgrounds should read the attached papers). There is nothing wrong with looking at details, but there is an infinity of detail in any direction one wants to venture. If we just observe what is lying before us, isn't it very plausible that, with this stable water cluster, we are looking at a basic, basic primary building block, which has its facets arranged perfectly to form a double helix—a kind of nature's Lego? Was not water present prior to life on Earth? Are we as biological entities (at least our protoplasmic part) not mostly water?

So what is this discovery? It would be wrong to imply that this is something chemical or pharmaceutical or that we are creating something that is meant to cure the ills of the world. What we must be careful to do is to steer this down a road where the science stays science and we don't venture into the total commercialism avenue, which Norman so aptly summarized in the introduction.

But it would also be wrong to stay silent about our work and not make it available to the public at large. So that is why this book is being written.

And quite honestly, we are getting to the most interesting part of the story—what has happened in the last three years.

Chapter 7

Stepping Further into the Water

It was because of my experience and background in what one might call "outside of the box" engineering that, in 2006, I was approached by several people who were experimenting with a piece of electronic equipment that they felt had healing properties. Now, I may give the wrong impression by characterizing my background as nonstandard, so I should rephrase that and say that my last thirty or more years of lab experience has nearly always been focused on what one would call experimental or *uncharted science*. The scientific community is a rather conservative group and not very many people want to step too far out of the agreed-upon circle of acceptance, as you can quickly get a reputation for being a bit weird. You can be eccentric, just not *weird*. Look what happened to Benveniste; there is a good example of what can occur if you stray too far from the flock. Hopefully this book is not Yin's and my introduction into the "weird hall of fame."

The problem in research always comes back to, if you stay within the accepted mainstream, you will only know the already known. I recall one occasion of describing my original encounter with the backyard inventor (I am talking now about the person who gave me the first sample of catalytic water that started Yin and me down this fifteen-year research line). I was telling the story of that encounter to another engineer who at the time was working for Chevron up around Santa Barbara, and I can remember the look in his eyes as I described why I was fascinated with the sample. He looked at me as if I were beginning to grow horns, and the more I said, the more his eyes described his opinion about my competence; you could tell that he was thinking, "How could I have missed it with this guy? He is surely on drugs."

But if you look at what Norman said in the introduction—*"Any good scientist (as I consider any good physician) at some point in his or her career begins to 'feel' this element of hypocrisy. What do I mean by that? One should not fear discovery or fear researching an area because it is considered outside the current accepted 'comfort zone' of knowledge"*—boy, is that true!

I saw the effect as I spoke to this other engineer. He was a good, competent guy, but I had just stepped outside his *comfort zone*; I was inferring something that existing science said couldn't happen.

OK, back to my story here about the guys with their electronics. I told them, "Bring it over and let me see what you've got." I was expecting to see some circuits that would generate Royal Rife's frequencies* or something similar but instead was shown a very large direct-current magnet. It had a big transformer attached that made me instantly nervous, as one was dealing with some sizable currents, and I quickly began to form the idea that I was a bit leery of working on it—too much current, plus why would someone want to sit under such large magnetic fields?

But never mind the electrical safety issues; I was certain the FDA would build me a new padded jail cell if I went down that road—this agency absolutely regulates all electronics used in the treatment of illness. Also, what had happened to the original inventor? Surely there was some dispute over the ownership of the technology; otherwise, why was I being asked to re-engineer the thing? So, I bowed out of the offer, even though a very fat pay check was being waved under my nose.

To politely say "No, thank you," without appearing rude or arrogant, I told this gentleman—we will call him "Bob" from Oklahoma—that if

---

* **Royal Raymond Rife** (1888–1971): An American scientist, who developed a therapy using resonant frequencies to selectively kill numerous viral cells such as cancer.

I were to go down the health line searching for some device, I would first look at very subtle, gentle frequencies, not the huge magnetic ones that their machine generated. That comment brought on a frown, as he was very intent on getting this machine understood and, as he stated, upgraded. As the conversation progressed, I found out that his interest in the equipment was that he had a friend who was going into hospice due to brain cancer. Evidently, the device that he wanted me to work on had had some effect on another person's illness but was being unsuccessful on his friend. His idea was to try and improve the device, make it better and save his friend. He kept saying, "What is your fear? She's in hospice; she's been through chemo, been through radiation; the tumors are inoperable; the docs have sent her home to die. Why are you so hesitant to help?"

Good, strong argument, but the problem was (1) I did not have a clue as to why something like that (his big magnetic generator) would help, so I did not know what to focus on to "improve" it; and (2) I just think that high energy fields around people are probably a factor in the growth of tumors, not in their destruction. Anyway, I continued to say "No, thank you," and Bob kept insisting that I help.

He was absolutely sincere. What do you do? One would normally say, "Send her to the hospital"; he was saying, "They have sent her home to write her will." It was at that point I decided to venture into this no man's land. I began to tell him about the early work that Yin and I were involved in at UCLA with the first trials on the stable water cluster. I gave him a brief description of the tests that were run on live T-cells with Bonavida (see, in part two, "Induction and Regulation of Human Peripheral Blood TH1-TH2 Derived Cytokines by I$_E$ Water Preparations and Synergy with Mitogens"). I told him that this water had created a significant effect on stimulating T-cells and the best part was that it should be very safe, as it was water not a drug or chemical. I truly believe that safety should be foremost in anyone's mind if they want to help someone who is ill, and I just could not wrap my wits around heavy magnetic fields as a treatment.

As you can imagine, his thoughts then focused on the T-cell stimulant research that had been published and he began to question and bug me for more information.

What's in it?

It's water, and Yin and I strongly believe, and the research is very solid, that it is an undiscovered stable molecular phase of water.

What happened in the studies?

T-cells were stimulated and secreted large numbers of cytokines. Cytokines are part of the body's defense against numerous viral attackers.

Well, that is where, about three days later after many phone calls, I agreed to give Bob some of the water. He had spoken to his friend and she desperately wanted to try it.

I sent him 15 milliliters and, out of the blue, told him to put 20 drops into a gallon of distilled water. I had no reason to pick that dosage other than it just came into my head; it would be at least one drop per glass at that dilution, and I suggested that she drink two glasses per day.

I had no hopes or aspirations that his friend would improve. But as he and I and, let's call her "Jane," discovered, she did improve—not only improve, but that was nearly three years ago and today she is cancer free.

Now, if you were to speak with Jane, she would tell you that she made her peace with Jesus during those first weeks she was sent home to die and it was that bonding with her God that healed her. I have to say that her conviction and her faith were absolutely critical to her recovery, but it should also be noted that she drank the water religiously for several years and *she is not the only person who has recovered.*

She was the first of many, and as I write this I realize that I am taking my own career and possibly my life's work and putting it all at risk. But I believe, as a human being sitting on this blue globe in space, that I have a responsibility to share wisdom with my fellow man. And that is how I must refer to this information; it is merely another piece of the puzzle of what makes this biological form we reside in tick. Am I saying that the water "cured" her cancer? *No, she* cured her cancer, just as Norman pointed out in the introduction: we heal because of the stored information within our DNA. What Yin and I believe is that this water is simply one of the basic building blocks of that healing process. We believe that our bodies manufacture this water internally, and if that is the case, what organization has the right to prevent us from having what is ours to begin with? We all have the God-given right to know something about ourselves.

No vested interest, no company nor government, should be allowed to seize or take away your right to know about *you* and to *heal yourself*. To dream up some law or legislation to regulate the treatment of self-healing would be the most insane computation in the healthcare arena yet.

Our research is now pointed toward finding the source of this phase of water in the body. There must be specialized cells that make this phase and there must be a reason that these cells are overwhelmed in the ill people who have shown up at our door. This water must be simply a component of the immune system.

Now, before someone wants to send Yin and me to jail, we have known exactly what we have been giving out—and the word is *giving*: water. All samples have been verified in the best labs in the country as water—ultrapure water—thousands of times cleaner than the distilled you purchase at your local grocery store. Plus—and you can ask all of the individuals—not one person was charged during these past years of research. All was freely given; all who participated were volunteers. Sure, some have wanted to donate to the research and many have, and their support and help was vital to this work. But the work and focus has been on discovering the fundamentals of water and how it applies to the healing process, using hard—core particle physics, not statistical analysis, which is the norm within the healthcare industry.

Yes, the "pure" scientist will ask, "Well, then, gentlemen . . . where's the proof?" And my answer to them is, "Well, gentlemen, where have you been?" Read the last fifteen years of work that forms the second part of this book. The proof is there in the pictures, experiments and papers that have been published and are currently being repeated in major universities around the world. Of course it will be challenged; what change in science has not been? But do not look for dogmatic authority; look for applied science and the results that are obtained. It is only through legitimate observation that discoveries can be made. And at this juncture, quite frankly, I really do not care if existing authority agrees with our findings or not. We are not looking for accolades; we are simply looking for a trail that takes man out of his lack of knowledge into a new age of understanding the body.

Stop being so frightened of the boogeyman. Yes, Benveniste was hanged, drawn and quartered, but we all owe it to our friends, families and fellow researchers to pick up the torch and deliver the straight scoop; and after nearly fifteen years we can say the straight scoop is exactly this: There is a hitherto undiscovered molecular phase of water and all indications point to it being a basic building block of the body. It's true that it can be found through homeopathic procedures, but we have discovered that strict controls must be present for any strong concentrations to occur.

Through word of mouth, we have been sought out and begged by people who were ranging from seriously ill to near death to let them have some of this water, and 80 percent of these people have either completely recovered from or are still recovering from, not just cancer, but a host of other so-called incurable illnesses, including Parkinson's disease, diabetes, lupus and arthritis. Did this water *cure* them? Again, NO—*they* cured themselves; but this water must have supplied some integral part of what they needed to build their own defenses.

So, that double-helix photo must mean that the stable water cluster is not a drug, not a nutrient, but a fundamental brick in the body and somehow is linked directly with the body's ability to heal.

There is no lag in time with the effect from this water. The body instantly uses it. Look at the photographs below. For the past three years we have taken hundreds of thermal images of people ranging from critically ill to completely healthy and all of these photos have something very much in common—immediate dramatic change occurs when people drink this water.

The first image is of a man's chest *prior* to drinking one glass of distilled water containing several drops of stable water clusters.

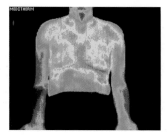

The second image is *after* drinking the glass containing the stable water clusters.

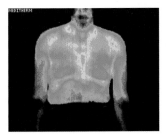

The time lapse is five minutes and, yes, there is a startling change. The temperature of his chest has changed dramatically in those few minutes. How can we be sure the change is not just due to the water itself? Each subject first drinks a glass of the same distilled water but without the stable water clusters and there is no or very minor change.

In addition, each subject acted as his or her own control, first drinking the distilled water without the stable water clusters and then later drinking the same water *with* the added stable water clusters and being photographed on both occasions.

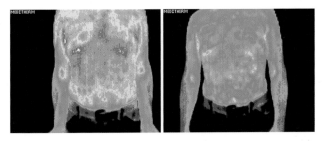

Before and after male subjects

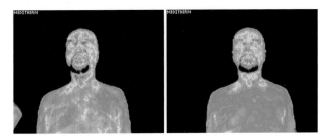

As I said, we have hundreds of these photos. The results repeat, repeat, repeat. You can see more examples in the second section of the book, in the paper titled "Sample Thermograph Images."

Now, the right question to ask is, "Why such a dramatic change?" Why are we seeing this rapid heat dissipation throughout the body by simply drinking this water? What can we learn from this? Are we looking at a component of the underlying healing mechanism that we continue to see with seriously ill people who drink this water?

Does it act as some type of anti-inflammatory agent? Arthritis is definitely improved. Look at the following letter from a seventy-plus-year-old woman. She is writing here to her sister, who had sent her the water that she had first gotten from me.

> *I must tell you about the "Water." Started on it: 2 drops to 6–8 oz of distilled water. It's really incredible. I said it was in my mind; but if I don't take it, my arthritis hurts all over my back, hips, hands. Now after taking it I'm sitting here like I had another person's body. I have a finger on my right hand—I'm sure you know the one on my right hand—it hurt like hell, was swollen like a sausage and almost unusable. Now the swelling is down and I can cut food and write. I feel like I may have found what they had in* Lost Horizon. *My shingles, "the bane of my life," are better, the itching and burning going away. My hips don't hurt, so now I can walk without looping along. What can I say but Thanks, Thanks, Thanks!*

Is there any question that we should continue to understand this phase of water? Is there any question why Yin and I have pursued this quest for so many years? We may have found that magical potion that was referred to in *Lost Horizon*, and the most ironic part of the story—it was always there within us.

Chapter 8

Homeopathy and the Stable Water Cluster

The question that Yin and I have been asked about a hundred times is, Have you found a scientific basis for homeopathy? And I can truthfully say, yes, in our opinion, the stable water cluster is the basis of homeopathy and, with further investigation, it is our absolute belief that there exists a true workable, affordable and safe healthcare system awaiting the world once a thorough understanding of the physical/biological mechanism of the stable water cluster (SWC) is known.

But the key here—and I cannot stress this strongly enough—is *with further investigation*. First, the traditional homeopathic dilution process will produce only a very small quantity of stable water clusters; second—and this is to be fair and truthful to both sides of this twenty- or thirty-year-old raging debate—it is difficult to predict "what type" of SWC one will make using the existing traditional homeopathic preparation procedure.

The manufacturing processes that we have been shown in several homeopathic facilities and those that we have read about in other locations follow a very strict standard but do not control atmosphere, nor do they control ion concentration in their preparation water. Ions are the trigger, and the ion present when the first SWC forms is going to determine the outcome of your manufacturing process. And in today's atmosphere, the ion most likely to trigger that first SWC is going to be the ever present product of CO_2 and clean water, which is carbonic acid. Today's atmosphere contains about 400 parts per million CO_2, and pure water is very, very thirsty for CO_2.

Now, carbonic acid may make a great SWC and the body may use it easily and quickly to its benefit; as a matter of fact, it is our opinion that any SWC is better than no SWC. We can only speculate at this time as to the truth of that statement, since more research is needed to prove or disprove it. But if our current research verifies that the SWC is a precursor to DNA, then it might also be true that all formations of SWCs represent some prime fundamental building block; and if that proves out, how then could such an integral first principle of biological existence not be linked somehow to the body's defenses—i.e., immune function?

When we look at the normally stated definition of homeopathy—*a system for treating disease based on the administration of minute doses of a drug that in massive amounts produces symptoms in healthy individuals similar to those of the disease itself* *—we see the first questionable datum: *minute doses of a drug.* (1) The product of the dilution is going to be a SWC; and (2) the most likely SWC currently being manufactured would be based on carbonic acid or possibly some other contaminate that was in the air or in the water, not necessarily a SWC based upon the drug that was originally diluted.

So if one wants to make the claim that the preparations made from homeopathy are remedies specific to the properties that come from the original undiluted drugs, chemicals, organics, etc., then one must control all atmospheres in the manufacturing process as well as all ion content in the preparation water.

I can say that I believe the stable water cluster *could* become a specific shape or structure depending on the original contaminate if all variables were controlled. Also, it could be true that the body might respond well to a specific shape or electrical signal that would be formed due to the union of a particular drug or ion. We are currently in the process of

---

* *The American Heritage Dictionary of the English Language*, Fourth Edition. © 2000 by Houghton Mifflin Company. Updated in 2003. Published by Houghton Mifflin Company.

proving this assumption by examining various SWCs that have been formed from different base contaminates (the original stuff used to dilute), and the results of that work may or may not be available by the time we publish this book.

But let's look at the differences in how we prepare a stable water cluster compared with the traditional homeopathic production process.

First, we start with ultrapure water, while most traditional methods start with distilled. Distilled water is not clean enough, as you have thousands of stray ions present, and, again, you want to control all ions. Remember, once formed, the SWCs beget themselves. So if there is truth to the homeopathic belief that more dilute means stronger (which makes total sense from what we have seen in the lab), the specific remedy that you are planning to make may not necessarily be the one that is getting stronger.

Therefore, if you are beginning your homeopathic preparation with distilled water, there is a strong possibility that what you end up with will be a SWC made from something other than what you thought—something that was originally in the distilled water, not added to it.

Second, what you dilute must go into solution—it must produce a plus and a minus ion. If your substance will *not* go into solution because of a balanced stable charge, then you will not produce a SWC (the only exception to this rule would be a large organic molecule where the charges [plus and minus] had sufficient distance between them to create enough single-pole charge).

Third, you must continue to dilute with ultrapure water in order to create distance between the plus and minus particles. Again, the reason you want the distance between these plus and minus ions is so they will not connect; because when they don't connect (remember they are intrinsically attracted to each other), their outward-reaching charge snaps back and, since they are "in water," those water molecules that are nearest to them are squeezed into a new phase of water—the stable water cluster (SWC). If you are using distilled water rather than ultrapure water, chances are that you are just adding more ions and you will not reach the above needed dilution.

Next, if you do not control the atmosphere at all times, you will not have a clue as to what you are making. As I explained, CO_2 is so abundant right now in the atmosphere and has so much affinity for pure water that it would probably be the most prevalent ion and consequently the cornerstone of the first SWC. Don't get me wrong; a carbonic acid SWC may be very useful and may be why homeopathy has shown such workability in the past. Look at the statistics: there is no question that homeopathy has been an extremely effective method to help the body heal. In fact, as we stated, we think all SWCs are helpful; and now with this latest research, the door should be open for a complete new understanding of how homeopathy could become an exact science based upon unambiguous specific remedies.

So there is our answer. There is no reason homeopathy should not flourish into a vast and exact science with major discoveries within the healthcare industry. And why not? Its products are much cheaper than allopathic remedies and far safer; plus, as Norman pointed out so concisely, the current pharmaceutical scene could use a bit of an overhaul.

But we want to go further with an explanation of why the SWC has shown such promise in our friends who have taken this water. Recall that Yin is a theoretical physicist and, yes, he has been using quantum theory to predict a hypothesis as to the exact role of the SWC. Although this may sound a bit "out there" for most western minds, just recall that it was his original mathematical model that first predicted the existence of the SWC, and that model has continued to predict more and more of our findings for the past fifteen years. I tend to listen closely when he speaks, and he has become very confident that the SWC is the basis of the body's *electrical* system. Now, notice that I did not say nervous system; I said *electrical* system.

Because of its "polar" charge nature, the particle, the SWC, wants to form long end-to-end circuits (this can be seen in numerous atomic force microscope photographs).

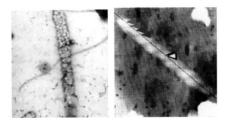

The picture on the left was taken by an electron microscope, showing a chain of the stable water clusters. You can see that the chain is several clusters wide, and the size of the small circular clusters inside the chain is about 0.3 microns in diameter. The picture on the right (atomic force microscope) shows similar water clusters joining together one after another in a long chain. The size of clusters on the right is similar to those on the left.

In Chinese medicine, of which Yin has become a very avid student the past ten years, there is an *electrical* system in the body and that system is referred to as *the meridians.*

Up to this time there has been no physical evidence for the actual existence of meridians, but one does find very precise maps indicating their exact locations and these have some four thousand years of history within the Chinese culture. The concept is that the meridians are channels or pathways that form a unified network throughout the body and carry a very specific type of energy. The Chinese call this energy *qi* (pronounced "chee"). Shock to the body in the form of trauma or illness disrupts and imbalances this flow, and practices such as acupuncture and acupressure are used to bring the flow back to optimum levels, thus restoring health.

According to its practice, there are fourteen meridians, which relate to all vital organs of the body, and it is interesting to find that this same practice appears throughout Japan and even in ancient civilizations such as the Yucatan Mayans.

Now, many in the West have sort of pooh-poohed the entire concept of meridians and its corrective practice of acupuncture; but before we start to write off Yin's new theorem, you should know that Norman Shealy, the world-renowned neurosurgeon who so thoughtfully wrote the foreword and introduction, has been practicing and employing acupuncture for nearly forty years, including publishing medical papers on such.

So, when Yin told me of his most recent theory of the function of the SWC in the body, I not only found it fascinating but expect we shall soon prove it in the lab.

Yin believes that the stable water cluster is the electrical circuit material of the meridians.

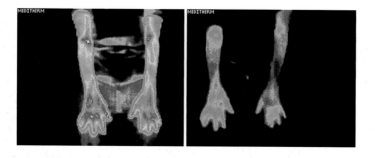

That could account for the rapid change (thirty minutes) in temperature of this person with arthritis, seen above in the infrared images of an otherwise healthy male before and after drinking the water. If the SWC is a conductor, the heat energy or charge could be normalized as the person drinks a glass of water that contains literally millions of SWCs; or these ready-made circuit builders might somehow trigger an internal healing response, thus affecting inflammation.

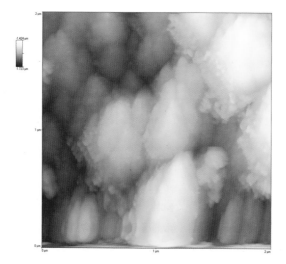

In this atomic force microscope photograph of stable water clusters, which we first showed you in chapter 3, the smallest discernible particles are in the 30-nanometer range. The larger particles are made up of multiples of the smaller particles. This is a 2-micron scan. An average drop of water is approximately 500 microns across. So each drop of water will contain over 100 million SWCs.

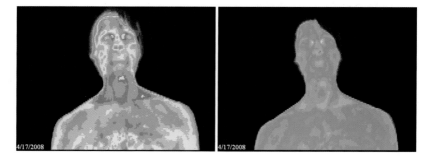

If it is true that by drinking the stable water clusters one adds millions of ready-to-go-to-work circuit builders, it would be possible to see such a rapid change in the thermal images as shown above.

So, there is evidence for Yin's new theory, and what we hope to establish soon is a way of codifying the existence of this electrical (meridian) system. Each water cluster should emit some slight frequency and with a delicate instrument we should be able to find these circuits. With the establishment of a frequency and a flow, we should then be able to map the existence of these four-thousand-year-old mystery circuits.

If they do exist and we can empirically show their existence, and if we are correct in our assumption that they are made from SWCs, well, hold on to your hat, because science—especially those branches of science related to the healing arts—will take a quantum leap. It would then be a quick jump to locating breaks in the circuits with simple detectors (sounds like Bones on *Star Trek*, doesn't it?). You could just scan a detector across the person's body to find the problem.

Software could be designed that would utilize a database of all known existing health problems identified with similar electrical frequencies, and soon one would have a diagnostic tool straight out of *Star Trek*.

So, yes, again, we need to move forward with the research.

This idea that a particle forms around an ion in pure water and makes up a specialized part of the immune function is not such a hard concept to get. What we need is more proof.

Help us find it.

Thank you for reading our story.

Epilogue

A n evolving science is a moving target with a steady stream of new details and exciting data to chase. The *stable water cluster* is no exception. Yin and I realized we needed to add this epilogue to include some of the more recent information, available just prior to this book going to print.

You will see in part two, among the first several papers, "Evidence for the Existence of Stable-Water-Clusters at Room Temperature and Normal Pressure." Published in October 2009 in the *Physics Letters A* journal, this paper has now been presented at four scientific conferences in the last four months and will be presented several more times before the end of 2009.

It is a rather exciting step forward, as it describes a process whereby the stable water cluster has been removed from the liquid phase of water and formed into a powder. That powder was then analyzed with several different types of sophisticated analytical equipment and—guess what? The powder said it was water.

So even if you do not plan to read part two, you should take the time to review this paper. It is an easier read than most of the attached work (no math), and I think you will find it interesting.

In addition, since we completed the first section, Yin commented that we should be sure to distinguish this work from traditional homeopathy, as even though there are many similarities, the stable water cluster absolutely stands alone on its own merits as a research subject. What we want to avoid is being labeled as simply another investigation into the mechanism of homeopathy.

Yes, we believe without question that homeopathy owes its efficacy to the stable water cluster, but in the same breath one must state that the stable water cluster is as old as life itself and rightfully belongs in its *own* category. It existed long before any practice or art of healing—period.

I feel confident that in the years to come this research path will be found to be a fundamental component in the understanding of the self-healing process. Our focus for study this coming year will be on how this charged solid water particle fits into the evolutionary line of protoplasmic organisms. We know that water covered this sphere (Earth) in its earliest beginnings and, in some primordial series of steps, sunlight and water played an elementary role in the evolution of biological organisms; and if we view the countless complex organisms alive today, it is obvious that something was extremely workable to keep this protoplasmic line alive for another billion years or so. It is interesting to see the rapid acceleration of research into the photochemical conversion of cholesterol to vitamin D—D_3 being the only vitamin the body manufactures from sunlight. I strongly believe that we as a culture are about to embark on a rocket ride of understanding of our roots, but this time there will be a physics viewpoint included as to how this conversion and transfer of energy is a key component of the healing mechanism.

The simplicities will uncover the fundamentals—the basic principles that will be the common denominators to multiple processes.

But the reason for this epilogue, other than to introduce the above paper, is to further distinguish the similarities and the differences between homeopathy and the study of the stable water cluster (SWC).

First, in preparing homeopathic remedies, shaking is traditionally shown to be an important step. Contrary to what we said earlier, we have found that in making SWCs, shaking is not necessary.

In homeopathy, the extent of the dilution is always indicated and is considered a key part of the process. We have not found evidence that higher dilutions create necessarily higher concentrations, unless contamination is completely controlled. Also, there may be a saturation point, although more study is needed to determine this.

With our study of SWCs, the dilution is only important in that there is a trigger point, a place where the stable water cluster is formed. As stated earlier, this is due to the exchange of charge or electrical pressure (inward collapsing forces) to first create the "seed" from which the other SWCs form. Once that first seed SWC is formed, there are numerous factors that control the concentration of the SWCs and simply diluting has not proven to be significant.

The important factor in the manufacture of the stable water cluster is the actual number of SWCs. Our research has been focused on quantifying this number and working toward higher and higher numbers.

Next, within the manufacture of homeopathic remedies, the mechanism of the Law of Similars is considered to be a vital part of the practice.

We believe that the Law of Similars is incidental to the manufacture of the SWC. The crucial factors (and we are confident these will eventually be discovered as the decisive health factors) will be the geometric shape as well as the molecular structure of SWCs. There will come about an understanding of a lock-and-key type of functionality.

Therefore, I must state that from a strict traditional sense the stable water cluster does not qualify as a homeopathic remedy, since (1) shaking is not necessary; (2) the number of dilutions must be specified for each homeopathic remedy, whereas the number of dilutions is not important for us, but the number of SWCs *is* important; (3) the mechanism of the homeopathic Law of Similars, to the SWC, is merely incidental, and we believe the crucial health factors to be the geometric shape and the molecular structure; (4) we do not concur with the statement "the higher the dilution, the more potent the remedy," as the potency of water with SWCs is determined by the final number/density of SWCs, regardless of how the solution is produced; (5) the industrial standard in homeopathy for clean water is double-distilled water; we regard this as insufficient.

The above are the dissimilarities. Now here are the similarities: (1) High dilution is necessary. (2) The materials that high dilution starts from are important in determining the characteristics of the remedy. (3) High dilution has significant health benefit.

We wanted to clarify these points, as we have already been asked these questions and thought it best to include the answers here before this book goes to print.

DAVID AND YIN

DOUBLE-
Helix
WATER™

PART TWO

Research Documents and
Published Scientific Papers

Sample Thermograph Images

Infrared images (Thermographs) before (left) and after (right) drinking double-helix water

1. First subject 9/30/2009, male, had prostate cancer 10 years prior.

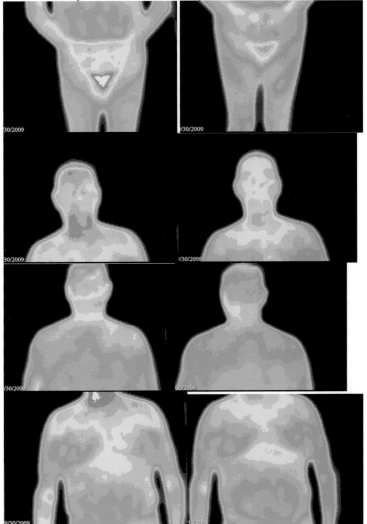

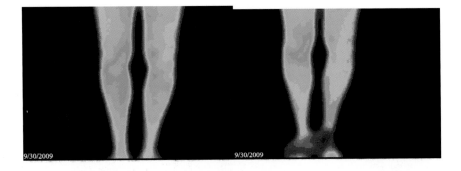

2. Subject with prostate cancer, 63 year-old male, hypertension, heart problem

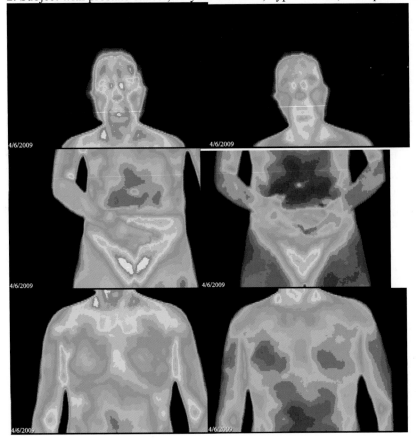

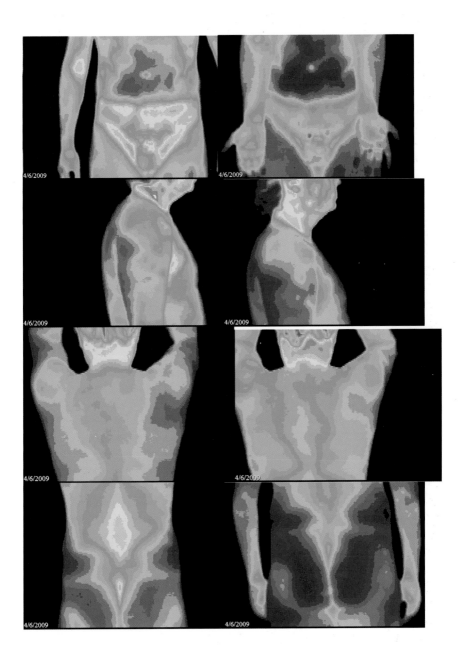

79

3. Woman, cancer in late fifties, CP, malignant melanoma 7/95 and lung surgery 6/25/01 lower right lobe removed

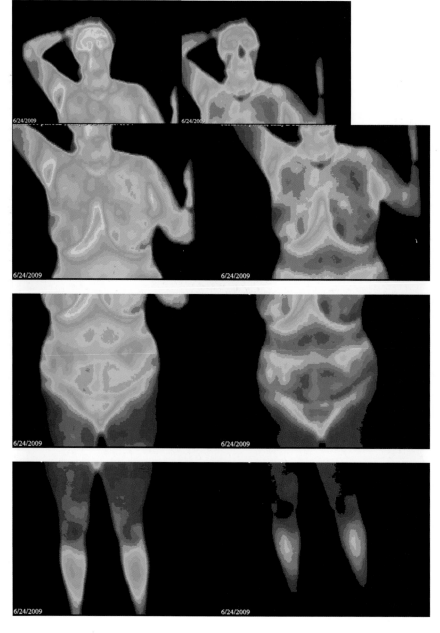

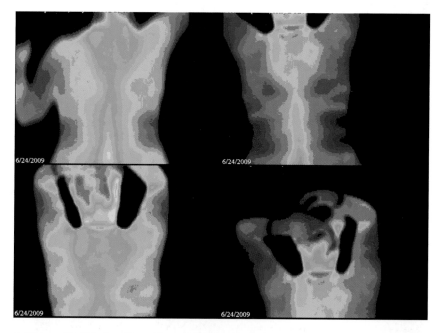

4. Woman 71, DS, thyroid problem, frequent urination

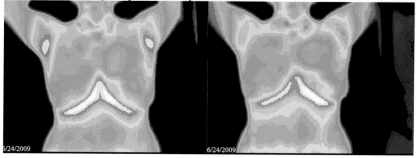

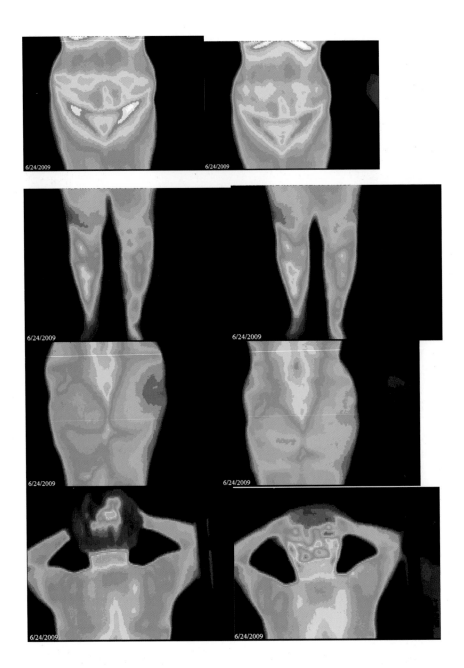

82

5. Male, 72 years-old: excessive urination, Prostate radiation treatment Feb 2005

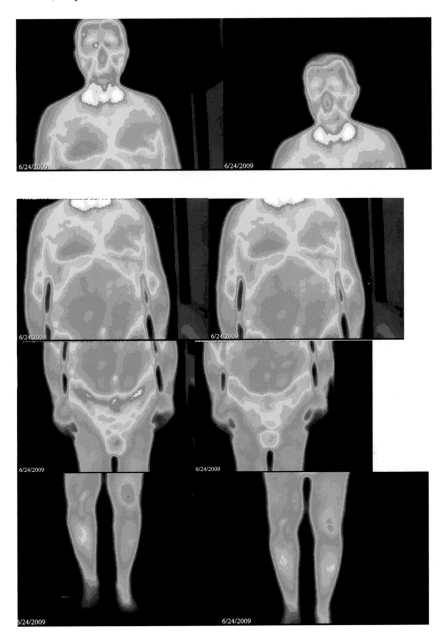

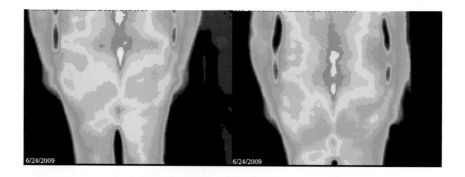

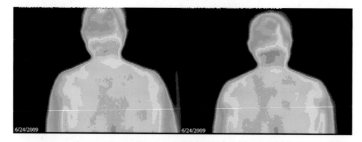

6. Male 54, cancer in kidney and lung

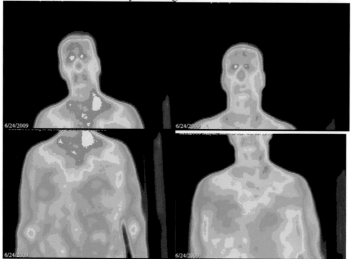

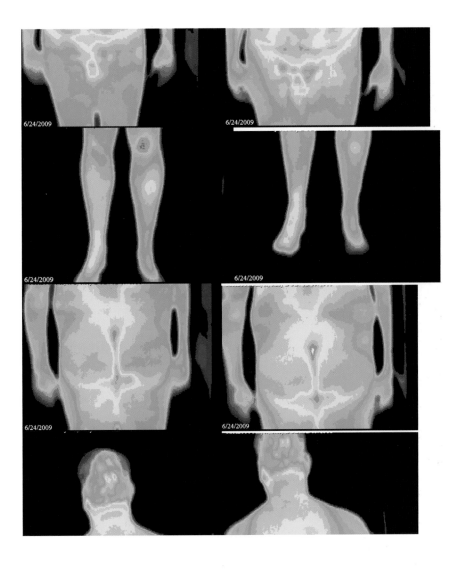

6/24/2009

6/24/2009

6/24/2009

6/24/2009

6/24/2009

6/24/2009

Physics Letters A ••• (••••) •••–•••

Contents lists available at ScienceDirect

Physics Letters A

www.elsevier.com/locate/pla

Evidence for the existence of stable-water-clusters at room temperature and normal pressure

Shui Yin Lo [a,*], Xu Geng [b], David Gann [c]

[a] *Quantum Heath Research Institute Pasadena, CA 91107, United States*
[b] *Department of Physics, Zhongshan (Sun Yat-Sen) University, Guangzhou, China*
[c] *D&Y Labs Reno, NV 89501, United States*

A R T I C L E   I N F O

Article history:
Received 12 August 2009
Accepted 16 August 2009
Available online xxxx
Communicated by V.M. Agranovich

A B S T R A C T

We report the finding of isolated stable-water-clusters of tens of nanometers to micron size from the evaporation of very dilute sodium chloride solution at room temperature and normal atmospheric pressure. The stable-water-clusters are found to be electrically charged by examination via an Electric Force Microscope (EFM). Raman scattering and infrared spectrum of residues from the evaporation show similar but not identical characteristics of liquid water.

© 2009 Elsevier B.V. All rights reserved.

One of the greatest advances on our understanding of water comes from the study of water-clusters. Most water-cluster studies have been focused on smaller water-clusters, below 100 water molecules [1–5]. There exists a few studies on stable-water-clusters from tens of nanometers to micron size. These water-clusters are reported to be stable at room temperature at normal atmospheric pressures [6–11]. These clusters are reported to be created from very dilute solutions made from a variety of different materials.

Here we report further evidence of these stable-water-clusters created from diluting minute amounts of NaCl in ultra-pure water.

In order to reduce the possibility of contamination to our sample, we take the following steps:

1. Experiments are performed in a Class 100 clean-room (Industry standard) that requires room to be free of no more than 100 particles no larger than 0.5 microns per ft^3. Whenever it is necessary, we perform our experiment in an atmosphere-free glove-box or bottle, devoid of atmosphere and maintained a slightly positive pressure utilizing pure (99.999%) Argon gas so as to prohibit carbon dioxide contamination. Carbon dioxide can cause damage to the sample due to the fact that it dissolves easily in water and introduces unwanted ions in the water solution.

2. We use two commercially available systems that produce ultra-pure water which is characterized by its 18.2 MΩ cm resistivity. The large system, commercially available through

Siemen's International, is used to provide bulk water for general use as well as feed water into the Purelab Ultra, Elga Lab Water, with TOC 3–10 ppb. This system is located inside the clean-room to protect against the introduction of contamination to our ultra-pure water during the preparation of samples and cleaning. We use a Laser Particle Counter (Lighthouse LS-60), which can detect and count separate particles ranging in size from 0.1 micron to 0.5 microns to ensure that our sample water has less than 10 particles no larger than 0.1 microns per 1 ml. Distilled water purchased from commercial supermarkets show particle counts of 5000 to 10,000 counts per 1 ml.

3. All utensils must be as clean as possible. We used the Lighthouse LS-60 Laser Particle Counter to ensure that all beakers are free of contamination after rinsing with 18.2 MΩ cm ultra-pure water by sampling the water for particles that might be left in the beakers after cleaning. It is critical to the success of this experiment that absolute care is taken to avoid contamination. Utensils, including containers, tubes, caps, pipettes, rotating flasks, condensing tubes, and slides that may be used to prepare the sample must be free from any contamination. We use only two kinds of containers: glass or those made from polypropylene. We shake/clean these utensils in ultra-pure water using ultrasound and then flush them with ultra-pure (18.2 MΩ cm) water. We repeat this process until we obtain a particle count of the flushed water to be below 100 particles or less, no larger than 0.1 microns per 1 ml.

4. We use NaCl with purity 99.99%.

In dilute solution of NaCl, sodium and chlorine ions coexist with water molecules, which have permanent electric dipole moment. The electric interactions of the dilute solution consist of those

---

* Corresponding author.
E-mail address: ideaclinic@Yahoo.com (S.Y. Lo).

0375-9601/$ – see front matter © 2009 Elsevier B.V. All rights reserved.
doi:10.1016/j.physleta.2009.08.061

Tapping,Topo Frw, 1.7 x e-7 diluent

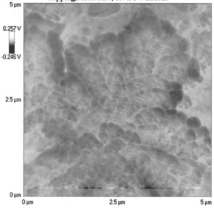

5 μm

-0.037 μm

-0.421μm

2.5 μm

0 μm

0μm   2.5 μm   5 μm

Tapping,Phase bkw, 1.7 x e-7 diluent

5 μm

0.257 V

-0.246 V

2.5 μm

0 μm

0μm   2.5 μm   5 μm

Fig. 1. Residues from evaporated 1.7×10^{-7} M NaCl solution taken with AFM and with EFM, shown in Fig. 2. For the AFM, the size of the picture is 5 μm × 5 μm. The different color code from bright to dark indicate the height of the clusters running from -0.037 μm to -0.421 μm. For the EFM picture (Fig. 2) the different color from bright to dark indicates the existence of electric potential from 1.257 V to -0.246 V. The different shades of color on the (Fig. 2) clusters indicate that there are charges on the surface of the clusters that generate electric potentials that are measured by the tip of the EFM.

Fig. 2.

among ions and dipoles. When the density of ions is high, the dominant interactions are those among ions. As the concentration of NaCl decreases, there are less and less ions per unit volume. The interaction among ions becomes less and less. The interaction among dipoles becomes more and more important. There comes a point when the dipole–dipole interactions dominate. The transition point when this occurs is found experimentally to be at the concentration about 10^{-4} M(mol/liter) [6]. At concentration below this transition point, water molecules will attract to one another to form clusters that have permanent electric dipole moment, much like small magnets stick together to form a big magnet.

For this experiment we diluted our NaCl solution to 10^{-7} M, far below this transition point. We then place drops of the solution on a glass slide and wait for it to dry. The residue is visible under an ordinary light microscope. To detect more structures of clusters we use an Atomic Force Microscope (AFM), the Innova model made by Veeco with includes an EFM (electric force microscope) mode. The clusters are soft and tapping mode of AFM is necessary. In the forward motion of the tip in the tapping AFM mode, the topography of the clusters is shown. The electric force microscope (EFM), works simultaneously with the AFM. When the tip scans backward at a slightly higher height concurrent with an electric potential, it records and shows as a different shade of color representing the influence created by the different values of electric potential emitting from the sample. When there is no charge on the cluster, there is no change in electric potential and the color is unchanged. Any variation of color indicates that local charges are present on the sample. In Figs. 1 and 2 we show one set of AFM and EFM pictures taken of our sample.

As a control, we put drops of pure water on similar glass slide under similar conditions and let them dry — we see no such structures as in Fig. 1 in AFM pictures.

There is a great variety of snow-flake like shapes. Similarly, there is a great variety of stable-water-clusters. We report one spe-

cific type, which we believe may give more weight to the idea that these stable-water-clusters may have a permanent electric dipole. Since one isolate water molecule has permanent electric dipole moment, it is likely that the stable-water-clusters made up of numerous water molecules would have a permanent electric dipole moment.

Let us have a group of small magnets with permanent magnetic dipole moments. If we put many of them in a small space, they will clamp together. If we spread them out evenly, these magnets will line-up because of their contained magnetic forces. Instead of small magnets, we suggest stable-water-clusters with permanent electric dipole moments. When the density of clusters is high from evaporating 10^{-7} M on a glass slide, they will clump together as in Figs. 1 and 2. If the density of clusters is not as dense, the clusters will spread out in straight lines as shown in Fig. 3(a). Here, they form straight lines most likely due to the electric attraction between the permanent electric dipole moment of the stable-water-clusters.

There is an interesting point of the lines formed by the clusters in Fig. 3(a). All the horizontal lines intersect with the vertical line at 102°, which is the same angle sustained by two hydrogen atoms interacting with the oxygen atom in a water molecule. One might conclude that such could be accidental, but the authors suggest it is a manifestation of the scaling law.

Most of the pictures are not as regular as Fig. 3. In Fig. 4(a), we show another example, which has less regular structures. Such structures are also quite common in the distillate, which is obtained from using a standard glass distillation unit to distill the 10^{-7} M, NaCl. One drop of distillate is left to dry on a glass slide and the optical picture of its residue is shown in Fig. 4(b).

We consider the fact that the residue from distillate also contains similar structures as that of the original solution gives strong evidence that the clusters we see are made of water molecules and not from contaminants.

The AFM pictures from the residues of distillate, such as those shown in Fig. 4(b) are similar to those from the original 10^{-7} M NaCl solution, as shown in Fig. 1.

In order to ascertain the molecular content of these residues, we have obtained infrared spectra as well as spectra from Raman scattering:

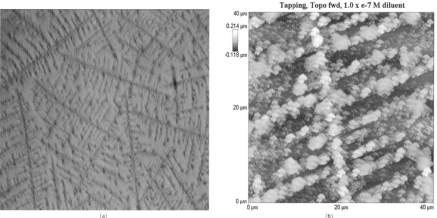

Fig. 3. On the left (a), is a picture taken with an ordinary light microscope. On the right (b), is the AFM picture showing the straight lines shown in (a). The size of the AFM picture is 40 μm × 40 μm.

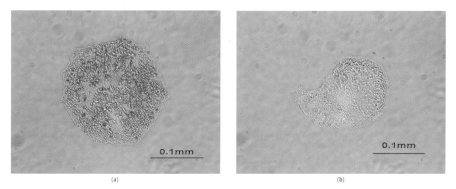

Fig. 4. On the left (a) is the picture from an optical microscope of the residue of one drop of 10^{-7} M NaCl. On the right (b), is that of the residue of the distillate from 10^{-7} M NaCl.

(a) Infrared spectra:

To strengthen the signal of infrared spectra, we have obtained a large amount of solid residues by evaporating more than a hundred drops of 10^{-7} M NaCl on the same slide. For optimum results, one drop is allowed to dry before we add a second drop. Then a third drop, and so forth. The infrared spectrometer we use is FT-IR Nicolet 380 with ATR from Thermo Electron Corporation. The results are shown in Fig. 5.

(b) Spectra from Raman scattering:

We place one drop of 10^{-7} M NaCl on a silicon slide, which is coated with TiO_2. Then the residue is obtained on the surface of the silicon slide by placing it to dry in a dry box. We use a Raman microscope made by RENISHAW, UK, which uses an Argon ion laser with wave length of 514.5 nm and power 20 mW to sweep a range from 100 to 4000 cm^{-1}. The Raman spectrum is obtained from sweeping an area of 2 μm × 2 μm, where there is residue. The curves are shown in Fig. 6. We focus the Argon laser beam on two separate residue spots on the silicon slide, we obtain two curves SP2 and SP3. For comparison we also obtain the Raman spectrum of liquid water SP1 by focusing the Argon beam on to inside of a capillary which holds the liquid water. The dominant Raman peak of liquid water is at 3426.42 cm^{-1}. The Raman spectra of the residues do not have a peak there, but have three peaks next to it at 3145.33 cm^{-1}, 3049.51 cm^{-1}, 2860.34 cm^{-1}. There are, in addition, smaller peaks at 2011.24 cm^{-1}, 1754.81 cm^{-1}, 1709.31 cm^{-1}, and 1404.86 cm^{-1}, *which may be related to the Raman peak of liquid water at* 1651.52 cm^{-1}. It may be interpreted as the molecular structure of stable water clusters is quite similar but not identical to that of liquid water. For back-

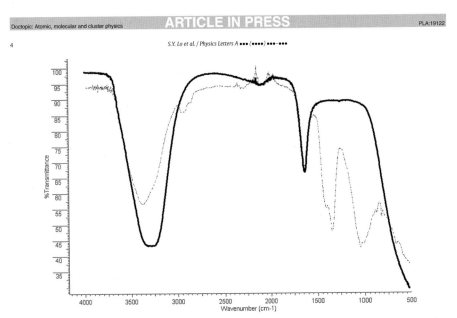

Fig. 5. Infrared spectra for pure water (solid line) and solid sample of stable-water-clusters (broken line). The absorption peaks for pure water are 3283.5 cm^{-1} and 1634.5 cm^{-1}. The absorption peaks for stable-water-clusters are 3371.4 cm^{-1}, 1639.5 cm^{-1}, 1342 cm^{-1}, 822.5 cm^{-1}.

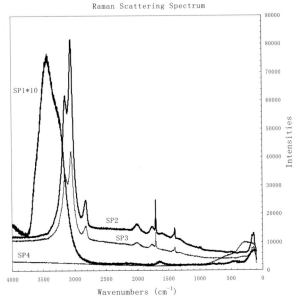

Fig. 6. Raman spectra: the Raman spectrum for liquid water is labeled as SP1, SP2, and SP3 represent the Raman spectra at two separate spots with residues on the silicon slide. SP4 is that of blank spot on the silicon slide where there is no residue.

Please cite this article in press as: S.Y. Lo et al., Physics Letters A (2009), doi:10.1016/j.physleta.2009.08.061

ARTICLE IN PRESS

S.Y. Lo et al. / Physics Letters A ••• (••••) •••–•••

ground noise we also focus the Argon laser to spot on the silicon slide where there is no residue. We see a flat curve and no peak.

Acknowledgements

We wish to thank Dr. Scott E. McKay, Department Chair & Professor of Chemistry, University of Central Missouri for providing help on the infrared spectra; Dr. Chen Jian, Director of Instrumental Analysis and Research Centre of Zhongshan (Sun Yat-Sen) University, China for help in obtaining spectra of Raman scattering; Prof. S. Senkan of UCLA, Prof. B. Bonavita of UCLA, and Dr. James Lo for interesting discussions.

References

[1] F.N. Keutsch, R.J. Saykally, Proc. Natl. Acad. Sci. USA 98 (2001) 10533.

[2] J.-W. Shin, N.I. Hammer, E.G. Diken, M.A. Johnson, R.S. Walters, T.D. Jaeger, M.A. Duncan, R.A. Christie, K.D. Jordan, Science 304 (2004) 1137.

[3] M. Miyazaki, A. Fujii, T. Ebata, N. Mikami, Science 304 (2004) 1134.

[4] K. Johnson, M. Price-Gallagher, O. Mamer, A. Lesimple, C. Fletcher, Y. Chen, X. Lu, M. Yamaguchi, X.-C. Zhang, Phys. Lett. A 372 (2008) 603.

[5] For more references, Cambridge Data Group, http://www.watersch.cam.ac.uk.

[6] S.-Y. Lo, W. Li, Mod. Phys. Lett. B 13 (1999) 885.

[7] S.-Y. Lo, et al., Mod. Phys. Lett. B 10 (1996) 909.

[8] S.-Y. Lo, S.-Y. Lo, A. Lo, W.C. Li, T.H. Li, H.H. Li, X. Geng, Mod. Phys. Lett. B 10 (1996) 921.

[9] C.Y. Wong, S.Y. Lo, Possible mechanism of formation and stability of anomalous state of water, in: S.Y. Lo, B. Bonavida (Eds.), Proceedings of the 1st International Symposium on Physical, Chemical and Biological Properties of Stable Water Clusters, World Scientific, 1998, p. 48.

[10] S.Y. Lo, W.C. Li, S.H. Huang, Med. Hypotheses 54 (6) (2000) 948.

[11] S.N. Magonov, in: S.Y. Lo, B. Bonavida (Eds.), Proceedings of the 1st International Symposium on Physical, Chemical and Biological Properties of Stable Water Clusters, World Scientific, 1998, p. 91.

Multi-Frequency Electromagnetic Homeopathic Solution©

C. Norman Shealy, M.D., Ph.D. and Paul Thomlinson, Ph.D.

In 1997 Bonavida and associates at the UCLA Department of Immunology reported that homeopathic multi-frequency electromagnetically imprinted water markedly increased immune antibody production by human leukocytes. Specifically, in that test tube study, TNF-a, IL-6, IL-12, IL-b, and IFN-y were increased by 30 to 100 fold.

In the fall of 2007, we enlisted, in an IRB approved protocol, 10 healthy subjects who had baseline blood drawn to measure TNF-A, IL-1B; IL-6, and IFN-Y. The serum was frozen and saved until completion of the study. There were 3 males and 7 females, aged 26 to 74. All were asked to drink one quart daily of purified or distilled water, to which they added 20 drops of homeopathically potentized water, prepared by the same technic as the original Bonavida study. The potenization of the water was carried out with a Multi-Frequency Electromagnetic process. Each bottle of the water was to be shaken vigorously by the subjects and kept refrigerated during the day. After 6 weeks blood was drawn again and both baseline and final blood samples were sent to a research lab at University of Pennsylvania, Hershey, for analysis. One subject failed to return for the final blood draw.

The sample size is too small for definitive statistical certainty. However, statistical analysis, revealed the following: Results indicate no reliable change in Interleukin-1B or Interleukin-6 measurements.

Name	Collection date	Collection time	Pre/Post	TNF-A pg/ml	Interleukin-1B pg/ml	Interleukin-6 pg/ml	Interferon-Y pg/ml
JD	10/15/2007	0430 pm	pre	2.2	2.9	9.5	20.8
JD	11/30/2007	1155 am	post	6.6	3.5	9.2	21.3
DW	10/16/2007	1100 am	pre	<1.0	<1.0	4.3	19.5
DW	11/29/2007	0935 am	post	<1.0	<1.0	<1.0	21.5
TS	10/16/2007	1145 am	pre	<1.0	<1.0	1.9	21
TS	11/30/2007	1255 pm	post	1.5	<1.0	3.6	22.5
PT	10/16/2007	0500 pm	pre	<1.0	<1.0	4.5	19.8
PT	11/30/2007	0620 pm	post	<1.0	<1.0	3.9	20.3
ER	10/19/2007	1150 am	pre	<1.0	<1.0	4.1	20.5
ER	11/29/2007	1120 am	post	<1.0	<1.0	5.5	21.3
LL	10/19/2007	0140 pm	pre	<1.0	4.6	<1.0	20.5
LL	11/30/2007	0935 am	post	2	1.6	<1.0	22.3
JP	10/19/2007	0200 pm	pre	<1.0	2.1	3.9	22
JP	11/30/2007	1130 am	post	1.8	7.1	3.4	22
NS	10/19/2007	0210 pm	pre	<1.0	6.1	2.4	19.3
NS	11/30/2007	1135 am	post	<1.0	<1.0	1.8	21.8
CS	10/20/2007	0630 pm	pre	<1.0	<1.0	5.3	21.3
CS	11/30/2007	0620 pm	post	1.4	2.9	3.8	21.8

Results indicate a marginally significant increase in TNF-A, if one uses the onetailed test ($p=.065$).

Results show significant increases in Interferon-Y ($p=.004$ using 2-tailed, $p=.002$ if using 1-tailed).

DISCUSSION

This pilot study suggests that Multi-frequency Electromagnetic Homeopathically Potentized water may produce a significant enhancement of immune function in human beings. Larger studies should be done with perhaps a broader overview of immune function. Dysfunctions of the immune system are major factors in allergies, autoimmune diseases, cancer and even atherosclerosis and diabetes.

The implications for immune health are obvious.

PROTOCOL FOR A STUDY OF THE EFFECTS OF HOMEOPATHICALLY/ENERGETICALLY IMPRINTED WATER ON SELECTED IMMUNE FUNCTIONS

Protocol Number

LOCATION: Shealy Wellness Center

5607 S. 222nd Road

Fair Grove, MO 65648

PRINCIPAL INVESTIGATOR: C. Norman Shealy, M.D., Ph.D.

IRB APPROVAL:

1.1 OBJECTIVE

To evaluate the changes in white immune function in vivo in a pilot study of 10 individuals and expanding this to a total of 50 individuals if the initial pilot results are positive.

1.2 BACKGROUND

An earlier in vitro study of a specifically homeopathically imprinted water revealed that in a test tube situation this water strikingly increased the production by white cells of immune activity.

Induction and regulation of human peripheral blood TH1-Th2 derived cytokines by IE water preparations and synergy with mitogens
Bonavida, B en X H Gan (1997) In: S Y Lo & B Bonavida, Proceedings of the first international symposium on 'Physical chemical and biological properties of stable water IceElectromagnetic clusters', 167-183. World Scientific, New Jersey.

Anecdotal evidence suggests that this water may have health benefits. At least a dozen individuals have reported marked improvement in a variety of medical conditions when drinking very small amounts of this water.

1.3   STUDY DESIGN

Initially 10 individuals with no known major medical illnesses will be solicited to participate in the study. They will be screened with a Symptom Index (attached), urine tested for free radicals, and blood will be drawn and sent to a laboratory at the University of Pennsylvania in Hershey, PA for measurement of **tumor necrosis factor alpha (TNF-α), interleukin-6 (IL-6), IL-b, IL-12, and interferon-γ(IFN-γ).** They will then be given 1 ounce of the homeopathically imprinted water and 15 gallons of distilled water with instructions to place 20 drops of the homeopathic concentrate into each gallon of water just prior to opening that particular bottle. The bottle is then shaken vigorously and placed in the refrigerator and they are to drink four 8 ounce glasses each day for 45 days. At the end of 45 days, they will come back for a redraw of blood for the same measurement a repeat symptom index and a urinary free radical test.

1.4   SUBJECT POPULATION

This study will involve at least 10 subjects.

1.4.1 INCLUSION CRITERIA

a. Subjects will show willingness to participate by signing a voluntary informed consent form and to fill out a baseline Symptom Index.

b. They will have the ability and willingness to follow the directions of the Principal Investigator.

c. Subjects will be in reasonably good health.

1.1.2 EXCLUSION CRITERIA

a. Individuals with a major medical illness or on prescription drugs.

1.4 POTENTIAL RISKS

There is no known risk other than that of a standard vena puncture.

1.5 DISCONTINUATION CRITERIA

Subject may be dropped from the study at any time at their request or that of the Principal Investigator and reported to the Institutional Review Board. If the subject stops participation in the study prematurely, the drop date and reason will be recorded and reported to the Institutional Review Board.

1.6 ADVERSE REACTIONS

If any adverse reactions occur during the study, the Principal Investigator can determine whether the subject should continue participation in the research and report to the Institutional Review Board in writing.

1.7 SAFETY

Safety will be evaluated by monitoring any adverse effects and adverse effects will be reported as follows.

a. Subjects will notify the Principal Investigator as soon as possible should unusual or adverse symptoms occur and the Principal Investigator will report to the Institutional Review Board.

b. The Principal Investigator will notify the Institutional Review Board Chair within 24 hours and the full board within 72 hours of any adverse reaction.

c. Any adverse reaction will be recorded in the complaint file and reported to the full Institutional Review Board.

d. In case of adverse effects, the Principal Investigator, in accordance with good clinical practice, will carry out proper therapeutic measures and follow up.

1.8   EFFICACY

Efficacy will be determined by comparing the measurements of the five selected immune functions, urinary free radicals, as well as the total number of symptoms before and at the end of the study. The participants' data will be analyzed using a mixed analysis of covariants (ANOVA) adjusting for baseline levels of observed difference. For each subject the mean difference will be calculated and considered the unit of measure.

2.0   SPECIAL INSTRUCTIONS

All subjects will be required to sign the informed consent form. They will be given 11 gallons of distilled water and 15 ml of the homeopathically imprinted water. They will also be instructed in the mixture of the water and its management by refrigeration after each bottle is mixed. At the initial screening visit, each subject will fill out the consent form, have a urinary free radical test, fill out a Symptom Index and have a blood sample drawn which will be submitted to the measuring laboratory in Pennsylvania within 24 hours.

2.1   MONITORING PERSONNEL

C. Norman Shealy, M.D., Ph.D.

2.1 REGULATORY CONSIDERATION

None known.

2.2 PROTOCOL AGENDA

The Principal Investigator will not implement a change or otherwise deviate from the protocol.

2.3 REGULATORY REPORTING

Reports of progress or lack of progress will be sent to the IRB within 3 months. It is anticipated that the pilot study will be completed within 60 days of approval by the IRB and at that time, it will be determined if there will be an additional 40 subjects enrolled.

2.4 PATIENT CONSENT FORM

Signed consent forms will be obtained by the investigator from each subject admitted to the study.

2.5   REPORTING FORMS

All completed reporting forms, appropriately signed and dated and maintained by the Principal Investigator. These will include:

    a. The Symptom Index

    b.   Urinary free radical result

    c. Immune functions as determined by reference lab

2.6   DATA RECORDING

    a. Only black ink will be used on reporting forms.

    b. All blanks will be filled in.

INDUCTION AND REGULATION OF HUMAN PERIPHERAL BLOOD TH1-TH2 DERIVED CYTOKINES BY I_E WATER PREPARATIONS AND SYNERGY WITH MITOGENS

B. BONAVIDA, X.H. GAN

Originally published as *Physical, Chemical and Biological Properties of Stable Water Clusters,*
Proceedings of the First International Symposium.
Reprinted here by permission of
World Scientific Publishing Company, 1998.

Recent studies by Lo *et al* [1,2] have reported on the physical properties of water with I_E structures. These structures exhibit a variety of distinct physical and chemical properties as compared to ordinary control water preparations. We have initiated studies to investigate the effect of I_E water in a biological system in order to establish a physiological role for I_E water. We investigated the induction and regulation of synthesis of several cytokines, mediators of both the antibody and cell-mediated immune responses to infection and cancer, by human peripheral blood-derived leukocytes and purified subsets. Cytokine secretion was determined by a sensitive and specific Elisa and transcriptional regulation of mRNA by RT-PCR. We demonstrate with one I_E water preparation provided by ATG that it possesses potent immunomodulatory activities in the absence and presence of suboptimal concentrations of T and B cell mitogens. The effects were specific for I_E water as no effect was seen with control water preparations from ATG or laboratory-derived water. The following findings were reproducibly obtained with I_E water preparations: (1) There was significant stimulation of several cytokines by human peripheral blood, namely tumor necrosis factor alpha (TNF-α), interleukin-6 (IL-6), IL-10, IL-12, and interferon-γ (IFN-γ). The amount secreted by I_E water was very significant, higher or similar to optimal concentrations of mitogen-induced stimulation of cytokines. The secretion of cytokines was also observed with purified subpopulations of lymphocytes and monocytes. (2) The induction of cytokine secretion by I_E water was a function of both the final concentration of I_E water and the time of incubation. There was a dose-dependent titration of cytokine secretion with different dilutions of I_E. Further, we observed a very rapid kinetics of induction of cytokines by I_E water as early as 2 h following stimulation. (3) In the presence of suboptimal concentrations of the B cell mitogen (LPS) and the T cell mitogen (PHA), we obtained a significant synergistic activity with I_E water but not with control water preparations. (4) The levels of cytokine induction differed from one individual to another but the pattern remained the same for all individuals. (5) In several instances, we observed a specific pattern of cytokine induction by TH1 and TH2 subsets. These two subsets regulate the outcome of several human diseases.

We were concerned about the possibility that I_E water was contaminated with bacterial products, like the lipopolysaccharide (LPS), which is mitogenic and stimulates high levels of cytokines by peripheral blood. We examined the effect of a specific inhibitor of LPS, polymixin B, in the cytokine response by human peripheral blood to both I_E water and LPS.

The findings demonstrate that whereas LPS-induced cytokines secretion is completely inhibited by polymixin B, the cytokine response by I_E water was not affected at all by polymixin B. These findings rule out LPS as a potential contaminant in the I_E water preparation.

Altogether, these findings demonstrate that I_E water preparations exert potent and selective immunomodulatory activities on human peripheral blood. Further, I_E water potentiates and synergizes with antigenic stimulation and thus may have an important role both as an adjuvant and/or as a regulator of specific immune responses. Since different water preparations can be prepared with different I_E crystals, we hypothesize that each might have a distinct and selective pattern of cytokine induction and immunostimulatory activities. The potential benefit of I_E water preparations in human diseases need to be explored.

1   Introduction

Infections (viruses, bacteria, fungi, protozoa and helminths) cause damage to tissues. Body surfaces are protected by skin epithelia and epithelia that line the gastrointestinal, respiratory, and genitourinary tract. Infections take place when pathogens colonize or crossover the epithelial barriers. When pathogens crossover epithelial barriers and begin to replicate in the tissues of the host, the host's defense mechanisms are required to eliminate the pathogens. The first phase of host defense is innate immunity. Different infectious agents cause markedly different diseases, reflecting the diverse processes by which they damage the tissues. Many extracellular pathogens cause disease by releasing specific toxic products or toxins. Intracellular infectious agents frequently cause disease by damaging the cells that host them. The pathology caused by a particular infection depends on the site in which it grows.

Host immunity can be divided into innate immunity and adaptive immunity. Innate immunity: exposure to infection is measured by host responses that are present at all times. These include epithelial barriers to infection, phagocytosis by monocytes and macrophages, secretion of mediators, and natural killer cells that kill infected cells and cancerous cells. Innate immunity is characterized by lack of specificity for a particular pathogen and lack of memory (responses do not increase with repeated exposure to the same pathogen). Adaptive immunity: it is characterized by the response of specific lymphocytes and the development of immunological memory. Adaptive immune responses are generated by clonal selection of lymphocytes. These antigen-specific lymphocytes, namely B and T cells, result in the production of antibody response and cell-mediated immunity, respectively.

While antibodies are useful in the blood and accessible spaces and can neutralize extracellular pathogens, bacterial pathogens and parasites and virus that replicate inside the cells cannot be detected by antibodies. These can be destroyed by T cell-mediated immune responses.

T cells have been subdivided into two types: cytotoxic (CD8[+]T) and helper (CD4[+]T). The T helper is subdivided into TH1 and TH2[3]. TH1 cells secrete soluble mediators or cytokines that regulate the antibody response by B lymphocytes. TH2 cells secrete cytokines that regulated delayed-type hypersensitivity and inflammatory responses. The cytotoxic T cells kill infected cells and cancerous cells.

The cytokines activated by pathogens are responsible for directing the immune response towards a preferential TH2-dependent B cell antibody response or a preferential TH1-dependent cell mediated response, or both. Different pathogens are eliminated preferentially by either antibodies or by cell-mediated responses. Thus, the regulation of cytokines that are synthesized and secreted is important in the final outcome of the two arms of the immune response and their effect in the elimination of infections.

The objective of this study was to initially examine whether I_E water cluster preparations, used alone or in combination with antigens, have any effect on the regulation of cytokine synthesis and production by human peripheral blood leukocytes and to determine whether there exists a selective triggering of TH1 vs. TH2 type of cytokines.

2.   Materials and Methods

2.1 Monocyte Isolation

This was done as described[4]. Briefly, monocytes were isolated from EDTA-anti-coagulated human peripheral blood using a modification of the Fogelman method[5]. Briefly, white blood cells, WBC, were separated by mixing 10 parts of blood, 1 part of 6% Dextran 500 (Accurate chemical) and leaving the tube standing at room temperature for 40 min. The WBC, after a serial hypertonic treatment with a gradually increased osmolality, were laid on monocyte isolation buffer (Nycoprep 1.068) and centrifuged at 600 g for 15 min. The monocytes (PBM) at and below the interface were harvested, washed once with PBS, and suspended in RPMI with 10% autologous serum for further use. The preparation of peripheral blood lymphocytes (PBL) was done according to Jewett et al.[4].

2.2 Whole Blood Cytokine Induction

Blood drawn from normal donors was sampled into sodium heparin-containing sterile blood collecting lubec (Vamtamer, Becton Dickenson & Co.)[6]. For cytokine induction, 0.3 ml of blood was added to 1.2 ml of RPMI-1640 containing 50% of either control water or I_E water, with or without other indicated treatments. For LPS treatment, the samples were incubated for 18 h, and for PHA stimulation, they were incubated for 48 h, except as otherwise indicated. At the end of the culture, the samples were gently mixed by swirling the test tube, and cell free supernatants were harvested after centrifugation.

For cytokine induction from PBM, PBL and monocytes, 100 µl of cells (10^7 cells/ml) were added to each sample (900 µl of RPMI-1640 containing 50% of control or I_E water) and incubated for 18 h for monocytes, 48 h for PBL, and for 18 h or 48 h whole blood depending on the stimulation.

2.3 Quantitation of Cytokines

This was done according to our published procedures[4].

3. Results

We have investigated the effect of I_E water preparations, alone or in combination with mitogens, on the induction of cytokines by human peripheral blood-derived leukocytes and subsets. The cytokines were assayed by sensitive and specific quantitative Elisa methods as described[4].

3.1 Effect of I_E Water on Human Peripheral Blood Leukocytes

3.1.1 Spontaneous Induction

We examined the effect of I_E water preparations on the spontaneous induction of several cytokines by human peripheral blood. The final concentration of I_E water was 50% as it was mixed with 2x medium. Table 1 shows a representative experiment whereby TNF-α, IL-6 and IL-12 were measured. Clearly, two different batches of I_E water (I_E #1 and #2) stimulated significant levels of all three cytokines. Control water from the laboratory or from ATG resulted in very low levels of TNF-α (< 45 fold) and no IL-6 or IL-12. These findings demonstrate that the culture of peripheral blood in I_E water-containing medium stimulates the secretion of significant levels of several cytokines.

Table 1: I_E water-induced cytokine production by whole blood.

Water	Cytokine (pg/ml)		
Preparation	TNF-α	IL-6	IL-12
Laboratory	260	0	8
ATG Control	260	0	9
I_E #1	12190	3906	1041
I_E #2	10735	4797	1190

The laboratory medium (RPMI 1640) was pretreated at 2x concentration. It was used to dilute (1:1) with various water preparations. Whole peripheral blood was diluted (1:5) in the medium and incubated for 18 h at 37°, 5% CO_2 incubator. Thereafter, the cell free supernatants were removed and stored for analysis for cytokines. The results presented are mean of duplicate tests of 3 different experiments.

3.1.2 Titration of Potency of I_E Water

We then examined if the spontaneous induction of cytokines by I_E water is dependent on the final concentration of I_E water clusters present in the culture. Different dilutions of I_E water were made and tested for their induction of cytokines. Table 2 shows a representative experiment for TNF-α and IL-12. Clearly, the secretion of both of these cytokines is a function of the final I_E water concentration. Significant cytokine induction was observed after ten fold dilutions.

3.1.3 Effect of I_E Water on Mitogen-Induced Cytokine Production

Several mitogens, such as lipopolysaccharide (LPS) and phytohemagglutinin (PHA), stimulate the proliferation and secretion of cytokines by peripheral blood leukocytes. We examined the effect of I_E water on both LPS and PHA-mediated cytokine secretion. Table 3 represents data obtained from LPS-mediated stimulation of peripheral blood. LPS is a potent mitogen for monocytes. Clearly,

Table 2 Effect of titration of I_E water on cytokine production by human whole blood.

Type of	Cytokine (pg/ml)			
cytokine	1:2	1:6	1:18	Non I_E Control
TNF-α	14176	4649	1593	430
IL-12	2405	1893	529	39

The laboratory medium (2x) was diluted with water preparations (1:1) to give a final concentration of 50%. This was diluted three fold and the experiment was performed as in the legend of Table 1.

Table 3   Effects of I_E water on LPS-induced cytokine production by whole blood.

Water	Cytokine (pg/ml)		
Preparation	TNF-α	IL-6	IL-12
Laboratory	8065	4014	1008
ATG Control	7211	4153	907
I_E #1	13222	4331	1040
I_E #2	12933	4902	1239

The peripheral blood was prepared as in the legend of Table 1 except that LPS (10 ng/ml) was used for mitogenic stimulation.

Table 4   Effect of I_E water on PHA-induced cytokine production by whole blood.

Water Preparation	Cytokine (pg/ml)			
	TNF-α	IL-6	IL-12	IFN-γ
Laboratory	131	19	40	703
ATG Control	117	19	41	703
I_E #1	13197	2414	1228	1043
I_E #2	10204	2657	1026	2230

The peripheral blood was prepared as in the legend of Table 1 except that the cultures were stimulated with PHA (5 μg/ml) and incubated for 48 h before harvesting.

while control water shows significant production of TNF-α, IL-6 and IL-12 by LPS, the combination of LPS and I_E water resulted in significant potentiation of the secretion.   Table 4 shows representative results of cytokine secretion by PHA stimulated human peripheral blood. PHA is a potent mitogen for T cells. The data in Table 4 show that PHA does not stimulate, as expected, significant TNF-α, IL-6, and IL-16 (monocytes derived) but stimulate T cell-derived IFN-γ.   The combination of I_E and PHA potentiate the secretion of IFN-γ.

These findings demonstrate that combination of I_E water with mitogens potentiate the secretion of selective cytokines by peripheral blood.

3.1.4   Synergy

We investigated whether I_E water can potentiate the cytokine secretion of primed cells. Human peripheral blood was activated with PHA and then restimulated in the presence of LPS in control medium or I_E water medium. The results are shown in Figure 1 and are representative for TNF-α. Clearly, in the absence of prior activation, I_E water stimulates TNF-α secretion as expected. However, following priming, the response obtained in I_E water is significantly and synergistically higher than the response obtained in control water.

These findings show clearly that I_E water preparations can potentiate the recall response and act in a synergistic fashion.

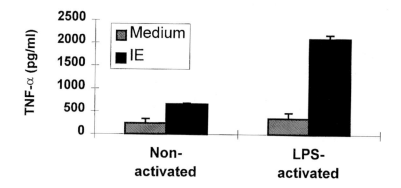

FIGURE 1 Synergistic response to PHA in activated blood cells.

Human peripheral blood was prepared as described in the legend of Table 1. The cells were cultured with or without LPS (10 ng/ml) for 18 h. The cultures were replaced with fresh medium in the presence of PHA (5 μg/ml) and incubated for 48 h. Cell-free supernatants were harvested and stored for assessment of cytokines.

3.2 Effect of I_E Water on Peripheral Blood Monocytes (PBM)

3.2.1. Spontaneous Induction

In the previous sections, we examined the effect of I_E water preparations on whole blood which mimics the *in vivo* system. However, we wished to investigate the effect of I_E water preparation on separated subsets of human blood leukocytes in order to determine if there is a preferential induction of cytokines by the subsets and if there is also a selective triggering of certain cytokines over others. We examined the cytokine secretion of purified human peripheral blood monocytes (PBM). Table 5 shows that I_E water significantly stimulated the secretion of TNF-α, IL-6 and IL-12 by PBM as compared to control water preparations. The induction of cytokines is at the level of gene induction and transcription as shown in Figure 2. We performed RT-PCR to determine the regulation of TNF-α synthesis. Clearly, control water has no detectable mRNA for TNF-α while I_E water induced significant levels of mRNA and was comparable to control LPS- induced TNF-α. These findings demonstrate that I_E water stimulates TNF-α secretion by gene induction.

Table 5. I_E water-induced cytokine production by human peripheral blood monocytes.

Water Preparation	Cytokine (pg/ml)		
	TNF-α	IL-6	IL-12
Laboratory	1359	168	11
ATG Control	979	169	6
I_E #1	16740	2579	76
I_E #2	22851	2534	215

The purified peripheral blood monocytes were prepared as described in Materials and Methods. The cultures were prepared as described in the legend of Table 1.

3.2.2 Kinetics of Secretion

We examined the time kinetics of TNF-α secretion by PBM cultured in I_E water and compared it to a control medium preparation. Figure 3 is a representative experiment which demonstrates that TNF secretion is detected early after culture in I_E water (<4 h) and increases as a function of incubation time. It reaches a plateau at 1 day and depending on the subjects, either it remains at plateau level for several days as shown in Figure 3 or declines (not shown). PBM in control medium show some spontaneous induction at 8 h and plateaus thereafter.

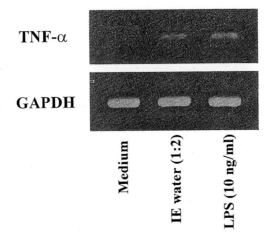

FIGURE 2 Gene induction of cytokines by I_E (PCR).

RT-PCR was done as described previously[7] using human peripheral blood monocytes.

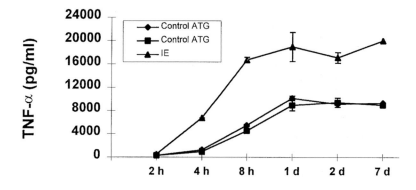

FIGURE 3 Kinetics of TNF-α secretion by human monocytes.

This experiment was done according to the procedure described in the legend of Table 6.

Furthermore, the kinetics of secretion of other cytokines (IL-6, IL-10, IL-12) is shown in Table 6. When compared to LPS, we found that for IL-10, the I_E water stimulation was significant but less effective than LPS. In contrast, for IL-12, I_E water stimulated higher levels than LPS and increased from day 1 to day 2 (Figure 4).

Table 6 Time kinetics of I_E-induced cytokine secretion by monocytes.

Time	TNF-α		IL-6		IL-10		IL-12	
	Control	I_E	Control	I_E	Control	I_E	Control	I_E
2 h	668	5305	57	82	4	4	13	14
4 h	2220	19274	188	1997	4	4	14	14
8 h	2245	24999	1689	2835	4	13	18	50
24 h	610	9465	2372	2775	4	190	34	139
48 h	241	992	3125	3125	5	109	37	155
7 days	4072	819	2741	2741	5	41	41	78

In this experiment, 10^6/ml purified monocytes were incubated with I_E medium (50%) or control medium. At different time points, cell free supernatants were harvested and stored at 70°C, for future use, for cytokine determination.

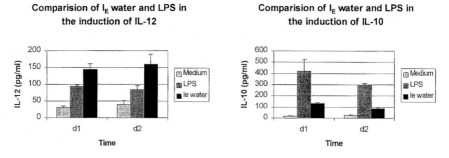

Comparision of I$_E$ water and LPS in the induction of IL-12

Comparision of I$_E$ water and LPS in the induction of IL-10

FIGURE 4 This experiment was done according to the legend of Table 3.
The cultures were harvested at d1 and d2 and cell-free supernatants stored for assessment of cytokines.

3.3 Effect of I$_E$ Water Preparations in Non-Adherent Peripheral Blood Leukocytes

We examined the effect of I$_E$ water on cytokine secretion by non-adherent lymphocytes (T, B, NK). The findings in Table 7 demonstrate that significant levels of TNF-α and IL-12 were stimulated by I$_E$ water compared to control. These findings demonstrate that I$_E$ water can also stimulate lymphocytes in addition to monocytes as described in 3.2 above.

Table 7 Effects of I$_E$ water on cytokine secretion by nonadherent PBMC.

Water	Cytokine (pg/ml)		
Preparation	TNF-α	IL-6	IL-12
ATG Control	13,000	2016	120
I$_E$ #1	38,765	2119	720

Peripheral blood mononuclear cells were isolated by Ficoll Hypaque and adherent cells were depleted by adherence to plastic plates. Two million cells/ml in different media were incubated for 48 h and cell-free supernatants collected for assessment of cytokines.

3.4 Absence of Endotoxin in I$_E$ Water Preparations

Since I$_E$ water preparations stimulated several cytokines by peripheral blood, we examined whether contaminating levels of endotoxins, powerful mitogens, might be responsible for the I$_E$-mediated effects.   We used an LPS-specific inhibitor, polymixin B, which inhibits the potent LPS mitogen. The findings in Figure 5 demonstrate that while polymixin B inhibits LPS-mediated stimulation of TNF-α, polymixin B has no effect, albeit enhancing effects on I$_E$ induced TNF-α secretion. These findings clearly indicate that the I$_E$-mediated cytokine induction is not due to endotoxin contamination in the I$_E$ water preparations.

4   Discussion

The findings in these studies suggest that human peripheral blood-derived leukocytes cultured in medium prepared with I_E crystal water undergo a state of activation resulting in cytokine production. Several cytokines are secreted albeit at various levels. Furthermore, certain cytokines are preferentially secreted over others. In addition, I_E water preparations act synergistically with T and B mitogenic stimulation. Noteworthy, the induction of cytokine secretion is rapid and is detected at less than 4 h following culture and increases progressively and reaches a

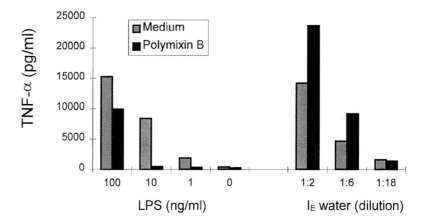

FIGURE 5   Absence of endotoxin in I_E preparations. The cell preparations were incubated with LPS (10 ng/ml) in the presence or absence of polymixin B (10 µg/ml) and incubated for 18 h. Cell-free supernatants were harvested and stored for cytokine measurement.

plateau which is maintained for several days. The stimulation of cytokines by I_E water is mediated through gene induction. Altogether, these findings demonstrate for the first time that water containing I_E crystals affect human blood leukocytes in a manner that mimics mitogenic or antigenic stimulation.

The I_E water preparation used in these studies did not contain detectable endotoxin contaminants like LPS that may be in part responsible for the induction of cytokines. This was demonstrated by the use of specific endotoxin inhibitors. Further, water preparations made under similar conditions, with the exception of induction of I_E crystals, did not have any detectable activity.

The stimulation of significant levels of cytokines by I_E and potentiation with antigenic stimuli suggest an important regulatory role in the immune response. The nature and level of cytokines produced will influence a particular immune response. The Mossmann et al.[3] reported an intriguing and conceptual revolution in immunology by dividing T helper (TH) cells into two populations (TH1 and TH2) with contrasting and cross-regulating cytokine profiles. This new paradigm was enthusiastically endorsed in many areas of immunology and infectious diseases.

The TH1 response evolves around the production of IFN-γ and the subsequent activation of macrophages. These features of cell-mediated immunity are certainly important for the resolution of intracellular infections[8, 9]. The paradigm that TH2 cells protect against extracellular parasites arise in part from the established role of antibodies in the control of many extracellular pathogens and the role that the TH2-type cytokines IL-4, IL-5 and IL-6 play in the generation of an effective antibody response[10, 11]. In addition, autoimmune diseases appear to be in general TH1-mediated[12]. For example, experimental work in insulin-dependent diabetes mellitus and experimental allergic encephalitis are TH1-mediated immune manifestations. Likewise, immune defense mechanisms against cancer are, in some instances, mediated by TH1-type responses. Further, transplantation studies show that graft rejection in TH1-mediated and graft acceptance is TH2-mediated[13].

Todate, it is more appropriate to define the combination of cytokines and effector cells required for a successful immune response than to attempt to clarify protective immunity as TH1-type or TH2-type. Other cells than T cells (example NK and monocytes) produce cytokines that may achieve a TH1 or TH2 effect[14].

Clearly, the findings of the present study are provocative as they demand understanding of the underlying molecular mechanisms by which I_E crystals initiate the activation machinery in the cells to secrete cytokines. Clearly, one of the most important questions to answer is the initial trigger between water and cells. It is possible that I_E water introduces changes in cell membrane potential that can result in triggering receptor-like signaling pathways. It is also possible that I_E water bypasses membrane effects and activates intracellularly enzymatic activity that initiates the cascade of activation signaling resulting in gene transcription and translation of cytokine gene products. Other yet unknown effects can also be induced by I_E water. These and other studies are urgently needed.

The present findings with I_E crystal preparations were all performed with one particular type of cluster. It is possible that different cluster preparations will have different effects and will activate cytokines differentially. Schematically shown in Figure 6 are the possible outcomes of different I_E crystal preparations (crystals A-D). Briefly, preparation I_EA may selectively regulate cytokines involved in cell-mediated immunity by potentiating TH1 cytokines. Preparation I_EB may be potentiating TH2 cytokines and regulates antibody responses. Preparations I_EC may be potentiating cytokines that regulate phagocytosis of pathogens. Preparation I_ED may regulate autoimmune responses and allergies. These and other preparations may be, in principle, customized by the preparations of different crystals or mixture of crystals. Clearly, the implication of these various water preparations *in vitro* and *in vivo* in the regulation of immune responses must be investigated.

114

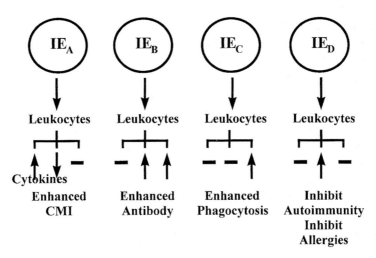

FIGURE 6. Cytokine regulation by I_E.

Schematic diagram showing regulation of cytokine production by leukocytes. ↑ represents upregulation; ↓ represents downregulation; - represents no effect.

In conclusion, these studies provide the initial phase of our long term objectives by exploring the biological effect of I_E water preparations on mammalian tissues and immunity. Furthermore, the principles of I_E crystal preparations must be examined as they may also apply in homeopathic remedies.

REFERENCES

1.   S.-Y. Lo, *Phys. Lett. B* 10, 909 (1996).
2.   S.-Y. Lo et al., *Phys. Lett. B* 10, 921 (1996).
3.   T.R. Mosmann et al., *J. Immunol.* 136, 2348 (1986).
4.   A. Jewett A et al., *J. Clin. Immunol.* 16, 46 (1996).
5.   A.M. Fogelman et al., *J. Lipid Res.* 29:1243, 1988.
6.   I.J. Elenkov et al., *Proc. of the Assoc. of American Physicians* 108, 374 (1996).
7.   S. Mori et al., *Cancer Res.* 56, 1874 (1996).
8.   K.C. Carter et al., *Eur. J. Immunol.* 19, 779 (1989).
9.   G.E. Grau and C. Behr. *Research in Immunol.* 145, 441 (1994).
10.   S. Sell and P.L. Hsu. *Immunol. Today* 14, 576 (1993).
11.   L. Romani et al., *J. Exp. Med.* 176, 19 (1992).
12.   R.S. Liblau et al., *Immunol. Today* 16, 34 (1995)
13.   T.B. Strom et al., *Curr. Opin. Immunol.* 8, 688 (1996).
14.   J.E. Allen and R.M. Maizels, *Immunol. Today* 18, 387 (1997).

SURVEY OF I_E™ CLUSTERS

S. Y. LO

Originally published as *Physical, Chemical and
Biological Properties of Stable Water Clusters,*
Proceedings of the First International Symposium.
Reprinted here by permission of
World Scientific Publishing Company, 1998.

Water clusters, referred to as I_E Crystals, that are stable at room temperature, have been discovered and studied recently. Three different sizes of I_E Crystals centering around 15nm, 300nm and 3 microns were identified by means of laser autocorrelation method. The larger, micron size clusters were also detected by transmission electron microscopy (TEM). Additionally, three-dimensional structures of I_E Crystals were observed with atomic force microscopy (AFM). The electric dipole nature of I_E Crystals was demonstrated by crystallization of sodium phosphate solution under an external electric field. The sodium phosphate crystals obtained from I_E-based solution were formed in a very regular manner, along the electric field lines, while a random crystallization was observed in the case of sodium phosphate solution prepared with a pure water control. The measurements of resistivity and electromotive force of I_E solutions also indicated a presence of electric dipole potential. A detected shift of hydrogen peak position in nuclear magnetic resonance (NMR) spectra of I_E solutions suggested a changed arrangement of water molecules in I_E solutions as compared to regular water. The possible applications of I_E Crystals and their solutions to physical, chemical, biochemical and medical processes are discussed.

1   Introduction

Water is one of the crucial components of life and its structure, unusual physical and chemical properties have been studied comprehensively. A number of models was proposed, based on the clustering of water molecules, to account for its negative volume of melting, density maximum at 4°C, and anomalous high melting and boiling temperatures[1-21]. Negatively charged water clusters of eight or more molecules were observed by Armbruster[18]. Larger clusters with 50-100 water molecules were predicted by other research groups[19,20]. Advances in laser spectroscopy and theoretical dynamics allowed highly detailed studies of small water clusters and offered insights into hydrogen-bond network rearranging dynamics[21].

It has been established that at least 10 types of ice structures exist[22-34]. Stable rigid structures, such as ice VI and VII, are known to be formed by water molecules at room temperature and at pressure above 7 kilobars[22] (Figure 1). A dissolved salt appears to cause an effect on water similar to that produced by high external pressure[35,36]. Rigid associations of water molecules, called I_E Crystals, were observed in specially prepared dilute aqueous solutions at room temperature and normal pressure[36,37].

In this study, we describe the structure of I_E Crystals and demonstrate that their formation is governed by the large electric dipole moment of water molecules.

2   A Possible Mechanism of I_E Crystal Formation in Aqueous Solutions

A new kind of stable water cluster[38], I_E Crystal, formed by the electric dipole moment of water molecules has been proposed[36,37]. We have discovered that I_E Crystals can be created from a dilute aqueous solution, for example sodium chloride, by their repeated dilution and shaking until the desired result is achieved.

To better understand the interaction between electric dipole moments of water molecules, an analogy can be made with a magnet made of iron atoms. Each iron atom can be viewed as a small magnet with a North and a South pole. When the magnetic dipole moments of iron atoms align, a magnet is created with a large magnetic dipole moment equal to the sum of the individual dipole moments. Similarly, when permanent electric dipole moments of water molecules line up, a stable water cluster with a large electric dipole moment is formed (Table 1).

Table 1 A comparison of an I_E cluster formed from water molecules with a magnet made of iron atoms

	Water Molecules	Fe Atom
Microscopic	Permanent electric dipole moment (nm)	Magnetic dipole moment (nm)
Macroscopic	Stable water clusters (μm); 10^{10} molecules	Magnet (m)

The water molecules, in ordinary water are at their lowest energy state in a potential well. A computer modeling of the potential energy of the surface of water,

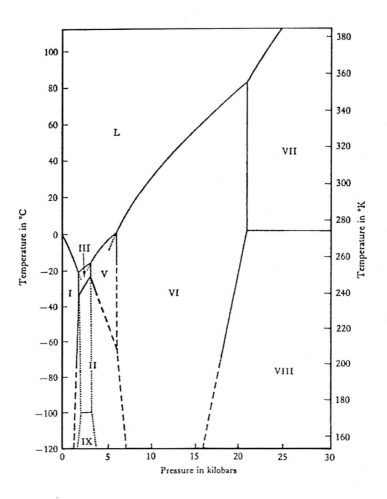

Figure 1 Phase diagram of ice based on temperature and pressure.

119

suggests an existence of several local minima besides the lowest energy state (Figure 2a). A dipole moment D_o presents the lowest (ground) stable state, and a larger dipole moment D_1 corresponds to a metastable state. The term "metastable" describes a stable, but not the lowest energy state. Its stability is due to a potential barrier that prevents molecules from falling back into the lowest stable state. The detailed mechanism is discussed in Wong and Lo[39].

When a charged ion, e.g. Na^+, is present in a dilute electrolyte solution, a local electric field around the ion is created. This electric field distorts the energy potential of local water molecules as shown in Figure 2b. As a result, the metastable state becomes lower in energy than the ground state, and the water molecules can then form easily into a larger dipole moment entity. A vigorous shaking of the solution results in a separation of charged ions from associations of water molecules. As a result, the shape of potential wells quickly restores and the ground state becomes the lowest energy state again. The restored potential barrier between metastable and ground states prevents the water clusters from sliding into the ground state.

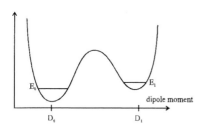

Figure 2a Potential wells for water molecules in water, and in I_E clusters as a function of dipole moment.

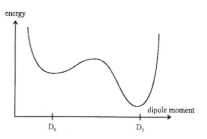

Figure 2b Potential wells change shape under the influence of an ion.

3 Detection of I_E Clusters

Three methods were used to detect stable I_E clusters: Photon Autocorrelation, Transmission Electron Microscopy (TEM) and Atomic Force Microscopy (AFM).

3.1 Size Distribution of I_E Clusters as Determined by Photon Autocorrelation

Photon Autocorrelation method, which utilizes the self-interference phenomenon of photons, was used to study the size distribution of I_E clusters. A helium-neon laser (Model BI-9000, Digital Correlation, Brookhaven Instruments Corporation) emitted light on a glass bottle containing an I_E Crystal aqueous solution. The interference between the light scattered by I_E Crystals and the transmitted light, allowed us to estimate the size of I_E clusters (Figure 3). Three major sizes of I_E clusters were observed: approximately 15nm, 300nm and several microns (Figure 3a).

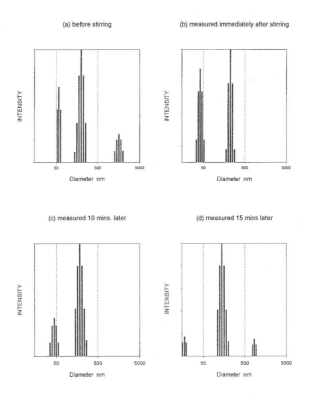

Figure 3   Size distribution of I_E clusters as determined by *in situ* laser autocorrelation measurement.

Vigorous stirring of I_E Crystal solution led to the complete disappearance of the largest I_E clusters, while the number of smaller, 10nm and 100nm size, clusters increased (Figure 3b). This observation indicates that stirring (or shaking) breaks down large I_E clusters into the smaller ones. The smaller I_E clusters have strong electric dipole moments, which act like magnets to attract one to another to form larger I_E clusters. Approximately 15 minutes after stirring, many of the smaller I_E clusters reassembled back to their original larger size, and the solution became stable again (Figure 3d).

121

3.2 Observation of the Two-Dimensional Structure of I_E Crystals with TEM

The following EPA approved method for Asbestos Fiber Analysis (EPA-600/4-83-043) was used to prepare I_E Crystal samples. About 25 ml of I_E solution was filtered through a 0.1 μm pore size Nucleopore filter. The filter was then coated with carbon in a vacuum evaporator. The obtained carbon coated filter was cut in small pieces and placed on top of an electron microscope copper grid. The assembly was then placed onto the chloroform-saturated lens tissue and incubated for 24 h. to partially dissolve the filter. The residual filter was dissolved in a chloroform condensation washer. This method allowed us to preserve particles, including I_E structures, under a carbon film and then to transfer them to a microscope grid with a minimum of particle movement and breakage of carbon film.

Various I_E Crystal solutions were prepared using ATG's proprietary technologies. The I_E Crystals were deposited on microscope grids (as described above), and were observed with a Hitachi H600A TEM. Different shapes of I_E clusters were noticed (Figure 4). Such a variation in I_E Crystal structure is not surprising, since quantum mechanical calculations of the potential energy surface of water clusters, suggest existence of many local metastable energy minima. Theoretically, each of these minima can produce a different cluster.

In the 1970's, a notion about a new form of water, called polywater, and its unusual properties caught tremendous interest among scientists. However, a more careful investigation of the phenomenon later established that the observations of "polywater" are due to silicon in laboratory glassware. To ensure that I_E Crystals are not related to a silicon contamination, the x-ray spectra of control pure water and I_E Crystal samples were examined (Figure 5). There were some particles of dirt observed in the purified water control sample. When the electron beam was focused on those particles, a characteristic Silicon peak was identified in the x-ray spectra obtained (Figure 5a). No such peak was detected when the electron beam was focused on any I_E cluster (Figure 5b). Therefore, I_E Crystals are far different from polywater.

3.3 Observation of three-dimensional Structure of I_E Crystals with AFM

The 3-D conformation and packing of I_E Crystals were studied on mica surface with NanoScope® Multimode AFM (Digital Instruments, Santa Barbara, CA) in TappingMode™. AFM is a high resolution technique for studying surface

122

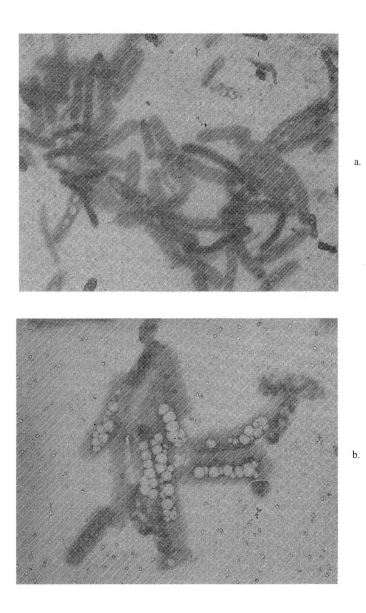

a.

b.

Figure 4 (a,b) Electron Microscopy images of different I_E clusters obtained from different I_E solutions and prepared using different initiators: (a) Isomaltose, amplification 5,000x, (b) cellalose, amplification 5,000x.

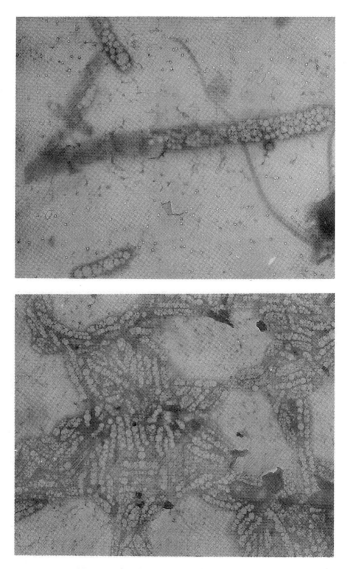

c.

d.

Figure 4 (c,d) Electron Microscopy images of different I_E clusters obtained from different I_E solutions and prepared using different initiators: (c) sophorose, 6,000x, (d) DS, proprietary solution 3,500x. The Electron Microscope is Hitachi H600A, 100keV electron beam. The small holes in the images are filter paper hole of 0.1 μm size. Qualitatively the clusters look different.

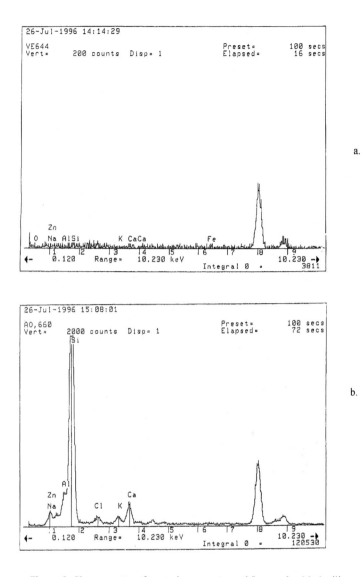

Figure 5 X-ray spectra of control pure water and I_E sample. (a) A silicon peak was observed at approximately 1.7 keV when the electron beam was focused on a dirt particle in control water. (b) No silicon peak was detected when the electron beam was focused on the I_E clusters. The peak at 8 keV is from the copper grid that holds the sample.

125

topography and is used in a wide array of application areas, including biology, semiconductors, polymers, etc. In this method, an oscillating cantilever with a sharp tip at the end is moved across the sample. A reduction in amplitude of oscillation, as the cantilever contacts the sample surface, is monitored with a laser beam focused on the back of the cantilever. The recorded information about changes in oscillation amplitude is then used to identify and measure surface features[40].

I_E Crystal samples were observed in two different ways. (1) A few drops of I_E Crystal solution were placed on freshly cleaved atomic smooth mica substrate surface and were dried by heating the substrate with warm air. The height images of I_E adsorbates were then recorded (Figures 6a-c). (2) To avoid possible effect of drying on the structure of I_E clusters, a fluid cell was used. A fluid cell allows operation of an AFM with the sample and the scanning tip under a fluid. The I_E structures deposited on the bottom of the cell were then imaged in their natural fluid environment (Figure 6d).

Size distribution analysis of imaged I_E samples indicated three major sizes of I_E clusters: 10nm, 100nm and 1μm. The observed I_E clusters were shown to be relatively flat objects, with the heights of approximately 10% of their length.

4   Direct Evidence of the Electric Nature of the I_E Clusters

Three methods were used to establish the electric nature of I_E clusters:
a.   An observation of electric field lines emitted by I_E Crystals.
b.   Analysis of nuclear magnetic resonance (NMR) spectra of I_E solutions.
c.   Measurements of resistivity and electromotive force (emf) of I_E solutions.

4.1 Evidence of Electric Field Emitted by I_E Clusters

The magnetic field of a magnet can be visualized by spraying iron powder around a magnet. Particles of the powder will align themselves along the magnetic field line emitted from the magnet. Similarly, electric field lines emitted by I_E clusters were observed as described below.

Monosodium phosphate, NaH_2PO_4, was dissolved in water containing I_E Crystals, referred to as I_E water. A small amount of the solution was placed on a glass microscope slide and allowed to evaporate and crystallize. The slide was then examined with an optical microscope with a magnification of 100x. A control sample was prepared by dissolving the salts in deionized water (18 MΩ-cm, less than 10 ppb total dissolved solids). The monosodium phosphate crystals, precipitated from control solution, demonstrated no ordered pattern (Figure 7a). The monosodium phosphate crystals precipitated from I_E-based solution lined up in

126

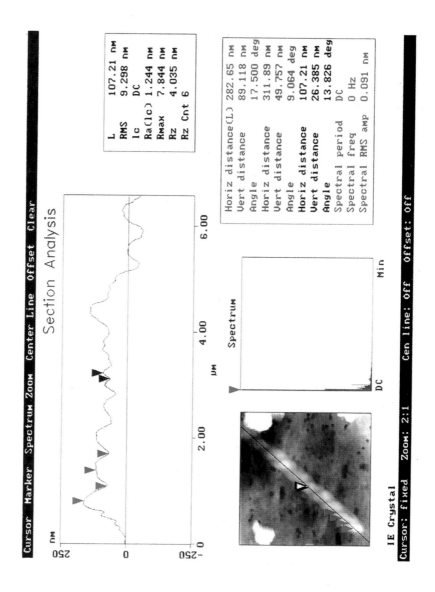

Figure 6a A 3-dimensional image of a micron size I_E clusters deposited on mica surface. The image was recorded in Tapping Mode™ with NanoScope AFM (Digital Instruments, Santa Barbara, CA).

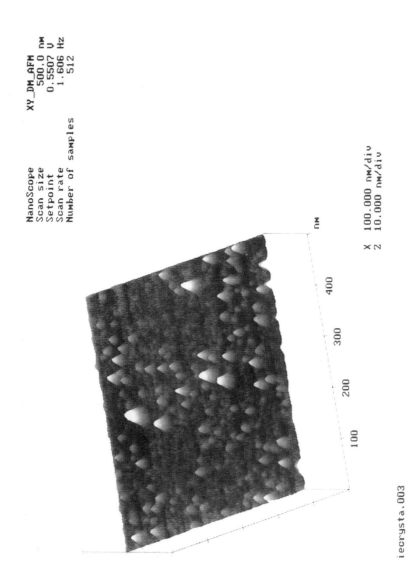

Figure 6b A 3-dimensional plot of ten nanometer size I_E clusters deposited on mica surface. The image was obtained in Tapping Mode™ with NanoScope AFM (Digital Instruments, Santa Barbara, CA).

128

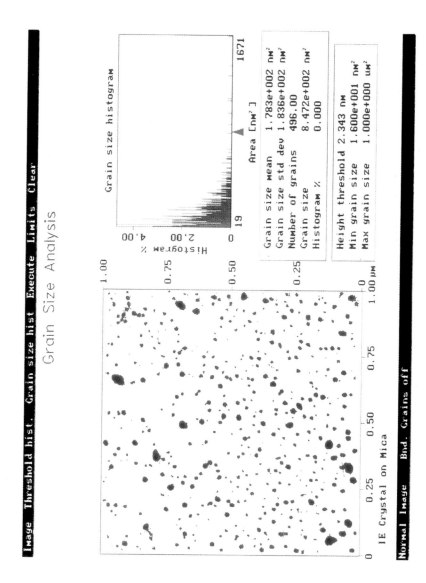

Figure 6c A 2-dimensional plot and a size distribution graph of small, ten nanometer size I_E clusters deposited on mica surface. The data was obtained by Tapping Mode™ scanning of I_E precipitate surface with NanoScope AFM (Digital Instruments, Santa Barbara, CA).

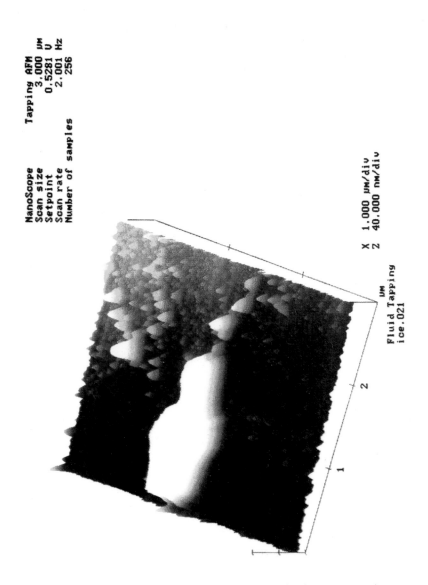

NanoScope   Tapping AFM
Scan size   3.000 µm
Setpoint   0.5281 V
Scan rate   2.001 Hz
Number of samples   256

X 1.000 µm/div
Z 40.000 nm/div

Fluid Tapping
ice.021

Figure 6d   Three sizes of I_E clusters: micron, hundreds of nanometer, and tens of nanometer size are all displayed together in this image recorded in a fluid cell with NanoScope AFM (Digital Instruments, Santa Barbara, CA).

a straight line (Figure 7b). These results strongly suggest that molecules, in this case molecules of monosodium phosphate, prefer to line up along the minimum energy position, which corresponds to the electric field lines emitted from the I_E clusters.

In order to further confirm the electric nature of I_E clusters, an external electric field of 20 volt/in or 100 volt/in was applied during the crystallization process. The electric field did not have any effect on the formation of monosodium phosphate crystals in control water solution (Figure 7c). However, the monosodium phosphate crystals, precipitated from I_E-based solution, aligned along the direction of the external electric field (Figures 7d and 7e). These observations can be explained by an interaction between the external electric field and the electric dipole moment of I_E clusters. The I_E clusters rotate, to align themselves with the external electric field, in order to stay at the minimum energy configuration and serve as nuclei for monosodium phosphate crystallization. Control water, on the other hand, does not contain I_E clusters, so there are no permanent net electric dipole moments available for an interaction with an external electric field. Therefore, no alignment of the monosodium phosphate crystals is observed in the case of control water.

X-ray diffraction analysis was carried out on powdered monosodium phosphate crystals precipitated from control and I_E waters. The original monosodium phosphate reagent (Sigma, St. Louis, MO) was also analyzed. The positions of the observed x-ray diffraction peaks (Table 2) were compared to the JCPDS-ICDD standard, that provides fingerprint information on various crystals. The original sample was, as expected, anhydrous. The crystals obtained from control water solution were monohydrates ($NaH_2PO_4 \cdot H_2O$), and the crystals precipitated from I_E-based solution were dihydrates ($NaH_2PO_4 \cdot 2H_2O$). This data indicates a difference in the crystallization process in the presence and in the absence of I_E Crystals.

4.2 A Shift of Proton Peak Position in NMR Spectra of I_E Solutions

To demonstrate that water molecules inside I_E clusters arrange themselves differently from water molecules in ordinary water, the positions of protons in water molecules were measured by NMR. NMR is a very sensitive way to detect the change of environment that protons find themselves in, since the method allows separation of signals from water and contaminants.

Figure 7(a,b) (a) Monosodium phosphate crystals precipitated from control water solution. No obvious pattern was observed. (b) Monosodium phosphate crystals precipitated from I_E-based solution. The observed radial lines were interpreted as due to electric field lines from the dipole of I_E clusters.

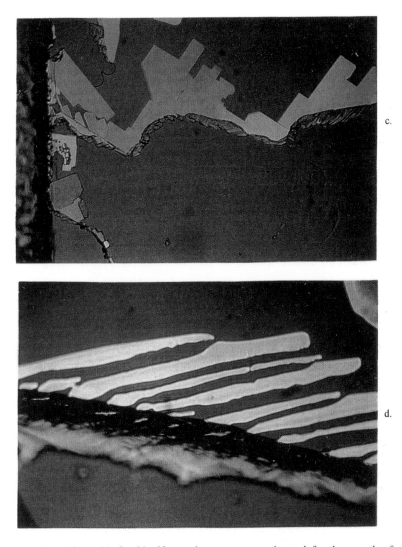

c.

d.

Figure 7(c,d)   (c)   No regular pattern was observed for the growth of monosodium phosphate crystals from control solution.   (d)   Sodium monophosphate crystals grew along the external electric field line, when a DC voltage of 100 volts was applied across the one inch slide containing I_E-based solution. The photograph was taken 3 hours after the beginning of the crystallization.

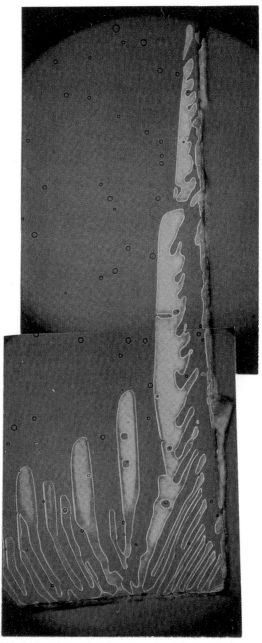

Figure 7(e) Sodium monophosphate crystalized from I_E-based solution in external electric field. The photograph was taken 20 hours after the beginning of the crystallization.

Table 2 X-ray diffraction peaks (2θ°)* of sodium phosphate crystals

Original sample	Crystals from deionized water solution	Crystals from I_E water
NaH_2PO_4 monoclinic	$NaH_2PO_4 \cdot H_2O$ orthorhombic	$NaH_2PO_4 \cdot 2H_2O$ orthorhombic
21.8	16.50	14.60
22.5	24.20	15.61
24.3	25.45	18.20
25.2	26.45	19.90
26.4	28.20	24.19
27.0	29.22	24.60
28.2	32.80	27.10
29.0	33.85	29.30
30.2	35.00	29.90
31.5	35.40	31.40
33.0	36.20	31.60
		33.80

* X-ray radiation CuKCl; lambda 1.5405

The electro-magnetic wave with frequency ω will be absorbed by the proton with magnetic moment μ in a magnetic field B, as it obeys the following law (1):

$$\hbar\omega = \vec{\mu} \cdot \vec{B} \tag{1}$$

$$\omega = \omega_0 + \omega_1 + \omega_2 \tag{2}$$

$$\vec{B} = \vec{B}_0 + \vec{B}_1 + \vec{B}_2 \tag{3}$$

where ω_0 is the resonance frequency of a free proton in vacuum with an external magnetic field B_0. The additional magnetic field B_1 comes from electric current, caused by the electron cloud surrounding the proton, in ordinary water. A 500 MHz resonance in vacuum, produces a shift in ω_1 of approximately 2400 Hz for a proton in water. When water molecules rearrange themselves to form a larger electric dipole moment, one expects that the electron cloud would be pulled away from its normal position in ordinary water. The change of electron cloud position will cause a change in magnetic field, which is defined as B_2. The change in magnetic field will cause additional shift in frequency ω_2, that can be registered by NMR (Figure 8).

135

Principle of NMR

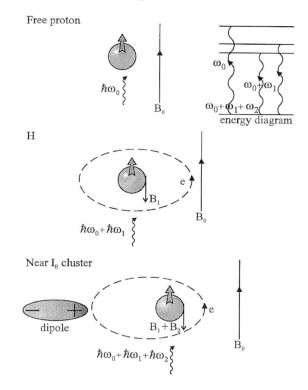

Free proton

$\hbar\omega_0$

B_0

ω_0

$\omega_0+\omega_1$

$\omega_0+\omega_1+\omega_2$

energy diagram

H

e

B_1

B_0

$\hbar\omega_0+\hbar\omega_1$

Near I_E cluster

dipole

B_1+B_2

e

B_0

$\hbar\omega_0+\hbar\omega_1+\hbar\omega_2$

Figure 8 The principle of NMR method.

A free proton under external magnetic field B_0 has a resonance frequency of $\hbar\omega_0$.

It is not possible to precisely calculate the value of the shift ω_2 without extensive computer calculations and detailed knowledge of the electron wave function. However, one can attempt to understand the shift in the following way. Assuming a linear relation between the electric field, E, felt by an electron to the magnetic field, B, felt by a proton, the relationship (4) can be written:

$$B_1 / B_2 \sim E_1 / E_2, \qquad (4)$$

where E_1 is the an electric field on electron in hydrogen atom, and E_2 is the electric field that comes from the electric dipole moment of an adjacent water molecule. In normal water, E_2 cancels out. However, in the I_E cluster, the parameter is not negligible.

$$E_1 \quad = e \,/\, r_0 \tag{5}$$

$$E_2 \quad = \eta e r_0 \,/\, r^3, \tag{6}$$

where e is an electron charge, r_0 is the radius of hydrogen atom 0.51 Å, r is the size of water molecule (0.28 nm), and $\eta e r_0$ is a permanent electric dipole moment of water clusters, η is a scale factor.

Therefore, $E_1 \,/\, E_2 = \eta (r_0 \,/\, r)^3$ is on the order of several parts in thousand if $\eta \sim$ 1/10. From this rough estimate, it is expected to get a shift of several Hz using a 500 MHz NMR.

A very concentrated I_E water solution contains more than 10% of I_E clusters. Water molecules in an I_E solution can be inside or outside of I_E clusters. A proton inside an I_E cluster will be affected more than a proton of bulk water molecules by the permanent electric dipole moment of I_E clusters. Therefore, two different shifts in proton peak position are expected.

It is proposed, that the smaller the I_E cluster, the larger the electric dipole moment. When two I_E clusters of the same size and same electric dipole moment come together, the lowest energy state for them is the one when a larger cluster is formed from two smaller ones, so that the two electric dipole moments align opposite each other with a net zero electric dipole moment. Therefore, the larger association of the I_E clusters, the smaller its electric dipole moment.

In order to maximize the influence of electric dipole moment on a proton, a concentrated I_E solution (P1) was sonicated by ultrasound for 1.5 minutes, and the NMR spectrum was recorded at timed intervals. A shift in proton peak position of water was observed immediately after sonication and became smaller over time (Figure 9a). These results can be related to the breakage of large I_E Crystals by sonication, with their further spontaneous recombination (Figure 10), similar to the phenomenon observed in the laser autocorrelation experiments. No shift was detected in control water (Figure 9b). Less concentrated I_E solutions, P2 and P3, were studied with NMR. P2 and P3 were, respectively, 10 and 50 times less concentrated than P1 solution. A dependence of the magnitude of proton peak shift on I_E Crystals concentration was established (Figures 9a,c,d).

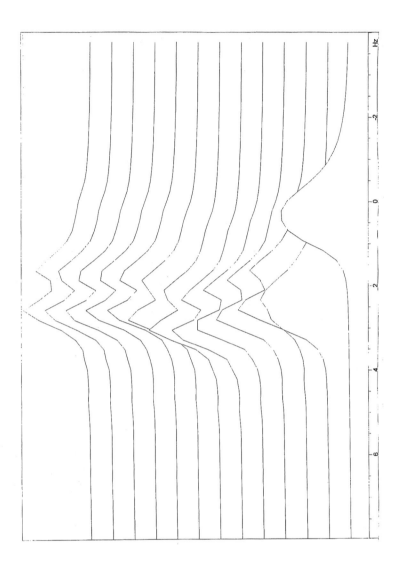

Figure 9a A concentrated I_E solution (P1) was studied by NMR prior to the sonication which shown in the bottom curve. After a 1.5-minute sonication, the next 12 spectra (from the bottom to the top) were measured in time intervals of 2 min., 4 min. × 6, 9 min., 6 min., 8 min., and 7 min. respectively. A proton peak shift of approximately 3 Hz was observed.

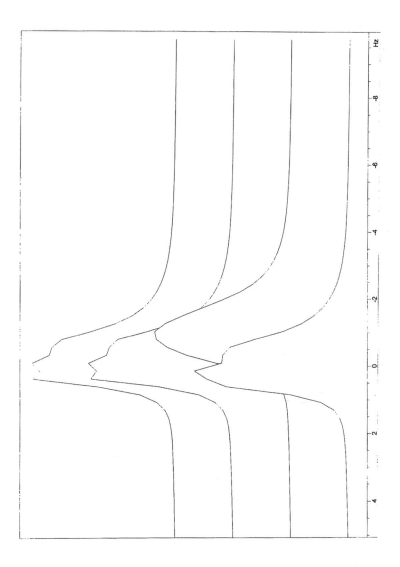

Figure 9b A sample of control water was studied by NMR. The bottom spectrum was recorded prior to the sonication. After a 1.5-minute sonication, the next three spectra were measured in time intervals of 2 min., 5 min., and another 5 min. respectively. The top two curves are the same as before shaking, as expected, with no observed proton peak shift.

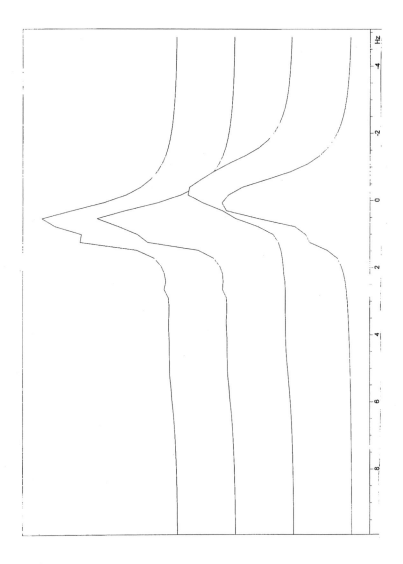

Figure 9c   A sample of low concentrated I_E solution (P3) was studied by NMR. The bottom spectrum was recorded prior to the sonication. After a 1.5-minute sonication, the next three spectra were measured in time intervals of 2 min., 3 min., and 4 min. respectively. The top two curves demonstrate a proton peak shift of 0.5 Hz.

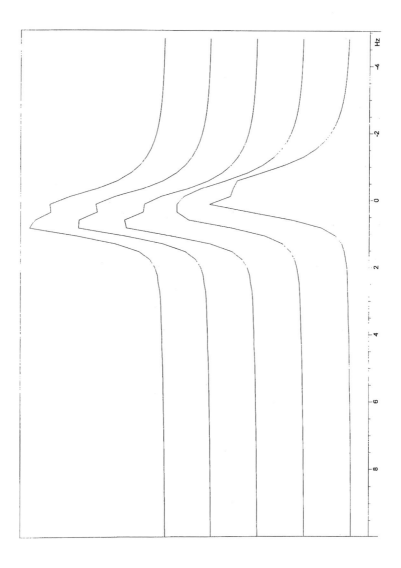

Figure 9d A sample of medium concentrated I_E solution (P2) was studied by NMR. The bottom spectrum was recorded prior to the sonication. After a 1.5-minute sonication, the next four spectra were measured in time intervals of 1 min., 4 min., 4 min., and 3 min. respectively. A proton peak shift of 1.5 Hz was detected.

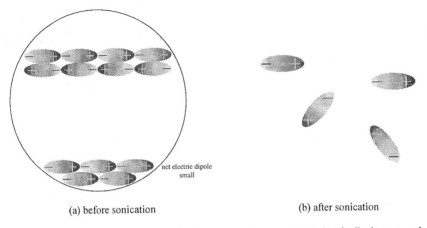

(a) before sonication   (b) after sonication

Figure 10 A large I_E cluster composed of smaller clusters has a small net electric dipole moment before sonication due to cancellation of the individual electric dipole moments (a). Sonication breaks the large I_E cluster into many smaller ones (b), and as a result a larger net electric dipole moment is produced.

4.3 Electric Potential Measurement

A strong electrostatic attraction is known to exist between ions, or monopoles, of the opposite charge, e.g. a positive ion Na^+ is strongly attracted to a negative Cl^- ion. Water molecules are dipoles, with one part of the molecule carrying a partial positive charge and the other a partial negative charge. An attraction force between a dipole and a monopole exists, but it is much weaker as compared to an attractive force between two monopoles. The attraction between water molecules in an I_E cluster is of dipole-dipole type and it is the weakest. An anthropomorphic analogy can be made. A single male and a single female are like monopoles of the opposite charge and they are strongly attracted to each other. A married man is a part of a couple (dipole), however, he can be also attracted to another woman (monopole), but such attraction is less. The attraction between two married couples (dipole-dipole interaction) is, of course, the weakest (Figure 11).

Previous studies[37] have reported that an emf of tens of mV was observed between two stainless steel electrodes immersed in I_E solution. In ordinary ionic solutions, no emf is established between two identical electrodes. However, in the case of I_E solutions, the electric dipoles of the I_E clusters can line up to establish an emf without any electrochemical reaction occurring.

In this study we used a pH meter (Fisher Scientific, PA) to measure an electric potential established by the electric dipole of the I_E clusters (Figure 12). The

142

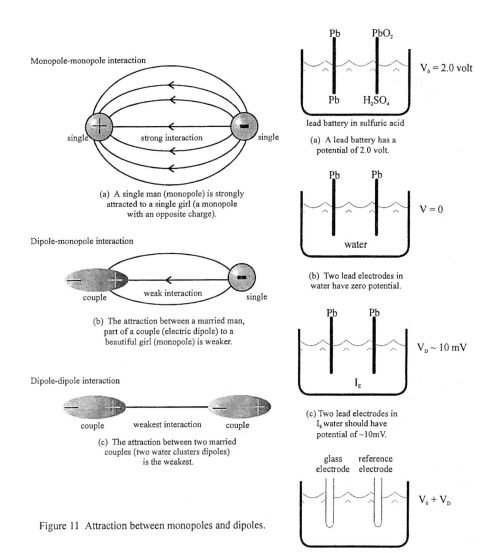

Monopole-monopole interaction

single — strong interaction — single

(a) A single man (monopole) is strongly
attracted to a single girl (a monopole
with an opposite charge).

Dipole-monopole interaction

couple — weak interaction — single

(b) The attraction between a married man,
part of a couple (electric dipole) to a
beautiful girl (monopole) is weaker.

Dipole-dipole interaction

couple — weakest interaction — couple

(c) The attraction between two married
couples (two water clusters dipoles)
is the weakest.

Figure 11 Attraction between monopoles and dipoles.

Pb   PbO$_2$

$V_0 = 2.0$ volt

Pb   H$_2$SO$_4$

lead battery in sulfuric acid

(a) A lead battery has a
potential of 2.0 volt.

Pb   Pb

$V = 0$

water

(b) Two lead electrodes in
water have zero potential.

Pb   Pb

$V_D \sim 10$ mV

I_E

(c) Two lead electrodes in
I_E water should have
potential of ~10mV.

glass   reference
electrode   electrode

$V_0 + V_D$

(d) Two electrodes,
a glass electrode and a
reference electrode of a
pH meter, were used to
measure dipole electric
potential of an I_E solution.

Figure 12
Measurement of dipole
electric potential

143

electric potential between a glass electrode and a reference electrode is given by the Nernst equation (7).

$$E = E^0 + (2.3R\ T_k\ /nF)\ \text{Log}\ a_i \tag{7}$$

where E^0 is the standard redox potential; R, gas constant, has a value of 8.314 Jmol^{-1}K^{-1}; F, Faraday constant, has a value of 96,490 Cmol^{-1}; T is absolute temperature; n is a number of electrons transferred in the reaction; a_i represents activities of participating species. We expect that the electric potential of an I_E solution will differ from the electric potential of ordinary water due to the additional contribution of the aligned electric dipole moments of I_E clusters:

$$E(I_E) = E + E_D, \tag{8}$$

where E_D is additional electric potential produced by dipole moments of I_E clusters.

We used a pH meter to study a deviation from the linear relationship between electrode potential and pH (9) in I_E solutions.

$$pH(X)=pH(S) + 1/k[E(X) - E(S)], \tag{9}$$

where S denotes a pH standard used to calibrate the pH meter; X is a sample; k=RTln10/F=59.2 mV at 25°C.

A wide range of pH, from pH=1 to pH=12 was analyzed. The test solutions were prepared either with concentrated aqueous I_E solution (UV absorbance of 2 at 195 nm, A_{195}=2) or deionized (DI) water. The desired pH was obtained with hydrochloric acid or sodium hydroxide The maximum deviation from the linear dependence between pH and E was observed at neutral pH, where dipoles strongly dominate the system's electric potential. The relative effect of electric dipole diminished at the extreme ends of the pH scale, where ionic (monopole) contribution dominates the potential (Figure 13). The addition of KCl (final concentration of 0.01 M) to I_E water-based solutions did not significantly change the shape of the pH-mV curve. Therefore, the electric potential of dipoles was not effected by the presence of additional ionic species. A linear relationship was found between electric potential and pH measurements in the case of control water for all pH values tested.

To study the effect of the solution's ionic strength on the observed phenomenon, a wide range (from 10 mM to 0.1 mM) of NaCl and KCl

144

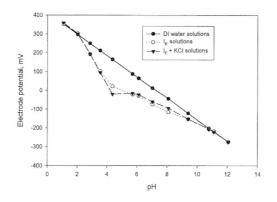

Figure 13 Electric potential of DI water and I_E water solutions.

concentrations in I_E and water solutions were tested. The average difference in measured electric potential between water- and I_E-based solutions was 92.4 mV for NaCl and 103.4 mV for KCl (Table 3).

Table 3 The electric potential measured in I_E and DI water solutions of NaCl and KCl

	DI+NaCl		I_E+NaCl		DI+KCl		I_E+KCl	
	pH	mV	pH	mV	pH	mV	pH	mV
0.00001 M	5.67	89.2	7.30	-4.1	5.60	92.7	7.30	-5.2
0.0001 M	5.69	87.6	7.30	-3.8	5.65	89.4	7.42	-11.1
0.001 M	5.65	90.0	7.29	-3.9	5.65	90.0	7.50	-15.6
0.01 M	5.67	89.4	7.24	-0.8	5.61	91.7	7.54	-17.8
Average	5.67	89.2	7.28	-3.15	5.63	91.0	7.44	-12.4

Very little variation in pH readings for different concentrations of NaCl and KCl was observed. However, it is important to note that the large difference between the pH of DI water and I_E solutions (ΔpH = 7.28 - 5.67 = 1.61 (NaCl) and ΔpH = 7.44 - 5.63 = 1.81 (KCl)) measured by pH-meter, was not detected by pH 0-14 indicator paper (VWR, West Chester, PA) and showed identical pH values for DI and I_E solutions. This observation can be explained by differences in the methods used for pH determination. A pH-meter is based on an electrochemical process. Since I_E Crystals produce an additional electric potential, the pH readings are affected. A chemical reaction takes place with pH paper, which is not influenced by the electric dipoles of I_E clusters.

The differences in electric potentials of water and I_E solutions were analyzed for concentrated (A_{195}=2) and diluted (A_{195}=0.8) I_E solutions. A greater difference in electric potential, covering wider range of pH, was found in the case of more concentrated I_E solution (Figure 14).

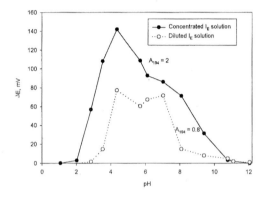

Figure 14 The difference in electric potential between I_E water and DI water versus pH. The more concentrated I_E solution has a larger dipole potential than the diluted I_E solution.

The UV absorbance at $\lambda = 194$ for deionized water and I_E solutions (concentrated, A_{195}=2 and diluted, A_{195}=0.8) was measured for a range of pH values. While there was no absorbance peak observed in the middle pH range (pH 4-9) for DI water, a prominent UV absorbance was registered for I_E water in the same pH range (Figure 15). The strong UV absorbance peaks were noted for all solutions under extreme acidic (pH<4) or basic (pH>9.5) environment, which can be explained by the dominating effect of monopoles in those areas.

The resistivity of two types of I_E solutions, called Y-R and C-R, was analyzed as a function of their relative concentrations, based on UV absorbance at $\lambda = 195$ nm (Figure 16). The I_E solution of higher concentration had lower resistivity. The

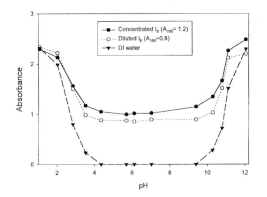

Figure 15   The UV absorbance at λ=195 nm versus pH value
for two different concentrations of an I_E solution, and DI water

resistivity of these two I_E solutions differed by more than a factor of 2, indicating difference in their mobilities, perhaps due to different shapes of the I_E clusters. Resistivity measurements may provide a way to distinguish different kinds of I_E solutions.   Another interesting feature was the large value of resistivity compared with that of an ionic solution.   For one mole of NaCl solution, the resistivity was about 32 Ω-cm.   The resistivity measured for the I_E solution, which is dipole solution, was 10,000 times smaller than that for the monopole ionic solution.

5   A Discussion on Contaminants

The crucial question in interpreting the above data is whether the results are artifacts. I_E samples were prepared in a clean room using water purified by deionization (Millipore Ultrapure System, San Francisco, CA), and contained less than 10 ppb of total dissolved solids. However, pure water is known to be very reactive, and its purity rapidly decreases when it is exposed to air. The resistivity of water processed by the Millipore Ultrapure System is 18.2 MΩ/cm, but as soon as the water exits the system, the resistivity drops to 6 MΩ/cm, then to 2 MΩ/cm and slowly drifts down to 1 MΩ/cm. The phenomenon is due to absorption by water of various contaminants and CO_2 from the air. Dissolved in water, CO_2 forms

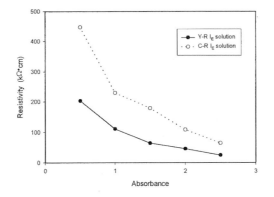

Figure 16 The resistivity of I_E water vs. its relative concentration
as indicated by UV absorbance at 195nm.

carbonic acid, which together with other dissolved impurities from the air contributes to an increase in the number of ionic species in water, which in turn causes a decrease in resistivity and an increase in conductivity of water. All reported results were obtained with DI water as a control. Typically, the measured parameters for I_E aqueous solutions were 4 orders of magnitude higher than the background. Therefore, the contribution of impurities from the water used for I_E solutions' preparations to the measured physical and chemical properties of I_E can be ruled out. Prior research results[37] established that there is about a 20% decrease in dielectric constant for a I_E water at 10^6 Hz, as compared with ordinary water.

Contaminants can be broadly classified into inorganic and organic. "Polywater" was claimed to have been discovered in the '60s and '70s, but later its anomalous properties were attributed to a silicon impurity. To distinguish I_E water from polywater, two classes of inorganic contaminants were considered: ionic and silicon. The organic contaminants were separated into two groups: volatile, which have a boiling point above that of water, and nonvolatile, with a boiling point below that of water (Table 4).

UV absorbance analysis of I_E solutions before and after distillation demonstrated that the characteristic UV signature of I_E solutions is not due to impurities. I_E clusters, composed of water molecules, evaporated and condensed together with ordinary water in a distiller, leaving non-volatile impurities behind.

Table 4 Properties of I_E solutions that allow to rule out inorganic, organic, and biological contamination

	Inorganic		Organic		Biological
			Volatile $T_{b.p.}>100°C$	Non-volatile $T_{b.p.}>100°C$	Micro-organism
	Ions	Silicon			
1. Distillation					
(1.a) UV absorbance of double distilled I_E water.	✗	✗	✓	✗	✗
(1.b) Residues from evaporation.	ppm	ppm	✓	ppm	ppm
2. Images					
(2.a) TEM (x-ray)	✗	✗	✗	✗	✓
(2.b) AFM	—	—	—	—	✗
(2.c) Laser autocorrelation	—	—	—	—	✗
3. Electrical properties[37]					
(3.a) Conductivity	✗	✗	✗	✗	✗
(3.b) Dielectric constant	✗	✗	✗	✗	✗
(3.c) Emf	✗	✗	✗	✗	✗
4. Physical properties[36]					
(4.a) Density	10 ppm	10 ppm	10 ppm	10 ppm	10 ppm
(4.b) Boiling point	✗	✗	✗	✗	✗
5. Electromagnetic response[37]					
(5.a) UV fluorescence		✗			
(5.b) IR	✗	✗	✓	✓	✗
(5.c) Low frequency AC	✗	✗	✗	✗	✗

✗ -- an effect of contamination can be ruled out, ✓ -- an effect of contamination cannot be ruled out

A concentrated I_E solution was distilled twice. Samples of the original solution, the first and the second distillates were analyzed with a Perkin-Elmer UV/Vis Lambda 2S spectrophotometer (Norwalk, CT) within 190-300 nm wavelength range (Figure 17). The maximum UV absorbance of I_E solution remained the same after the first and the second distillation. There was a small change in UV absorbance observed after the first distillation, but hardly any change in the UV absorbance occurred after the second distillation. The UV signature, with a peak around 195 nm and a shoulder between 200 - 210 nm observed in I_E solution prior to and after distillation, could not come from any non-volatile contaminants. Therefore, inorganic and non-volatile organic contaminants, as well as microorganisms can be ruled out as sources of the UV absorbance in the discussed region. This experiment, however,

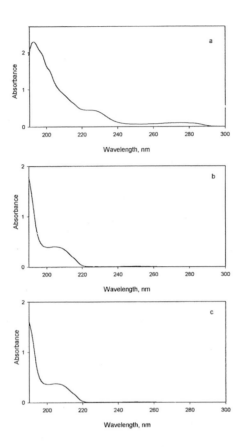

Figure 17 UV absorbance vs. wavelength for I_E water
(a) before distillation (b) after the first distillation
(c) after the second distillation.

did not rule out a possibility of contamination by volatile organic substances.

I_E Crystal samples for TEM analysis were prepared by depositing the I_E solution on filter paper, coating it with carbon, and then boiling in chloroform for twenty minutes. This process removed all volatile organic contaminants from I_E samples, and therefore the structures identified on TEM images cannot be attributed

150

to the presence of volatile organic contaminants. The analysis of x-ray spectra obtained by focusing the electron beam on any I_E cluster ruled out inorganic contaminants.

Even though single I_E structures do look like bacteria containing gas vesicles, the clusters that they form are too regular in shape to be described as microorganisms. Moreover, TEM of sterilized by boiling I_E solutions still revealed I_E clusters. It is highly unlikely, therefore, that the structures observed in TEM photographs are of microbial nature. The combined results of I_E distillation experiments and TEM analysis ruled out any conceivable contaminants above ppm level (Table 4).

Some of the properties of I_E solutions discussed in this paper present strong evidence against various contaminants and their effect on properties of I_E clusters:

a. Inorganic ions: As discussed in section 4, ions are monopoles. Monopole-monopole and monopole-dipole types of interaction can not account for electrical properties of I_E solutions.

b. Silicon: The x-ray spectra, recorded by focusing an electron beam on an I_E cluster detected with TEM, rule out silicon as a source of I_E Crystals. Silicon, however, was identified as a component of particles found in control water samples.

c. Volatile Organics: The method of I_E sample preparation for TEM analysis described above eliminates a possibility that the detected structures are due to volatile organics.

d. Nonvolatile organics: The UV absorbance measurement of distilled I_E solution rules out this type of contamination.

e. Microbial contamination: Microorganisms cannot contribute to the electrical properties of I_E solutions. Since microorganisms can be effectively removed by distillation, UV absorbance data of distilled I_E solutions indicate other than microbial origin of I_E clusters. Additionally, the morphology of I_E clusters viewed with AFM and results of laser autocorrelation experiments support this conclusion.

Industrial application of I_E water does not require ultra purity of I_E solutions. The presence of contaminants at ppm levels is acceptable, when a significant favorable effect is achieved in physical, chemical, or biological systems. Additional research is required to establish existence of I_E clusters without an initiator. Our main goal at this time, however, is to further improve the beneficial effects of I_E clusters in a wide range of applications.

6 Applications

Since I_E clusters are made of water molecules, almost unlimited possibilities for I_E clusters applications exist in the areas where ordinary water can be substituted with I_E water. Only a few potential I_E water applications have been investigated so far:

Application Area	Testing Area
Physical Processes	· Descaling
	· Cleaning
Chemical Processes	· Enhancement of combustion
	· Reduction of coke formation in ethylene production
Biotechnology	· Regulation of enzymatic activities and microbial growth
Medical	· Stimulation of immune responses to infection and cancer

6.1 Scaling Reduction and Cleaning Enhancement

It has been established by AFM and photon autocorrelation measurements that I_E clusters range from 10-20 nm to 1-5 μm in size (Section 3). Since smaller I_E clusters have larger electric dipole moments (Sections 4.2 and 4.3), it is necessary to break large I_E clusters into small ones, prior to an application, to achieve the maximum effect. A mechanical stirrer, a static mixer, or ultrasound can be used for this purpose.

Scaling of heat transfer equipment by calcium and magnesium carbonates is a common problem. Traditional chemical scale mitigation methods require higher running costs and produce a negative environmental impact. The use of the I_E water to eliminate scaling is an attractive cost-efficient and environmentally friendly alternative. I_E clusters provide a center of nucleation for the calcium carbonate growth, which prevents scale deposition on the walls of heat transfer equipment (Figure 18).

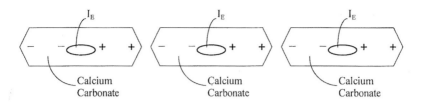

Figure 18 Effect of descaling by I_E clusters. Due to the strong electric field, calcium carbonate will nucleate around the I_E Crystals and not deposit on the wall.

The effect of I_E clusters on surface tension is being studied by several research groups. The sonication of I_E water has been observed to result in reduction of solution's surface tension.

In a traditional cleaning or washing process, soils are removed from a surface by surface active substances (surfactants). I_E clusters may enhance detergency due to electrostatic attraction between the electric dipole moment of the I_E clusters and the induced electric dipole moment of the soil, assuming the soil is made up of dielectric materials. Although, further in depth research is required, a potential for use of I_E water in commercial cleaning applications does exist.

6.2 Enhancement of Chemical Reactions

Current research indicates that I_E solutions enhance the oxidation of hydrocarbon, carbon, and carbon monoxide. These observations can be attributed to the effect of electric dipole moments of I_E clusters in chemical reactions.

Let us consider a very simple reaction in which A reacts with B to give products C and D:

$$A+B \rightarrow C+D$$

The reaction rate (R) of this reaction can be written as:

$$R = n_A \, n_B \, \upsilon_{AB} \, \sigma \, (AB \rightarrow CD), \tag{10}$$

where n_A, n_B are the densities of A and B, υ_{AB} is the relative velocity of A with respect to B, and $\sigma\,(AB \rightarrow CD)$ is a cross section of the reaction. The electric dipole moment of the I_E clusters can influence this reaction rate in two ways.

The densities n_A and n_B will be increased in the proximity of I_E clusters. Assuming that the chemical species are in equilibrium in a gaseous state, the distribution of chemicals n_A and n_B obey Boltzman distribution:

$$n_A = \exp(-\phi/kT)$$
$$n_B = \exp(-\phi/kT), \qquad (11)$$

where ϕ is an electric potential exerted by the permanent electric dipole moment D of the I_E clusters onto A and B. The electric field emitted by I_E clusters will induce an electric dipole in A or B, which will be then attracted to the I_E clusters. The value of electric potential ϕ depends on the distance (r) between an I_E cluster and a molecule A (or B):

$$\phi \sim 1/r^3 \qquad (12)$$

The closer a molecule to an I_E cluster, the larger the potential ϕ, the Boltzman factor, and as a result the density n_A (or n_B) is higher (Figure 19).

Additionally, a molecule A (or B) will be attracted by electric dipole force towards the I_E clusters, which will result in higher relative velocity υ_{AB}. A and B molecules will move faster around I_E clusters which will lead to a higher reaction rate.

Should the above hypothesis be true, then the catalytic effect of I_E Crystals is a volume rather than a surface phenomenon, which separates I_E clusters from such well-known catalysts as platinum. If the enhancement of the chemical reaction occurs mostly near the I_E clusters, then the particular surface or charge distribution of an I_E cluster is not critical. The only relevant factor is the net electric dipole moment of that particular I_E cluster.

(a) Electric field surrounding the I_E cluster similar to magnetic field surrounding a magnet.

(b) Molecules A and B in the neighborhood of I_E cluster will be polarized by the strong electric field line and attracted towards the cluster.

Figure 19 Enhancement of a chemical reaction by an I_E cluster.

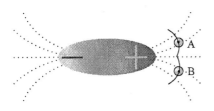 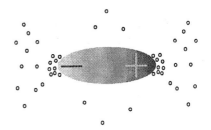

(c) When A and B collides, the relative velocity of collision is much larger than where there is no electric field from I_E.

(d) Due to strong electric field near the positive and negative pole of I_E clusters, the densities of molecules A and B are much higher than places where there is no electric field.

Figure 19(cont.) Enhancement of a chemical reaction by an I_E cluster.

6.3 Influence of I_E Clusters on the Activities of Enzymes

Enzymes, catalytic proteins, are known to enhance the rate of chemical reactions in biological systems by many orders of magnitude. Although, the mechanisms of a wide range of enzymatic reactions are under extensive investigation, scientists still cannot predict an enzymatic mechanism based on the known structure of an enzyme. Therefore, it is premature to make any definite conclusions about a mechanism behind the stimulating affect of I_E clusters on certain enzymes.

The following discussion is an attempt to propose a possible mechanism for I_E-enzyme interaction based on the known physical properties of I_E clusters. I_E clusters can form around a protein. Shaking of the protein solution will remove some I_E clusters from the protein, leaving some parts of I_E clusters intact. Further dilution and shaking of the protein solution may generate a negative-like image of the created water clusters, a template of a portion of the protein surface with similar charge density distribution. The obtained I_E clusters may act as catalysts, similar to the original enzyme. It is also conceivable that some I_E clusters may be attracted to the enzyme in a way that impairs its function as a catalyst, thereby reducing its activity.

The discussed hypothesis can be applied to the following simple enzymatic catalysis; the hydration of carbon dioxide by carbonic anhydrase:

$$CO_2 + H_2O \rightarrow HCO_3^- + H^+$$

The zinc ion plays a key role in the catalysis. Water bound to the zinc ion is converted into a hydroxide ion, which creates a high local concentration of OH^-. Zinc also helps orient the CO_2, so it is positioned better for reaction with OH^-.

155

It is expected that an I_E solution, prepared with carbonic anhydrase as a seed material, will contain some I_E clusters which resemble zinc ion in surface change density. Such I_E clusters might bind water and CO_2 similar to zinc ion, and therefore will catalyze the enzymatic reaction.

It is also possible that some I_E clusters might be attracted to the zinc ion of the carbonic anhydrase and block its function as a catalyst. In this case, the addition of an I_E solution may suppress or even inhibit the enzymatic activity.

It is possible, therefore, to both stimulate and suppress enzymatic reactions, by optimizing the type of I_E solution used in a particular application.

6.4 Medical Application

The human body, which is approximately 70% water by weight, is an extremely complicated biological system. Based on the various properties of I_E clusters and some anecdotal evidence, we can speculate relative to four areas of medical applications.

6.4.1 Shape and Charge Density of I_E Cluster

I_E clusters may act as templates of the material used to induce their formation (seed). Therefore, I_E clusters may act as a harmless antigen that stimulates the production of antibodies and enhances the immune response to an infection or cancer.

6.4.2 Effect of Ultra Low Dosage

I_E clusters exist even when the concentration of the seed material is diluted down to below 10^{-7} mole. The I_E clusters can then regenerate themselves in further dilutions. Although the concentration of the seed becomes very small (on the order of ppb), the percentage of I_E clusters is quite large in the solution. The cell membrane is an osmotic membrane and can locally create a small amount of very pure water which is required for formation of I_E clusters. Many I_E clusters can be then generated by a cell from a single seed molecule. Therefore, a single seed molecule can influence many cells through formation of high concentrations of I_E clusters. The above hypothesis can be a basis for an explanation of efficacy of ultra low dosages (homeopathic remedies in particular) on human functions.

6.4.3   Electric Properties of I_E Clusters

The I_E clusters can generate electric potential up to 100mV. The existence of I_E clusters may be the underlying physical basis for the observed increase or a decrease of electric potentials in acupuncture points, as well as the meridian theory of acupuncture in general.

6.4.4   Electromagnetic Waves (em)

Electromagnetic waves are widely used in medical applications. A very short electromagnetic wave, such as a gamma ray, is used to treat brain cancer. The radio frequency em wave is used in magnetic resonance imagining. I_E clusters absorb UV energy at 195nm, and demonstrate a fluorescence emission at 295nm. These characteristics may be useful as diagnostic tools. The three peaks of low frequency em wave at kHz can also be used in the future for diagnostic purposes or as treatment.

7   Acknowledgments

Many of the results reported here are obtained from collaborations with Dr. Wen-Chong Li, Dr. Cheuk-Yin Wong and Dr. Olga Berson

8   References

1. J. H. Jensen, and M.S. Gordon, *J. Phys. Chem.* **99**, 8091 (1995).
2. L. S. Sremaniak, L. Perera, and M.L. Berkowitz, *J. Phys. Chem.* **100**, 1350 (1996).
3. C. Lee, H. Chen, and G. Fitzgerald, *J. Chem. Phys.* **102**, 1266 (1995).
4. I.P. Buffey, W. Byers-Brown, and H.A. Gebbie, *Chem. Phys. Lett.* **148**, 281 (1988).
5. C. J. Tsai, and K.D. Jordan, *Chem. Phys. Lett.* **213**, 181 (1993).
6. C. J. Tsai, and K.D. Jordan, *J. Phys. Chem.* **97**, 5208 (1993).
7. K. Liu, M.G. Brown, J.D. Cruzan, and R.J. SayKally, *Science* **271**, 62 (1996).
8. C.J. Grueloh, J.R. Carney, C.A. Arrington, T.S. Zurei, S.Y. Fredericks, and K.D. Jordan, *Science* **276**, 1678 (1997).
9. A. Vegiri, and S.C. Farantos, *J. Chem. Phys.* **98**, 4059 (1993).
10. S.S. Xantheas, *J. Phys. Chem.* **100**, 9703-9713 (1996).
11. S.S. Xantheas, and T.H. Dunning, Jr. *J. Chem. Phys.* **99**, 8774 (1993).
12. S.S. Xantheas, *J. Chem. Phys.* **100**, 7523 (1994).

13. K.S. Kim, M. Dupuis, G.C. Lie, and E. Clementi, *Chem. Phys. Lett.* **131**, 451 (1996).
14. A. Khan, *Chem. Phys. Lett.* **258**, 574 (1996).
15. A. Khan, *Chem. Phys. Lett.* **253**, 299 (1996).
16. J. Smets, W.J. McCarthy, and L. Adamowicz, *Chem. Phys. Lett.* **256**, 360 (1996)
17. H. Sekiya, H. Hamabe, H. Ujita, N. Nakano, and Y. Nishimura, *Chem. Phys. Lett.* **255**, 437 (1996)
18. M. Armbruster, *Phys. Rev. Lett.* **47**(5), 323 (1981).
19. G. Nemethy and H.A. Scheraga, *J. Chem. Phys.* **36**, 3382 (1962).
20. S.W. Benson, *J. Amer. Chem. Soc.* **100**, 5640 (1978).
21. K. Liu, J.D. Cruzan, and R.J.Saykally, *Science* **271**, 929 (1996).
22. N. Fletcher, *The Chemical Physic of Ice*, (Cambridge University Press, 1970).
23. S. Dong, A.I. Kolesnikov, and J.C. Lo, *J. Phys. Chem. B*, **101**, 6087 (1997).
24. S.M. Jackson, V.M. Nield, R.W. Whitworth, M. Ogriro, and C.C. Wilson, *J. Phys. Chem. B*, **101**, 6142 (1997).
25. I. Morrison, J.C. Li, S. Jenkins, S.S. Xantheas, and M.C. Payne, *J. Phys. Chem. B*, **101**, 6146 (1997).
26. C.A. Tulk, H. Kiefte, M.J. Clenter, and R.E. Gagnon, *J. Phys. Chem. B*, **101**, 6154 (1997).
27. S.M. Jackson, and R.W. Whitworth, *J. Phys. Chem. B*, **101**, 6177 (1997).
28. I.M. Svishchev, and P.G. Kusalik, *Phys. Rev. Lett.* **73**, 975 (1994).
29. V.P. Dimitriev, S.B. Rochal, and P. Toledano, *Phys. Rev. Lett.* **71**, 553 (1993).
30. M. Garrish, R. Poporitz-Biro, M. Lahav, and M. Leisterowitcz, *Science* **250**, 973 (1990).
31. *Proceedings of the International Symposium on the Physics and Chemistry of Ice*, eds. N. Maeno, and T. Hondoh (Hokkaido University Press, Sapporo, Japan 1992).
32. *Seventh Symposium on the Physics and Chemistry of Ice, J. Phys. Chem.* **48**, Colloq. No. 1 Supplement, Fasc. 3, XV, 707 (1987).
33. *Sixth Symposium on the Physics and Chemistry of Ice, J. Phys. Chem.* **87**, 4015, 340 (1983).
34. *Symposium on the Physics and Chemistry of Ice, J. Glaciol*, **21**, 714 (1977).
35. W. Stumm and J.J. Morgan *Aquatic Chemistry. An Introduction Emphasizing Chemical Equilibria in Natural Waters* (John Wiley & Sons, New York 1981).
36. S.Y. Lo, *Modern Phys. Lett. B*, **10**, 909 (1996).
37. Shui Yin Lo, Angela Lo, Li Wen Chong, Lin Tianzhang, Li Hui Hua, and Xu Geng,, *Modern Phys. Lett. B*, **10**, 921 (1996).

38. There are a great deal of work on water clusters existing in isolation see examples from NATO Advanced Institute Recent Theoretical and Experimental Advances in Hydrogen-Bonded Clusters, 22, June 4, July 1997, Elounda, Crete, Greece, edited by S.S. Xantheas, to be published as a book. The water clusters discussed here are formed in water not in isolation.

39. C.Y. Wong and S.Y.Lo in *The Proceedings of The First International Symposium on the Current Status of the I$_E$ Crystal Technology*, (World Scientific, 1998).

40 S. Magonov in *The Proceedings of The First International Symposium on the Current Status of the I$_E$ Crystal Technology*, (World Scientific, 1998).

POSSIBLE MECHANISM OF FORMATION AND STABILITY OF ANOMALOUS STATES OF WATER

CHEUK-YIN WONG
SHUI-YIN LO

Originally published as *Physical, Chemical and Biological Properties of Stable Water Clusters,* Proceedings of the First International Symposium. Reprinted here by permission of World Scientific Publishing Company, 1998.

We examine the physical processes which are involved in the formation and stability of the anomalous states of water reported recently. The initial step of adding a small amount of ionic compound X^+Y^- to pure water leads to the formation of water clusters $X^+(H_2O)_n$ and $Y^-(H_2O)_n$ with $n \gg 1$. The structure of the cluster around the ion depends strongly on the equation of state. We explore the consequences of possible polymorphic states of H_2O in the liquid phase at room temperature. If there are low-lying polymorphic states, the local dipole moment and the local density will change discontinuously as a function of the radial distance from the ion, and regions of different polymorphic states will be found at different separations from the ion. Fragmentation of the cluster by vigorous shaking may break up the cluster into small domains to allow subsequent coalescence of these domains or the growth of the domains as seeds to form greater domains of polymorphic states. Further experimental and theoretical analyses are needed to study these pictures.

1 Introduction

Recently, experimental observations of anomalous states of water with I_E structures have been reported [1-3]. The existence of anomalous states of water is an interesting and new phenomenon with important experimental and theoretical implications. It is therefore essential that the observations be confirmed by an independent experimental group in order to ascertain or refute the existence of the anomalous states. While we await such a confirmation, it is useful to make plausible hypotheses on the nature of the anomalous states so as to guide further experimental and theoretical studies on this interesting subject.

The addition of a small amount of ionic compound X^+Y^- to pure water is a necessary step in the production of the I_E water. We shall first consider the formation of clusters brought about by the addition of a small amount of X^+Y^- in water. In such a dilute aqueous solution, the X^+ and Y^- ions are well separated and become isolated. Stable large water clusters of the type $X^+(H_2O)_n$ and $Y^-(H_2O)_n$ will form around the ions in the dilute aqueous solution since similar isolated clusters of $X^+(H_2O)_n$ and $Y^-(H_2O)_n$ are found to be stable aggregates in many experiments[4-13]. Specifically, individual assembly of $X^+(H_2O)_n$ and $Y^-(H_2O)_n$, with $X^+=H^+$, Li^+, Na^+, K^+, Ca^{+2}, and $Y^-=Cl^-$, Br^-, I^-, and OH^- have been observed[4-13]. Similar cooperative effects on complexes of alcohol with proton acceptors have also been observed[14]. For the $H^+(H_2O)_n$ cluster, a cluster size up to $n = 75$ has been identified[7], indicating the stability of large clusters with $n \gg 1$. The limiting size of n has not yet been determined. Computer simulation shows that the six water molecules in the $Na^+(H_2O)_6$ cluster prefer the 4+2 structure, with the Na^+ ion in the center of the shells[15]. Molecular dynamics calculations of the hydration shell around an ion in a supercritical aqueous solution also exhibits the clustering of H_2O molecules around an ion[16]. One expects, therefore, that in a water solution with a small amount of ionic substance, large H_2O clusters will form around the ions. These large H_2O clusters carry charges and interact among themselves. They may arrange themselves in an orderly manner in the aqueous solution to give rise to clusters of even larger sizes (superclusters) consisting of many $X^+(H_2O)_n$ and $Y^-(H_2O)_n$ clusters. While each $X^+(H_2O)_n$ or $Y^-(H_2O)_n$ may be only about 10 Å in radius, it is interesting to find out whether superclusters may be formed and may be an important component of the I_E water, where clusters of the size of 100-1000 Å have been observed[1,3]. Thus, the study of these clusters in I_E water will provide information on the stability and the interactions of the $X^+(H_2O)_n$ and $Y^-(H_2O)_n$ in aqueous solutions.

Other interesting physics questions can also be studied with I_E water. The consideration of cluster formation leads to the examination of the structure of the water cluster around an individual ion. One finds that the stability of the cluster arises from the strong Coulombic polarizing power of the ion, which attracts water molecules with their dipole moments aligned along the electric lines of force of the ion. The density and the average local dipole moment of the medium need not be spatially uniform near the ion. Their profiles depend on the equation of state of the water medium as a function of both the density and the average local dipole moment per molecule.

The dependence of the cluster structure on the equation of state leads to another related and interesting subject. It is well known that under different conditions H_2O molecules form different stable structures[17,18,19] represented by different energy minima around which the many-body state of H_2O can be locally stable. The study of the structure of the cluster around an ion in I_E water will provide vital information on the equation of state of water in the dipole moment and the density degrees of freedom. We shall see that if there are low-lying polymorphic states in water, the dipole moment or density will change abruptly as a function of the radial distance from the ion.

Rigorous motion of the liquid will lead to the fragmentation of the cluster into small domains. The dipole moment of each fragmented domain has been aligned by the ions. If the equation of state of water at room temperature has polymorphic states as exhibited by the presence of multiple minima in densities and dipole moments, then these small domains may coalesce to form larger domains of metastable phases of water [1]. The domains may also be the seeds for the growth of larger domains of the same polymorphic states [1]. The presence of these metastable polymorphic states of water may be important components of the I_E water. They may then appear as an immiscible mixture without the ions in the aqueous solution. The existence of polymorphic states can be examined by studying whether the medium responsible for the I_E water contains the X^+ and the Y^- ions in the anomalous state. This signature for the existence of polymorphic states can be tested with future experimental investigations.

In the following, we shall review the tetrahedron structure of a H_2O molecule, the structure of a water cluster around an ion, the existence of polymorphic states of H_2O in different phases, and the possibility of multiple energy minima of the states of water with different dipole moments and densities at room temperature.

2 Molecular Structure of H_2O

As is well known, the H_2O molecule has the structure of a tetrahedron. The six electrons of the oxygen atom in the outermost shell and the two electrons from the hydrogen atoms form an octet structure of four ee pairs. The four electron pairs coming out from the oxygen nucleus as the four supports of the tetrahedron, with the two hydrogen nuclei at two vertices of the tetrahedron, are shown in Figure 1. The

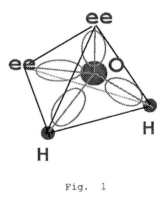

Fig. 1

opening angle between the two O-H bonds is 104.45° as compared to 109.5° for a regular tetrahedron. Thus, the four vertices of the tetrahedron can be characterized as two positively charged H vertices and two negatively charged ee pair vertices.

Because of the complex geometry of the tetrahedron, many possible arrangements of the tetrahedron network lead to stable configurations – the polymorphic states. They differ in their energies. However, under a change of thermodynamical conditions, the lowest-lying polymorphic state may change to lie higher than another polymorphic state and the role of the ground state changes. The change of thermodynamical conditions will lead to a phase transition between different polymorphic states. Phase transition in which the order parameter changes abruptly is a first-order phase transition. Phase transition in which the order parameter changes continuously is a second-order phase transition.

In the normal liquid state of water, the tetrahedrons of neighboring H_2O molecules are arranged in such a way that the H vertex of one tetrahedron is in the close vicinity of the *ee* vertex of another tetrahedron, forming a hydrogen bond. A hydrogen bond is weak. It is about 30 times weaker than a normal covalent bond, with a strength of 10-40 kJ/mol[20].

For a single H_2O molecule, there is an electric dipole moment with a magnitude of 1.87×10^{-18} esu which is $0.39|e|$Å. The electric dipole moment is a vector which points from the oxygen nucleus to the mid-point between the two hydrogen nuclei. For a collection of H_2O molecules, one can also speak of the specific dipole moment which can be defined as the local per-molecule average of the vector sum of the dipole moments of a local collection of H_2O molecules. Because of the vector addition of the dipole moments of individual molecules, the specific dipole moment of a many-body state of H_2O can be quite different if the orientations of the molecules are not random. Different arrangements of the orientation of the molecules will lead to different specific dipole moments. An orderly arrangement of the molecules such that the dipole moments are aligned nearly in the same direction will lead to an increase of the magnitude of the specific dipole moment.

For brevity of notation, we shall use the term "dipole moment" as an abbreviation to refer to the vector or the magnitude of the electric dipole moment, the vector or the magnitude of the electric dipole moment in units of the electron charge, or the vector or the magnitude of the local average of the dipole moment per molecule (the specific dipole moment), as the case may be. The meaning of the different cases can be simply inferred from the context. We shall use the unabbreviated term if its usage will help the understanding of the discussed concepts.

3   The Structure of a H_2O Cluster Around an Ion

Experimental observations [4-13] of water clusters of the type $X^+(H_2O)_n$ and $Y^-(H_2O)_n$ show that the occurrence of water molecules clustering around an ion is a common phenomenon. This arises from the strong Coulombic polarizing power of the ion. For an isolated assembly of large $X^+(H_2O)_n$ or $Y^-(H_2O)_n$, is the charge located at the center of an isolated cluster or at its surface? The interaction of the dipole moments of H_2O molecules with the ion depends on the orientation of the dipole moments. The energy of the system is lowest when the dipole moments are aligned along the lines of force of the ionic charge. Then the interaction between a H_2O molecule of dipole moment d with an ion of charge $q|e|$ varies with distance to the ion r as $-|q|e^2d/r^2$, and one can show that the energy is a minimum when the ion is located at the center. Thus, for a large H_2O cluster in equilibrium, the ion is located at the center.

The largest value of n in the $H^+(H_2O)_n$ cluster which has been observed [7] so far is 75. What is the limiting value of n for which the $X^q(H_2O)_n$ cluster is still stable? Those H_2O molecules with a binding energy greater than the thermal energy will not be evaporated by thermal motion. Thus, the condition for the H_2O at the outermost H_2O to be bound is

$$\frac{|q|e^2d}{r^2} \geq kT \quad \text{or} \quad r \leq \sqrt{\frac{|q|e^2d}{kT}}. \tag{1}$$

For room temperature with $kT = 0.025$ eV and a water molecule with $d = 0.39|e|$Å, the maximum radius of the cluster is $r \sim 15$ Å , and the maximum number of water molecules n is about 500. If the dipole moments are not completely aligned along the direction of the lines of force of the ion, these values will be reduced. One expects therefore that the radius of the cluster is of the order of 10-15 Å and a maximum cluster number of the order of 150-500. The measured heat of evaporation [8] of a H_2O molecule from a $H^+(H_2O)_n$ cluster with $n > 10$ is close to the bulk heat of evaporation of a H_2O molecule in water in the liquid phase ($\Delta H_v = 44.016$ kJ/mol), indicating that for large n, the water molecules in the cluster are in the liquid phase.

In the water medium, the addition of a small amount of ionic compound X^+Y^- will lead to ions dispersed over the water medium. When the medium is diluted enough with a X^+Y^- molar concentrations of 10^{-6} or lower, the ions can be considered to be well separated and isolated, and physical considerations similar to those for isolated ions are applicable. The strong polarizing power of the ions leads to a similar formation of $X^+(H_2O)_n$ and $Y^-(H_2O)_n$.

We consider the isothermal case and place an insolated ion of charge $q|e|$ at the origin $\mathbf{r}_0 = 0$. To study the response of the water medium to the presence of the charged ion, we can specify the properties of the water medium by the "equation of state" function $W(n,d)$ which is the energy per H_2O molecule. The function $W(n,d)$ depends on the temperature, the (number) density n, and the specific dipole moment d (the local average dipole moment per molecule). This function W arises, at least in principle, from all interactions between H_2O molecules. Because of the tetrahedron structure of the H_2O moelcule, there is the additional orientation dependence of the equation of state on the magnitude of the average dipole moment per molecule d. The dipole moment $\mathbf{d}(r)$ at $\mathbf{r}$, in general, has both a magnitude $d(\mathbf{r})$ and a direction.

The total energy of the medium is

$$E = \int W(n(\mathbf{r}), d(\mathbf{r})) n(\mathbf{r}) d\mathbf{r} - \int n(\mathbf{r}) \frac{q e^2 d(\mathbf{r}) \cos \theta(\mathbf{r})}{r^2} d\mathbf{r}. \qquad (2)$$

Note that in the above equation, the interactions between H_2O molecules have been included in the equation of state $W(n, d)$.

The energy of the system (Eq.(2)) is a minimum when the angle θ is aligned along the electric lines of force of the ion, i.e. $\theta = 0$ for $q > 0$ and $\theta = \pi$ for $q < 0$. We shall assume that the dipole moments of the H_2O molecules have settled down such that this alignment has been achieved. Equilibrium is reached when the energy is stationary upon arbitrary variation of n and d,

$$\delta E = \int \left[\frac{\delta}{\delta n} \left\{ W(n, d) n - n \frac{|q| e^2 d(r)}{r^2} \right\} \delta n + \frac{\delta}{\delta d} \left\{ W(n, d) n - n \frac{|q| e^2 d(\mathbf{r})}{r^2} \right\} \delta d \right] d\mathbf{r} = 0.$$

Thus, equilibrium of the medium occurs when

$$\frac{\delta}{\delta n} \left\{ W(n, d)\, n - n \frac{|q| e^2 d(r)}{r^2} \right\} = \left\{ \frac{\partial [W(n, d)\, n]}{\partial n} - \frac{|q| e^2 d(r)}{r^2} \right\} = 0 \qquad (3)$$

and

$$\frac{\delta}{\delta d} \left\{ W(n, d) - \frac{|q| e^2 d(r)}{r^2} \right\} = 0. \qquad (4)$$

Condition (3) implies that equilibrium is reached at those densities for which

$$W_{ext}(n, d)\, n = \left\{ W(n, d)\, n - n\, |q| e^2 d(r) / r^2 \right\} \qquad (5)$$

is a minimum with respect to a variation in n, and (4) implies that equilibrium occurs for those dipole moment values where the energy per molecule

$$W_{ext}(n, d) = \left\{ W(n, d) - |q| e^2 d(r) / r^2 \right\} \qquad (6)$$

is a minimum with respect to a variation in d. The second term in the above two equations represents the polarization force which moves the location of the energy minima to different densities or dipole moments.

4 Density and Dipole Moment Profile of H$_2$O Cluster for a Single State

It is instructive to give the structure of the H$_2$O cluster when the state of the water medium consists of a single state whose equation of state is described by

$$W(n, d) = \frac{1}{2} K_n \frac{(n - n_0)^2}{n} + \frac{1}{2} K_d (d - d_0)^2,$$

(7)

where n_0 is the equilibrium density, d_0 is the equilibrium specific dipole moment, K_n is stiffness parameter with respect to the density variation and is related to the compressibility of water, and K_d is the stiffness parameter with respect to the dipole moment variation. We ssume again the alignment of the dipole moments around the ion, and we look for solutions of the density and the dipole moment around the equilibrium values. Then, Eq. (3) gives the density profile of the cluster as

$$n(r) = n_0 + \frac{\sqrt{|q|e^2 d(r)/K_n}}{r}.$$

(8)

Thus, the deviation of the cluster density from the equilibrium density is inversely proportional to the radial distance from the ion, depending on the compressibility K_n of water. Equation (4) leads to the dipole moment profile of the cluster as

$$d(r) = d_0 + \frac{|q|e^2}{K_d r^2}.$$

(9)

The deviation of the cluster dipole moment from equilibrium is inversely proportional to the square of the radial distance from the ion, depending on the stiffness of the variation of W with respect to d.

From this analysis, one notes that the density and the magnitude of the dipole moment of the H$_2$O cluster are greater than the corresponding quantities in the surrounding medium. It will be of interest to see whether such a difference may lead to observable sinking of the clusters due to gravity.

It is of interest to note the differences of two stiffness parameters K_n and K_d. The stiffness parameter K_n involves the compression of the medium. To compress water in the liquid phase, considerable energy is needed to overcome the repulsive overlap of the electronic densities of the molecules. One expects that the water medium is quite stiff against a change in density. On the other hand, the change of the specific dipole moment arises from the change of the local average of the vector sum of the dipole moments of the H$_2$O molecules, which can be brought about by reorienting the H$_2$O molecules without moving their centers-of-mass. As the energy involved in making a rotational motion is considerably smaller than the energy required to bring two molecules closer than the equilibrium separation, one expects that the water medium is much softer against dipole moment distortions as compared to density distortions. That is, it is easier to change the specific dipole moment than the density.

5   Polymorphic States of H_2O in the Liquid Phase

The dipole moments for normal water are randomly oriented, and the (average) specific dipole moment is essentially zero. Other arrangements of the H_2O moelcues different from that of the norm state of water are possible, and they may lead to polymorphic states of H_2O with different configurations, densities and dipole moments. Polymorphic states of H_2O in the solid phase manifest themselves in different structures of ice crystals where the tetrahedron structure of the molecule is maintained by joining the oxygen nuclei in tetrahedron network patterns, with a hydrogen nucleus between each link of two oxygen nuclei. These polymorphic states are well known [17]. We are naturally more interested in polymorphic states of H_2O in the liquid phase.

Polymorphic states of H_2O in the liquid phase are found experimentally in supercooled water by Mishima et al. [18,19] and shown theoretically by Poole et al. [21,22], and by Roberts et al. [23]. The polymorphic states of supercooled water exist as the low-density amorp (LDA) and the high-density amorp (HDA). The transition between the two polymorphic states has been observed to occur reversibly and abruptly at about 135° K and about 0.2 GPa with a volume change of 0.02 cm^3/g and some hysteresis [19]. The LDA has a volume-pressure relation very similar to Ice Ih, while the HDA is similar to Ice V and VI at supercooled temperatures (see Fig. 1 of Ref. [19]). One can interpret LDA and HDA as configurations of excited energy minima in the liquid phase in which the normal ground states at that temperature are different configurations of ice in the solid phase. For a given temperature in which LDA (or HDA) is the lower energy ground state, the transition from the other excited HDA state (or LDA) will involve the release of heat, and such a release of heat has been observed experimentally [19].

It is worth noting that metastable states in different energy minima have been found in many systems in physics. Hill and Wheeler discussed unstable shape isomers which differ from the stable ground state by their quadrupole moment [26]. In this case, the quadrupole moment plays the role analogous to the order parameter in thermodynamic systems. Isomers with different quadrupole moments have been found experimentally in many nuclei and can be understood as the manifestation of multiple minima in the energy surface as a function of the quadrupole moment[27]. They are locally stable because they reside in the energy minima associated with their own local variations.

Recent theoretical work on supercooled water indicates that there are polymorphic states of water in which the local density can be an order parameter[21,22,23]. The molecular dynamics computer simulations of Sciortino et al.[22] show a first-order liquid-liquid phase transition for water molecules interacting among themselves with the ST2 model interaction. These two phases can coexist at different spatial locations at a range of temperatures. They differ by about 15% in density and have different local structures, local dynamics, and mobility, with the molecules in the high-density phase much more mobile than the molecules in the low-density phase. In separate investigations on a supercooled, dense, equilibrium Lennard-Jones liquid using molecular dynamics, it is found that the more mobile particles form large-scale quasi-stable string-like clusters and their dynamics is correlated in a string-like motion[24,25]. The fraction of these large clusters is about 5% of the liquid in the model considered.

Recently Roberts et al. found from theory and simulations of network-forming liquid that the polymorphic states occur quite generally in systems in which the molecules interact via strong directional intermolecular forces, as in the case of the tetrahedron H_2O molecules or Si atoms[23]. The qualitative characteristics of the phase transition depend on the details of bonding and on the choice of the model parameters. For example, a calculated temperature-density phase diagram of a model network can exhibit a liquid-liquid phase transition in a pure substance, in addition to a vapor-liquid phase transition.

It will be of interest to study many tetrahedron networks similar to those of the ice crystals to see whether they lead to polymorphic states in the liquid phase. Furthermore, in view of the elongated shape of the clusters as observed in I_E water samples[1,3], it will be useful to study a network in which the simplest unit consists of two H_2O molecules with the H vertices of these molecules

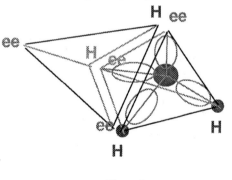

Fig. 2

in the vicinity of the ee vertices of the other molecule. The dipole moment of the whole complex is aligned along the symmetry axis of the two molecules, as in Figure 2. The repeated and parallel arrangement of these basic units along the same direction may lead to a state with a preferred direction as the symmetry direction, and may exhibit an elongated string-like behavior.

6 Structure of H_2O Cluster for Polymorphic States

We note in the last section the experimental observations of the existence of the polymorphic states in supercooled water [18,19]. Theoretical supports for the occurrence of these polymorphic states in water comes from the directional nature of the interaction of tetrahedron molecules [21,22,23]. There is also the occurrence of large-scale quasi-stable, string-like clusters in a simple Lennard-Jones liquid [24,25]. It is therefore useful to explore the possibility of polymorphism for water at room temperature. The strong polarizing power of the ion makes it a useful tool for such an investigation.

Accordingly, we consider the possibility of polymorphic states of water at room temperature by representing the equation of state of water with an energy surface containing low-lying secondary minima where the normal ground state has order parameter d_0, and metastable states with order parameter d_1 and d_2, ... The secondary minima are the anomalous states differing from the normal ground state water configuration by their order parameters which can be either the density or the specific dipole moment. Each energy minimum represents a configuration with distinct characteristics of the medium. The case for the dipole degree of freedom is shown schematically as the solid curve in Figure 3.

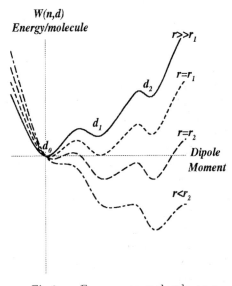

Fig.3. Energy per molecule as a function of the dipole moment for different distances r from the ion.

If the rate of change of the order parameter is rapid, the water molecule system will jump from the lowest energy surface to the higher energy surface, retaining the characteristics of its initial configuration, as in the case of large Landau-Zener jump probabilities [28]. On the other hand, if the rate of change of the order parameter is small, then the intrinsic energy surface of the water molecule will follow the lowest surface represented by the solid curve in Figure 3, and the configuration of the system may change slowly from one minimum to the next as the dynamics evolves. In the polarization stage of the process, we shall consider only this case of slow change of the order parameters. The anomalous states represented by the secondary minima at d_1 and d_2 are separated from the minimum for the normal state at d_0 by a barrier.

Assuming again the alignment of the molecular dipole moments along the lines of force of the ion, one can use the equilibrium conditions (3) and (4) to study the profile of dipole moment and density around the cluster. Consider first the dipole moment as the order parameter with an equation of state $W(n, d)$ in the form of the solid curve shown in Figure 3. The equilibrium dipole moment is determined by the condition that the function $W_{ext}(n, d)$ is a minimum of d. As $W_{ext}(n, d) = W(n, d) - |q|e^2 d/r^2$, the minimum will be located at different values of d for various values of r. In Fig. 3 the solid curve gives $W_{ext}(n, d)$ at a distance far from the ion in the bulk part of the water medium. The metastable minima d_1 and d_2 are above the normal ground state d_0. At a distance r_1 from the ion, the polarization term $(-|q|e^2 d/r^2)$ proportional to d distorts the function W_{ext} such that the minimum around d_1 is on the same level as that around d_0, and a state of coexistence of the two states is possible. At a shorter distance, the dipole moment will make a transition to d_2. Similarly, at distances closer than r_2, the minima at d_2 is pulled down lower than the minimum around d_1, and the system will make a transition to the dipole moment around d_2. Thus, the dipole moment is $\sim d_0$ for $r > r_1$, is $\sim d_1$ for $r_1 > r > r_2$ and is $\sim d_2$ for $r_2 > r$, and so on. Thus, in the presence of polymorphic states of water, the local dipole moment of the cluster abruptly changes as a function of the radial separation from the ion, corresponding to the different minima brought down by the polarizing interaction.

One can use a similar argument to discuss the density profile of the medium around an ion. The equilibrium density is determined by the condition that the function $nW_{ext}(n, d) = nW(n, d) - n|q|e^2 d/r^2$ is a minimum with respect to a variation in n. If the function $W_{ext}(n, d)$ possesses secondary minima, then $nW_{ext}(n, d)$ will also possess multiple minima. Using arguments similar to those for the dipole moments, one finds that in the presence of polymorphic states in density, the local density around a cluster changes abruptly as a function of the radial distance from the ion. After equilibrium is reached, water molecules at different distances will have different densities, being greater at shorter distances from the ion.

The abrupt changes of density or dipole moment arise only when the heights of the secondary minima in these two degrees of freedom are not too large so that they can be pulled down by the polarizing power of the ion. If the heights of these secondary minima are very large, then, for all intents and purposes, the medium is essentially a single state where the secondary minima play no role.

7 Cluster Interaction and Fragmentation

After equilibrium is reached and the clusters formed around the ions, each cluster remains charged, and there is a Coulombic interaction between different clusters. Each cluster has a radius of about 10 Å , and the Coulomb interaction energy between two touching clusters of opposite charge is about 0.7 eV which is still considerable. It may provide sufficient attractive interaction for the clusters to arrange themselves in an orderly manner, forming clusters of greater sizes (superclusters) with many $X^+(H_2O)_n$ and $Y^-(H_2O)_n$ entities. Another interesting possibility is the formation of a bridge linking the two clusters of opposite charge between which the dipole moments of the H_2O molecules line up in the same direction. It is of interest to examine in I_E water whether superclusters or bridges of H_2O molecules are components of the anomalous states in I_E water. Thus, the study of these clusters in I_E water will provide information on the stability and the interactions of the $X^+(H_2O)_n$ and $Y^-(H_2O)_n$ in aqueous solutions.

If the liquid is shaken vigorously after equilibrium is reached, then the cluster will fragment into many small domains. In each domain, the dipole moment has been properly aligned by the ion. If the water medium has only a single phase, these domains will relax and will return to the state of the normal water, with the orientation of the dipole moments of the H_2O molecules becoming randomized again. No new anomalous state will be formed as a stable entity.

The situation will be different if there are polymorphic states of water and the domains which break away from the cluster contain metastable polymorphic states, which have been produced under the strong field of the polarizing ion. Being a polymorphic state stable under local variations of its order parameters, these domains will not relax to the normal state of water. They will remain metastable and may coalesce with other similar domains. Fragmented domains of H_2O can also act as seeds for the growth of greater regions of polymorphic states. In this case, anomalous polymorphic states will contain metastable domains of H_2O molecules for which the dipole moment or the density may be different from that in the normal state.

8 Conclusions and Discussions

The anomalous states of water are peculiar and unexpected. Their existence may be connected to the occurrence of metastable polymorphic states of water at room temperature. It is therefore important to confirm or to refute the observations of these anomalous states by independent experimental investigations.

Looking at the process of the formation of the anomalous states, one finds that isolated ions have great polarizing power which attracts water molecules around it. Stable clusters in free assembly have been copiously found experimentally and their existence in dilute aqueous solutions is expected. The large polarizing power of the ionic charge leads to great change of the dipole moment and density of the medium around the ion. These changes depend on the stiffness of the equation of state against the variation of density and dipole moments. If there are low-lying polymorphic states of the liquid, the polarizing action of the ion will lead to local densities and local dipole moments which change abruptly as a function of the separation from the ion, being greater at shorter distances from the ion.

Fragmentation of the clusters upon vigorous shaking will produce domains of the liquid where the dipole moments are aligned. The coalescence of these domains and the seeding of these regions may allow the formation of polymorphic states of the liquid if these polymorphic states are possible metastable configurations of the liquid. Pending further experimental confirmations, the anomalous states of the I_E water may be such a substance.

The presence of the polymorphic state can be examined by looking for the decay of the metastable I_E state. It can also be studied by exciting the I_E state above the barrier which will lead to a change of the I_E state to the normal state, and will deplete the I_E water population. One can also measure the dielectric properties of the I_E water to show an enhanced dipole moment of the I_E water. The difference in the dielectric constants as discussed by Lo et al.[2] needs to be analyzed theoretically to understand its implications on the nature of the dipole moments in the anomalous states.

The foregoing discussions in the last few sections can be carried over to discuss many other liquids in which the molecules in the liquid have permanent dipole moments. Because the polarizing interaction for an aligned dipole depends on $-|q|e^2 d/r^2$, the interaction is greater, the greater the static electric dipole moment of a single molecule. Therefore, the addition of a small amount of ionic compound on a liquid whose molecules have a large static dipole moment will lead to a very strong clustering of the molecules around the ion. They can be well utilized to study polymorphism in these liquids to see whether domains of anomalous states with properties different from those in the ground states may exist in these liquids.

Acknowledgments

The authors would like to thank Profs. A. A. Chialvo and S. Christian for helpful discussions. The research of CYW is sponsored by the USDOE under Contract DE-AC05-96OR22464 managed by Lockheed Martin Energy Research Corp.

References

1. S.-Y. Lo, *Modern Phys. Lett.* **19**, 909 (1996).
2. S.-Y. Lo et al., *Modern Phys. Lett.* **19**, 921 (1996).
3. S.-Y. Lo, Proceedings of this Symposium, 1997.
4. A. Good, D. A. Durden, and P. Kebarle, *J. Chem. Phys.* **52**, 212 (1970).
5. R. Yamdagni and P. Kebarle, *Can. J. Chem.* **52**, 2249 (1974).
6. G. Caldwell and P. Kebarle, *Can. J. Chem.* **63**, 1399 (1970).
7. T. Schindler, C. Berg, G. Niedner-Schatteburg, and V. E. Bondybey, *Chem. Phys.* **201**, 491 (1995).
8. T. Schindler, C. Berg, G. Niedner-Schatteburg, and V. E. Bondybey, *Chem. Phys. Lett.* **229**, 57 (1995).
9. A. A. Viggiano et al., *J. Phys. Chem.* **94**, 8194 (1990).
10. X. Yang, X. Zhang, and A. W. Castleman, Jr. *J. Phys. Chem.* **95**, 8520 (1991).
11. K. Hiraoka, S. Mizuse, and S. Yamabe, *J. Phys. Chem.* **92**, 3943 (1988).
12. J. W. Larson and T. B. McMahon, *J. Am. Chem. Soc.* **106**, 517 (1984).
13. J. Coe, *Chem. Phys. Lett.* **229**, 161 (1994).
14. E. E. Tucker and S. D. Christian, *J. Am. Chem. Soc.* **106**, 517 (1984).
15. L. X. Deng, J. E. Rice, J. Caldwell, and P. Kollman, *J. Am. Chem. Soc.* **113**, 2481 (1991).
16. A. A. Chialvo, P. T. Cummings, J. M. Simonson, and R. E. Mesmer, Proceedings of the Fifth International Conference on Hydrothermal Reactions, Gatlinburg, June 1997, (Edited by D. A. Palmaer et al.), pp. 157-160.
17. N. Fletcher, *The Chemical Physics of Ice*, Cambridge University Press, 1970.
18. O. Mishima, L. D. Calvert, and E. Whalley, *Nature* **310**, 393 (1984).
19. O. Mishima, *Jour. Chem. Phys.* **100**, 5910 (1994).
20. R. Holyst, *Encyclopedia of Applied Physics*, (http://xxx.lanl.gov/abs/cond-mat/?9603062).
21. P. H. Poole, T. Grande, C. A. Angell, and P. F. McMillan, *Science* **275**, 322 (1997).

22. F. Sciortino, P. H. Poole, U. Essmann, and H.E. Stanley, *Phys. Rev. E.* **55**, 727 (1997).

23. C. J. Roberts, G. Karayiannakis, and P. G. Debenedetti, AICHE Talk, (November, 1997).

24. W. Kob, C. Donati, S. J. Plimpton, P. H. Poole, and S. C. Glotzer, *Phys. Rev. Lett.* **79**, 2827 (1997).

25. C. Donati, J. K. Douglas, W. Kob, S. J. Plimpton, P. H. Poole, and S. C. Glotzer, (http://xxx.lanl.gov/abs/cond-mat/?9706277).

26. D. L. Hill and J. A. Wheeler, *Phys. Rev.* **89**, 1102 (1953).

27. M. Brack, J. Damgaard, A. S. Jensen, H. C. Pauli, V. M. Strutinsky, and C. Y. Wong, *Rev. Mod. Phys.* **44**, 320 (1972).

28. L. D. Landau, *Z. Phys. Sow. Un.* **2**, 46 (1932); C. Zener, *Proc. Roy. Soc. (London)* **A137**, 696 (1932).

DIELECTRIC SPECTRAL STUDY IN LOW FREQUENCY OF I_E WATER AND SOME OTHER SOLVENTS

LI WENCHONG

LAI TIANSHU

LI HUIHUA

SHUI YIN LO

Originally published as *Physical, Chemical and Biological Properties of Stable Water Clusters,* Proceedings of the First International Symposium. Reprinted here by permission of World Scientific Publishing Company, 1998.

Spectra of dielectric constant ε and dissipation factor D of I_E water, distilled water; acid and base solutions; polar solvents: (methyl alcohol, methyl formate); non-polar solvents (CCl_4 and dimethyl benzene) were studied.

1. Introduction

As stated in our previous papers[1,2], I_E water contains stable water cluster. These clusters consist of highly ordered water molecules with their electric dipole lining up. It is well known that, dielectric constant ε is an important parameter reflecting the dipole property of materials. In the recent years, dielectric spectral methods are used in colloidal and aqueous solutions chiefly to gain information about chemical and physical properties of solutes and its interaction between the solute and solvent (3-6). I_E water is created by very low concentration of initiator, but contains many stable water clusters with a strong electric dipole moments. These stable water clusters are called I_E clusters. Dielectric spectroscopy studies may help us to understand the structural characteristics of I_E clusters. An experimental device was used to measure the complex dielectric constant. Some interesting results have been obtained.

2. Principle and Experimental Set-up

In principle, dielectric constant measurement of a medium is obtained by comparing the capacitance C_0 in air and capacitance C_i with the medium of a condenser. The ratio $\varepsilon = C_i / C_0$ is the dielectric constant. If the medium inside the gap of condenser is acted upon by an alternating voltage $V = V_0 e^{j\omega t}$ with angular frequency $\omega = 2\pi f$, the charge of the condenser is equal to $Q = C_i V$ and the charging current is:

$$I_c = \frac{dQ}{dt} = I_0 \exp[j\,(\omega t - \pi/2)] \qquad (1)$$

which leads the voltage in phase by 90^0. The material, which fills in the condenser, normally possesses conductivity, and the stray current component $I_1 = V / R_i$, I_1 is in phase with the applied voltage V. Thus, the full current passing through the condenser is equal to:

$$I = I_1 + I_c = \frac{V}{R_i} + C_i \frac{dV}{dt} \qquad (2)$$

where V and I are voltage and current of the condenser with the medium. They have a phase difference with each other and could be expressed as a complex variable. The dielectric constant, which is determined by I and V, is also complex:

$$\mathrm{Re}\,\varepsilon - j\,\mathrm{Im}\,\varepsilon \quad (3) \qquad (3)$$

$$\varepsilon = |\varepsilon| = \left(\mathrm{Re}\varepsilon^2 - \mathrm{Im}\,\varepsilon^2\right)^{1/2}\,; D = \tan\Delta = \mathrm{Im}\,\varepsilon/\,\mathrm{Re}\,\varepsilon \qquad (4)$$

where ε is dielectric constant. The ratio **Im** ε/ **Re** ε is equal to the ratio of stray current to charging current. It is called the dissipation factor D of medium. Its value is equal to the tangent of loss angle Δ. The angle in question is that on the complex plane between the vectors of full and the charging currents.

In dielectric spectroscopy, ε_i and D are measured as a function of scanning frequency. Therefore, we have:

$$\varepsilon_i(\omega) = \frac{C_i(\omega)}{C_0(\omega)}; \frac{(in\,medium)}{(in\,air)}\,, \quad D_i(\omega) = \frac{R_i}{1/\omega\,C_i} = \omega\,C_i\,R_i \qquad (5)$$

Generally, ε reflects the capacitance variation of a liquid medium compared with a dry air medium. This variation is created by permanent and induced dipole moments of liquids inside the condenser. Stray current, which is measured by R_i, is due to either the line up, or migration of dipole clusters in testing liquid between the gap of condenser. In the case of very thin solution, a variation in R_i causes a variation in D_i. However, $\varepsilon_i(\omega)$ mainly relates to the dielectric property of medium molecules, and $D_i(\omega)$ relates to the movement of dipole cluster in testing liquid. Obviously, these are related to the mechanical characteristics of clusters and the viscosity of solvent. A peak of $\varepsilon_i(\omega)$ in a certain frequency means a resonance in the creation of the induced dipole moment. The peak of $D_i(\omega)$ gives significant information on the mass, the size of clusters and rheological properties of testing liquid.

For example, a methanol molecule CH_3OH can be separated into two groups: OH, a polar group and CH_3, a non-polar group. Under the action of an applied alternative electric field, the OH group will have induced dipole moment resonance. Certainly, in this condition, the whole methanol molecule is in motion. This motion will consume energy, the reading is dissipation (Figure 1).

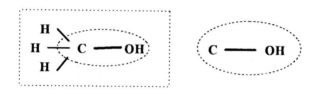

D ∝ whole molecular movement   ε ∝ induced dipole moment resonance

Figure 1: Dielectric constant and Dissipation

So far many authors have indicated that ε which measured at low frequency and high frequency are different. Frequency spectral methods have been extensively used in dielectric materials research in the last ten years. A commercial frequency scanning instrument, an Impedance Analyzer, is widely used for this purpose. Usually, this instrument is suitable for low dissipation medium studies. In the case of a high dissipation medium, it is difficult, to match the impedance with the built-in circuit. Figure 2 shows the set up of the equipment.

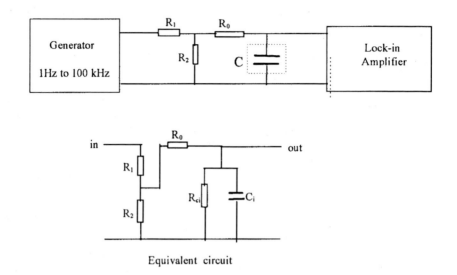

Equivalent circuit

Figure 2 Experimental set-up and equivalent circuit

Condenser C is a pair of aluminum planes with diameter of 60 mm. It is put into a plastic chamber where the testing liquid fills the whole chamber. The condenser in the measuring circuit is equivalent to C_i in parallel with R_{ci}. To match the impedance of various kind of samples, a variable resistance R_0 and voltage divider is put inside the circuit. A sinusoidal current from divider through R_0, feeds to the testing condenser. V_{ci} and ϕ_{ci} are read by a lock-in amplifier. The V_0 and ϕ_0 of input signals are measured by the lock-in amplifier as well. According to the alternating circuit analysis, we can easily calculate the R_{ci} and C_i, and then calculate ε_i and D_i for each medium by using special software. The scanning sinusoidal current is provided by a numerically synthetic oscillator from 1 Hz to 100 kHz.

3. Experimental Results and Discussion

Several classes of solutions are studied. They are:

(1) Water: Ordinary water and I_E water.

178

(2) Polar organic solvent: Methanol CH_3OH, and CH_3OH are dissolved in water at ratios of 5:1 and 1:50.

(3) Non-polar organic solvent: CCl_4, an entirely non-polar solvent. Dimethyl benzene $[C_6H_4(CH_3)_2]$, which has an induced dipole moment.

(4) Strong polar organic solvent: Methyl formate $[HCOOCH_3]$ has high solubility. We prepared the solutions at the ratios of 1:50, 1:200 and 1:2500 with water and measurements are then taken.

(5) Ionic solution: Similarly, a suitable amount of NaOH is added into water until a pH=12 is achieved. They are acidic solutions and alkaline solutions respectively. These are real ionic solutions.

In Figure 3a, variation of dissipation D vs. frequency of the applied AC field is shown for both ordinary water and I_E water. There is a gradual increase in D that begins from 100 Hz and has a peak at 3 kHz in water sample. In the D spectrum of I_E water, there is the same gradual increase in values from 100 Hz onward. At the peak position of 3 kHz, the reading is 2.5 times higher than that of ordinary water. In addition, at the lower and higher frequency side of the 3 kHz peak, in this spectrum, there are two additional shoulders, respectively. We plot the difference of dissipation between I_E and H_2O ($\Delta D = D_{IE} - D_W$) vs. frequency (Figure 3b) and we processed this difference of spectrum with a spectral analysis software. Three individual bands at 800 Hz, 3.6 kHz and 11 kHz are found. The peak at 3.6 kHz can be considered as a small frequency shift of the peak at 3 kHz, in water spectrum. Peaks at 800 Hz and 11 kHz can be attributed to I_E water alone. The spectra of the dielectric constant ε for distilled water and I_E water are shown in Figure 3c. In the frequency range of less than 150 Hz, the dielectric constant ε of I_E water is higher than that of DI water, however the dielectric constant ε of I_E is lower than that of DI water when the range is greater than 150 Hz. We plot the difference of dielectric constant between I_E and DI water ($\Delta\varepsilon = \varepsilon_{IE} - \varepsilon_w$) as a function of frequency (Figure 3d). Four peaks at 10 Hz, 70 Hz, ~300 Hz and 1 kHz appear in plus or minus direction. Comparing these with Figure 3c, we observe two peaks (70 Hz and 300 Hz) appearing simultaneously in both samples. The I_E water peak height at 70 Hz is higher than that of H_2O, while at 300 Hz, the reverse happens. It seems that structures reflected by these two peaks exist in both samples in varying amounts. Peaks of 10 Hz and 1 kHz are characteristic of additional structures that exist in I_E water only.

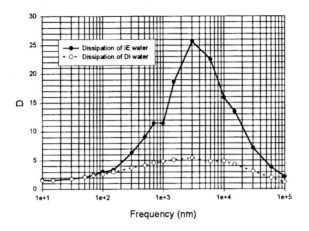

Figure 3a. Dissipated D spectra of I_E and distilled water

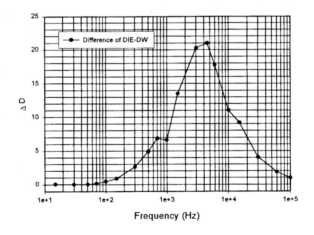

Figure 3b. Difference of dissipation Δ D spectra between I_E and distilled water

180

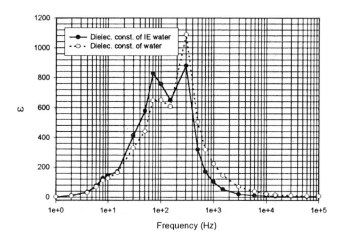

Figure 3c Dielectric constant spectra of I_E and DI water

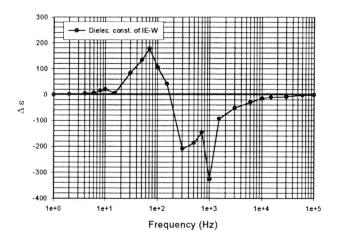

Figure 3d Difference of dielectric constant $\Delta \mathcal{E}$ spectra between I_E and DI water

The dissipation D and dielectric constant ε spectra of acidic and alkaline solutions are shown in Figures 4a and 4b. The peak values at 300 Hz are 3×10^5 and 7×10^4 for alkaline and acidic solution, respectively, and are three hundred times and seventy times higher than that of H_2O. The dissipation D spectra for alkaline and acidic solutions are quite different from that of H_2O and I_E water. In an acidic solution, only one dissipation peak appears at the low frequency region (≤2 Hz). In an alkaline solution, high dissipation appears at the high frequency region (≥60 kHz).

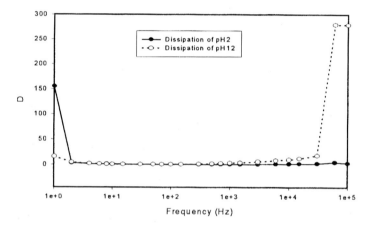

Figure 4a. Dissipation spectra of acidic (HC) and alkaline (NaOH) solutions

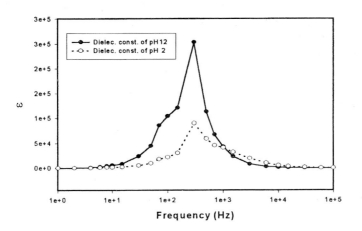

Figure 4b. Dielectric constant spectra of acidic (HCl) alkaline (NaOH) solution

For further understanding of the characteristics of the peaks, in Figure 4b several kinds of polar and non-polar organic solvents and ionic solutions are studied. The position and values of different peaks for different solutions are tabulated in Table 1 and 2.

The peak at 300 Hz appears in all kinds of aqueous solutions (Table 1). ε values of acidic or alkaline solutions are in the order of 10^5, and ε are about 10^3 for H_2O or I_E water. Polar solvents such as CH_3OH, $HCOOCH_3$ are about tens in value, but once those molecules bond with water, their ε immediately rise to 10^3. The rise in value indicates the increase of dipole strength due to the ordering of H_2O molecules, which are attracted and aligned around a polar site of the original molecule. Non-polar organic solvents such as CCl_4 and dimethyl benzene $C_6H_4(CH_3)_2$ have ε values are less than ten.

The dielectric constants ε of various solutions are plotted in Figure 5a. The curves could be classified into three groups: non-polar solutions (lower part), polar solutions, where molecules have permanent electric dipole polar (middle) and ionic solutions (upper). The dielectric constant ε of ionic solutions are ten to hundreds of times larger than those of polar solutions. The situation is quite similar to results by J.P. Hansen *et al*, 1998, where the pH measurements reflect ions in solution created hundreds mV between two testing electrodes. The corresponding measurements in dipole solutions have tens mV dipole potential between electrodes. These phenomena are consistent with the universal knowledge of physicists and chemists that dipole effects are always 2 to 3 orders lower than that of monopole (ionic) effects.

The dissipation D values of various peaks of solutions are found in Table 2. The peak at 3 kHz appears in following solutions: H_2O and I_E water, CH_3OH with or without water and $HCOOCH_3$ with or without water. The peak at 3 kHz does not appear in non-aqueous methyl alcohol or methyl formate solutions. As the concentration of methyl formate in water goes down the dissipation value goes up and approaches that of I_E water. This peak also does not appear in acidic, alkaline solution and non-polar solvent, such as CCl_4 and dimethyl benzene. Summing up above evidence, we suggest that this peak belongs to water cluster. Another peak of I_E water at 700 to 800 Hz also appears in CH_3OH, which are greatly enhanced in an aqueous solution.

Dissipation factors of various solutions are plotted together in Figure 5b. In the range of 10 Hz to 10 kHz, acidic and alkaline solutions have very low dissipation, and a very high ε (Figures 4 and 5). It is well known, that electrolytes have high dielectric constants and low dissipation. Accordingly, high capacitance (electrolytic) condensers, are widely used in low frequency electronic devices. Conversely, CCl_4 and dimethyl benzene have extremely high dissipation, but very low ε at the range of 30 Hz to 500 Hz. Perhaps in these solutions, molecules are grouped together and have a resonance absorption at above the frequency range.

Table 1. Peak values of ε in I_E water and other solvents

Frequency	8 Hz	10 Hz	70 Hz	100 Hz	300 Hz	500 Hz	1 kHz	3 kHz	10 kHz	60 kHz
H_2O		148	648		1089					
I_E water			828		880					
HCl in water pH = 2					8.9×10^4					
NaOH in water pH = 12				1.1×10^5	2.5×10^5					
CH_3OH	2.80		472.5		489.7	404.6	219.3			
$H_2O + CH_3OH$ 1:5	79.7		70.8		55.4	24.37	14.2			
$CH_3OH + H_2O$ 1:50	315		878		1294	607	280			
$HCOOCH_3$		2.0	2.54		5.67				1.77	
$HCOOCH_3$ in water 1:50		1456	1.7×10^4	1.8×10^4	3.8×10^4				692.4	
$HCOOCH_3$ in water 1:2500		785	2323	2020	2647		457.7	135.9	41.1	32.0
$HCOOCH_3$ in water 1:25000		320	614	525	619		115.5	36.9	16.9	11.5
$C_6H_4(CH_3)_2$					2.01					
CCl_4					2.98					

Table 2. Peak values of D in I_E water and other solvents

Frequency	1 Hz	8 Hz	70 Hz	150 Hz	300 Hz	700 Hz	1 kHz	3 kHz	10 kHz	60 kHz
H_2O								5.49		
I_E water						11.46		25.74	15.9	
HCl in water pH = 2	155.2									
NaOH in water pH =12										279.7
CH_3OH						5.29		5.85		
H_2O +CH_3OH 1:5						4.12		5.07		
CH_3OH + H_2O 1:50						86.82		47.42		
$HCOOCH_3$		40.4	130.7		131.3					
$HCOOCH_3$ in water 1:50								2.48		
$HCOOCH_3$ in water 1:2500								10.76		
$HCOOCH_3$ in water 1:25000								19.62		
$C_6H_4(CH_3)_2$			50 Hz 512.8	513	256					
CCl_4		42.7	50 Hz 170.8		170.7					

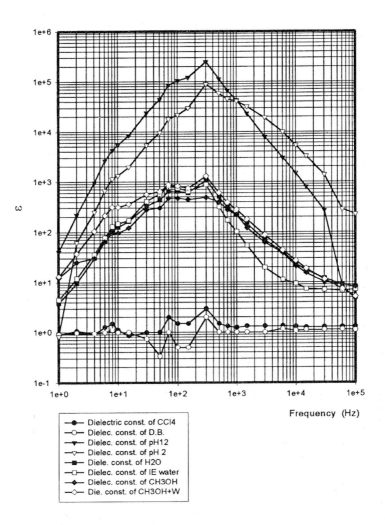

Figure 5a. $\mathcal{E}$ spectra of IE water and some other solutions

187

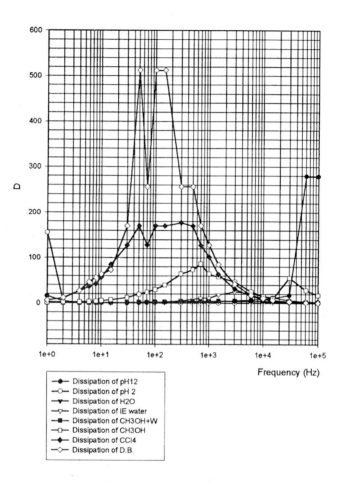

Figure 5b. Dissipation spectra of all kind of solutions

Electric dipole moment of CH_3OH in gas phase is 1.77 debyes, which is slightly lower than that of H_2O (1.85 debyes), however, they would have similar dielectric constant ε values. In general, small amounts of CH_3OH added into H_2O have the effect of increasing the ε value; whereas addition of a small amount of

H_2O in CH_3OH decreases the ε value. The ε at 300 Hz of CH_3OH is 489.7 (Table 1). When it is diluted with water at the ratio of 1:50, ε increases to 1294 by a factor of 2.6. The value is nearly that of H_2O ($\varepsilon_{300} = 1089$). However, if one fifth of H_2O is put into CH_3OH, the ε value decreases to 55.4. For methyl formate ($HCOOCH_3$), the ε is 5.67, and when diluted with water at a ratio of 1:50, the ε increases to 3.8×10^4 by a factor of 6.7×10^3. These results indicate the bonding ability of water with methyl formate (COO= group), which is much higher than that of methyl alcohol (OH group).

4. Summary

(1) Dielectric spectra provide a reasonable picture to classify the ionic, polar and non-polar solution. I_E water belongs to polar solutions where molecules have permanent electric dipole moments.

(2) Variation of ε value of some organic solvents between itself and its aqueous solution provide valuable information on aqueous affinity.

Under the action of low frequency electro-magnetic fields, each solution has some resonant dissipation peaks. These peaks probably reflect characteristic structures of the molecular cluster in the solution.

References:

1. S.Y. Lo, *Modern Physics Letter B*, **10**, 909 (1996).
2. S.Y. Lo *et al*, *Modern Physics Letter B*, **10**, 921 (1996).
3. S.S. Dukhin, *Surface and Colloid Science* ed. E. Malijevic; (Wiley-Interscience, vol. 3, 83 (1971).
4. F. Wilhelms *et al*, *Conference Lectures of Recent Theoretical and Experimental Advances in Hydrogen-Bonded Clusters* (1997).
   J.G. Paren in *Physics and Chemistry of Ice* ed. by E. Whalley et al, (Royal Society of Canada, Ottawa, 262 (1973).
5. A.F. Petrenko, *Electrical properties of ice*, Special report 93-20, US Army Cold Regions Research and Engineering Laboratory (1993).
6. E. Hawlicka and I. Dlugoborski, *Chemical Physics Letters*, **268** 325 (1997).
7. S.Y. Lo and Li W.C., *to be published.*

INELASTIC NEUTRON SCATTERING TECHNIQUES AND ITS APPLICATION TO I_E WATER

Y. WANG and J-C. LI

Originally published as *Physical, Chemical and Biological Properties of Stable Water Clusters,* Proceedings of the First International Symposium.Reprinted here by permission of World Scientific Publishing Company, 1998.

Using inelastic incoherent neutron scattering and Raman scattering techniques, we measured vibrational spectra for the I_E water and compared with high purity normal water (99.96% H_2O). We also tested the I_E water with our crystal growth system which is based on the Bridgman technique. In this paper we report these results.

1. Introduction

Hydrogen bonding is one of the most important and intriguing interactions which dominate our daily lives, and for a long time scientists across different disciplines have endeavored to understand the complex nature of water and of other H-bonded systems. Despite considerable scientific efforts, there are no completely acceptable explanations of most properties of water, often referred to as its 'anomalous' properties.[1-3] The large bond energy and the asymmetrical geometry of the H-bond, combined with the fact that the electrons in the $2s^2p^3$ orbitals of the oxygen atoms can rehybridise in response to the relative configurations of adjacent molecules, giving rise to a large number of abnormal properties of water/ice which cannot be explained by the ordinary rules of physics and chemistry. As a consequence, a large number of models have been proposed in attempts to interpret some of these properties of water, such as the high heat capacity, high melting/boiling temperature and the large density and entropy fluctuations. Meanwhile, a large number of H-bond potentials have also been proposed. Some of these are based on ab initio quantum mechanical calculations[4,5] while others are very arbitrary[6]. Some are good at reproducing the structure of water and others are good at reproducing its thermodynamic properties. No theory can yet provide a coherent explanation of (or complete model for) the water anomalies.

Experimental information about the strength of the H-bond interaction can be obtained by measuring vibrational spectra, because a particular phonon mode (or frequency) will determine the interatomic force constants which, in turn, are the double differentials of the pair-wise potentials. Therefore, measuring dynamic properties constitutes one of the most powerful ways of investigating pair-wise interatomic potentials in a given material. Inelastic incoherent Neutron Scattering (IINS) provides a most suitable probe for studies of vibrational dynamics for given solids. This is because a neutron can simultaneously give insight at the atomic and molecular level about where things 'are' and what they 'do'. Indeed, it is only when this structural and dynamic information is available at the atomic level that it becomes possible to build a complete picture of the behaviour of the world around us. The answers to questions depend on understanding the atomic behaviour of the material. Neutron provides this detailed information about the microscopic behaviour of solids and liquids, and in a major way, has shaped our experimental and theoretical understanding of phenomena ranging from water and biological systems to chemical surfaces and interfaces.

The advantages of neutron scattering, for the study of molecular dynamics, are due to several remarkable properties of thermal neutrons: for instance, the thermal neutron energy is comparable to the phonon energy and the wavelength associated with the neutron is of the same order as the interatomic distances in the condensed materials. Another characteristic of this probe is that the neutron mass is of the same order as the mass of the scattering nuclei. The scattering is, therefore, sensitive to the structure of the system. In an inelastic scattering experiment, the variation of scattering intensity with neutron energy and momentum transfer is observed. The energy and momentum transfer can be written as:

$$\hbar\omega = E_i - E_f = (\hbar^2 / 2m)(K_i - K_f) \qquad (1)$$

$$Q = (K_i - K_f) \qquad (2)$$

where E (or $\hbar\omega$), k and m are the neutron energy, wave-vector and mass, respectively, and i and f refer to the initial and the final conditions of the neutron. Neutron scattering is characterized by the range of $\hbar\omega$ and Q in which measurements are carried out. It is interesting to note that for molecular phenomena, the relevant energies are of the order of 10^{-4} to 10^{-1} eV and the wave-vectors are of the order of 10^{-3} - 1Å^{-1} Therefore, neutron scattering appears to be the only probe capable of revealing the scope of the dynamics of molecular solids and liquids on such short space and time scales. In the case of infrared absorption and Raman scattering, the ranges of the energy transfers are essentially the same, but the wavelengths are lengthened by at least three orders of magnitude in comparison with neutron scattering. Moreover, because of the characteristics of the interaction of neutrons with nuclei, there is another unique advantage: giving so called coherent and incoherent scattering. Together, coherent and incoherent scattering provide complete information about the vibrational motions of the atoms or molecules which can be derived from the peak positions, their intensities and their widths. The total neutron scattering cross-sections can be written as sum of the two contributions:

$$\frac{d^2\sigma}{d\omega\, d\Omega} = \frac{d^2\sigma_{coh}}{d\omega\, d\Omega} + \frac{d^2\sigma_{inc}}{d\omega\, d\Omega} \tag{3}$$

$$\frac{d^2\sigma_{coh}}{d\omega\, d\Omega} = \frac{k_f}{k_i}\exp(-2W)\sum_i \frac{\hbar\sigma_{coh}}{4Nm_i}\sum_{jq}[e_i(q,j)\cdot Q]^2 n(\omega)[\exp(-\frac{\hbar\omega}{2kT})]$$

$$\sum_n \delta(Q\pm q\pm 2\pi n)\delta(\omega\pm\omega_i) \tag{4}$$

$$\frac{d^2\sigma_{coh}}{d\omega\, d\Omega} = \frac{k_f}{k_i}\exp(-2W)\sum_i \frac{\hbar\sigma_{inc}}{4Nm_i}\sum_{jq}[e_i(q,j)\cdot Q]^2 n(\omega)[\exp(-\frac{\hbar\omega}{2kT})]$$

$$[\delta(\omega+\omega_i)+\delta(\omega-\omega_i)] \tag{5}$$

The equations, σ, σ_{inc} and σ_{coh} are the total, incoherent and coherent cross-sections. i labels an atom of mass m_i; $n(\omega)$ is the occupation number at temperature T for the phonon mode of frequency; ω is the phonon frequency in the jth mode for a wave-vector q and $e_i(q, j)$ is the associated eigen-vector on the ith atom in the unit cell in jth mode. The existence of the second delta function in the double differential of coherent cross-section means that coherent processes are fundamentally different from incoherent processes.

The vibrational spectra of ices have frequently been obtained using IR and Raman techniques. However, because of the proton disorder in most ice structures, the normal selection rules governing the interaction of radiation with the crystal are broken. Hence the analysis of these spectra is difficult. Secondly, the weak intensities associated with the lattice modes (<320 cm^{-1}) provide incomplete information on H-bond interactions and therefore these measurements have been seriously misleading. In contrast, IINS is a more direct probe, because with it all the vibrational modes can be measured with equal sensitivity. The IINS spectrum shows two molecular optic modes at 28 (or 224 cm^{-1}) and 37 meV (or 310 cm^{-1}) rather than one at 220 cm^{-1} as seen in the Raman and IR spectra. Using ice single crystals, these spectra show no dependence on crystal orientation. The spectra of the other forms of proton disordered ices, such as ice V, VI, IX and amorphous ices, show similar features.[7-9] These first direct observations of the two well separated molecular bands is a direct result of the very high flux of neutrons and the excellent energy resolution of the inelastic neutron scattering instruments on ISIS at the Rutherford Appleton Laboratory. The superiority of these measurements has been clearly demonstrated in comparison with earlier neutron data.[10,11]

These results are in direct contradiction to existing dynamical models[11-13] for ice and conventional explanations of the IR and Raman spectra, such as TO and LO splitting.[14] In order to reproduce these INS spectra using lattice dynamic calculations, all available H-bond potentials have been tried. The results of these calculations are far from satisfactory. The two well-separated molecular optic bands in the spectra can only imply that there are two distinct strengths of H-bonds,[15,16] which are related to the two types of proton (or dipole) arrangements in the particular form of ice. Thus, in ice VIII, because of the proton ordering, there is only one type of dipole configuration, which is related to the weak H-bond. Therefore, the higher energy band at 310 cm^{-1} disappears. When the protons in this structure become disordered at high temperature (namely ice VII), the other possible configuration also appears and hence the higher energy optical band reappears. Another interesting phenomenon is that the relative intensities of the strong and weak optical modes are entirely dependent on the relative number (or ratio) of the strong and weak H-bonds in the ice structure. For instance, in ice Ih or ice Ic, the protons are completely disordered, hence the statistics will give one weak H-bond for two strong H-bonds (ratio is 1/3:2/3) which are randomly and isotropically distributed in the ice structure. By partially ordering the structure, we could demonstrate that the relative intensities of the two bands could be altered, which implies that the ratio of the strong and weak dipole arrangements are also changed. Furthermore, the difference of the two H-bond force constants is very large indeed.[15] A simple calculation using the relationship, $\omega = (K/m)^{1/2}$ (where ω is the vibrational frequency and K is the force constant) gives a ratio of the two H-bond force constants as $K^1 : K^2 = (\omega^1 : \omega^2)^2 = 28^2 : 37^2 = 1 : 1.9$ (the exact values determined by the lattice dynamic calculation are 1.1 and 2.1 eV/Å^2). However, the large difference in force constants cannot be produced by the fixed electrostatic interactions (the maximum calculated difference between the strong and weak bonds is $<20\%$).[17] The fundamental source of the splitting of H-bond, therefore, lies at the quantum mechanical level. Based on the above hypothesis, lattice dynamical calculations for ice Ih were carried out for a large super-lattice, containing 64 molecules (8 unit primary cells), to represent the disordering of protons.[15,16] The results show remarkable agreement not only with the spectrum of phonon density of states, but also with the measured dispersion curves.

This remarkably simple model is capable of reproducing almost every aspect of the measured lattice dynamics of a wide variety of ice structures and indicates the existence of two strengths of H-bonds in the solid phases of water and provides insight into the "complex" nature of the H-bond. The properties of water are considered abnormal, based on the concept of water as a monodisperse system. However, when we realize that the H-bond interaction is actually bi-functional, all the "abnormal" properties of water become normal. We, therefore, concluded that, if these two types of bond also exist in liquid water, they would provide a mechanism to explain water anomalies, such as the high heat capacity, the high melting/boiling temperatures and the density fluctuations. Because the proportion of the weak/strong H-bonds in water/ice vary by geometric effects and by the laws of thermodynamics, these in turn, will determine the macroscopic properties which can be simulated by Lattice and Molecular Dynamic calculations.

2. Spectroscopic Measurements of the I_E Water

Using similar techniques, we were able to measure vibrational spectra for the I_E water provided by American Technology Group (ATG). These measurements could provide crucial information about the formation mechanism of the I_E clusters which are stable at high temperatures as indicated by Lo et al.[18,19] The IINS measurement was made using TFXA (Time Focused Xtal Analyser) spectrometer on ISIS (a pulsed spallition neutron source) at Rutherford Appleton Laboratory, UK.[20] TFXA is an inverse geometry time-of-flight spectrometer. A "white" energy neutron beam is inelastically scattering by sample, analyzed by graphite crystals (placed at 135^0 to the direction of the incident neutrons) and beryllium filters, and neutrons with final energy ~4 meV are registered. The measurements give hydrogen bonding vibrational frequencies in the inter- and intra-molecular modes regions up to 500 meV (or ~4100 cm^{-1}). The instrument provides energy resolution, ~1.5% (i.e. dE/E). The measured IINS spectra were transferred to the dynamical structure factor $S(Q,\omega)$ vs energy transfer $\hbar\omega$ by using a standard data treatment program at TFXA. The background from the empty-can was also measured at similar conditions and was subtracted from the original data. Finally, the measured data was then transferred to the one-phonon spectrum by subtracting the multi-phonon contributions calculated using the iteration technique.[21]

The IINS spectra of both I_E water and normal water at 15K are plotted in Figure 1. The comparison shows that there are no observable differences between the two spectra. This could be due to the fact that the concentrations of I_E clusters in the water used is less than 5% by weight. The IINS signal from the clusters is insignificant. Higher concentrations may be needed in order to see significant difference from the normal ice.

194

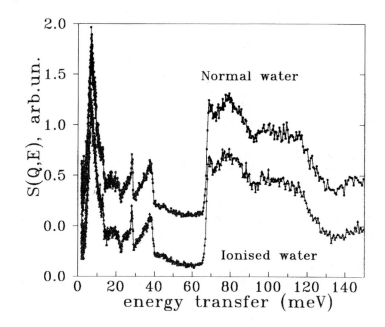

Figure 1. A plot of Inelastic Incoherent Neutron Scattering spectra of the I_E water and normal water measured on TFXA in the energy transfer region below 140 meV at temperature of 15K. The data show that difference between the two spectra is less than the experimental error.

Another series of measurements for the I_E water were made using a standard Raman spectroscopy at 77K. Figure 2 shows the comparison between the I_E water and normal water. We observed that a small peak at energy ~33 meV is stronger in spectrum for the I_E water than that for the normal water and is shifted slightly towards the high energy transfer. More detailed study is needed to understand the source of the feature.

195

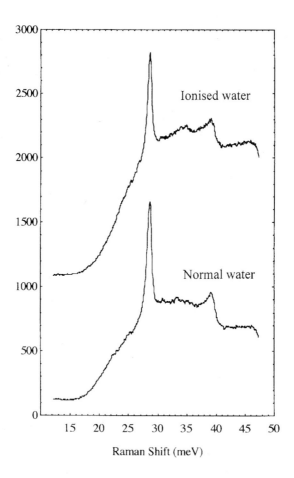

Figure 2. A plot of Raman Scattering spectra of both I_E water and normal water measured at temperature of ~77K. The two spectra are almost identical. There is only a small difference in the molecular optic modes region at energy transfer of ~33 meV.

3.   Using the I_E Water for Single Crystal Growth

Apart of spectroscopic studies of the I_E water, we have also attempted to understand the micro-structure of I_E water by growing ice crystals with it. It is our past experience that water which contains impurities inhibits and prevents high quality single crystal growth (i.e. polycrystalline samples can be obtained as the result). This is because ions or other biological materials in water may cause

196

changes in the surroundings and disrupt the growth.

There were two methods of producing ice crystal. One is by fast vaporization of water to cool the water surface down to minus. The crystallization occurs from surface and the single crystal gradually grows downwards.[22] The process takes a few hours. Using this method, we can rapidly produce single crystals and test the water quality. We found that using this method, we can produce ice crystals from the I_E water provided by ATG as easily as from normal water (99.96% H_2O), although they are less transparent (milking white) than the crystals produced by normal water.

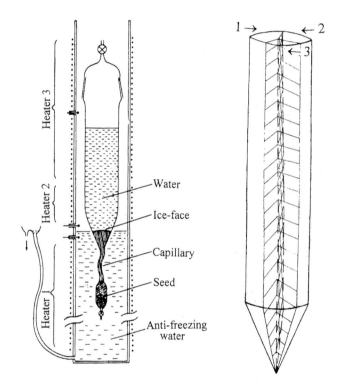

Figure 3. The left diagram shows a schematic illustration of the Bridgman method of crystal growth system[23]. The right diagram is a crystal of ice Ih produced by the system (using the I_E water). In most cases, we were able to produce ice crystals as easily as the high purity normal water. However, for the I_E water labeled with Ds-PB provided by ATG, we obtained 2-3 pieces of single crystals, after a number of attempts as shown in the right diagram.

Another method of producing ice crystal is by the Bridgman method. Figure 3 is schematic illustration of the basic set up for the system[23]. The growth process of ice crystals can be described as follows: Firstly, a growth tube filled with degassed water is dipped into antifreeze at below 8°C in order to form ice nuclei (i.e. seeds). The tube is then suspended inside a larger tube filled with antifreeze liquid at 1.0°C. The temperature above the antifreeze is kept at 0.5°C in order to prevent frozen water. The temperatures are controlled by three independent heaters (Figure 3). Secondly, the growth tube is gradually lowered into the antifreeze liquid in a rate of 1cm/day. One of the grains (seeds) will pass the capillary (i.e. a process of elimination) and a single crystal is grown while the tube is lowered. This system allows us to produce high quality ice crystals, with a very low concentration of dislocations, for neutron scattering experiments.

After several attempts with this system, we found that the I_E water gives as good a quality of single crystals, in most cases, as normal water with 99.96% H_2O. However, there are occasionally two or three column crystals produced along the length of the growth tube when we use the I_E water labeled with Ds-PB (see the right diagram in Figure 3). This may not be due to the I_E water itself, but the conditions surrounding the growth tube.

References

1. H.S. Frank *WATER: A Comprehensive Treatise, V1,* ed. F. Franks, (Plenum Press 1972).
2. D. Eisenberg and W. Kauzmann, *The Structure and Properties of Water* (Oxford University Press, Oxford 1965).
3. P.V. Hobbs *Ice Physics* (Clarendon Press, Oxford 1974).
4. H. Kistenmacher *et al, J. Chem. Phys.* **60**, 4455 (1972).
5. C. Lee, *et al, Phys. Rev. Lett.* **69**, 462 (1992).
6. M.D. Morse and S.A. Rice, *J. Chem. Phys.* **76**, 650 (1982).
7. J-C. Li *et al, J.Phys.: Condens. Matter* **4**, 2109 (1992).
8. J-C. Li *et al, Chem. Phys. Lett.* **241**, 290 (1995).
9. J-C. Li and D.K. Ross, *J. Condens Matt.* **6**, 10823 (1994).
10. H. Prask *et al, J. Chem. Phys.* **48**, 3367 (1968).
11. B. Renker, in *Physics and Chemistry of Ice*, ed. E.Whalley *et al*, (University of Toronto Press, Toronto 1973).
12. P. Bosi *et al, J. Chem. Phys.* **59**, 4578 (1973).
13. D.D. Klug and E. Whalley, *J.Glaciol*, **21**, 55(1978), and comment, *J. Chem. Phys.* **71**, 1513 (1979).
14. T.T. Wong and E. Whalley, *J. Chem. Phys.* **65**, 829 (1976).
15. J-C. Li and D.K. Ross, *Nature*, **365**, 327 (1993).

16. J-C. Li, *J. Chem. Phys.* **105**, 6733 (1996).
17. J-C. Li, *J. Phys. Chem. B,* **101**, 6237 (1997).
18. S.Y. Lo, *et al, Modern Phys.Lett. B,* **10**, 921(1996).
19. S.Y. Lo, *Modern Phys. Lett. B,* **10**, 909 (1996).
20. S.F. Parker *et al, The TFXA User-Guide*, Rutherford Appleton Laboratory: Technical Report No.RAL-TR-95-036 (1995).
21. A.I. Kolesnikov *et al, J. Phys.: Condens. Matter,* **6**, 375 (1994).
22. N.N. Khusnatdinov and V.F. Petrenko, *J. Crystal Growth,* **163**, 420 (1996).
23. M. Ohtomo *et al, J. Physique,* **48**, C1595 (1987).

ATOMIC FORCE MICROSCOPY OF ADSORBATES FROM I_E SOLUTIONS

SERGEI N. MAGONOV

Originally published as *Physical, Chemical and Biological Properties of Stable Water Clusters,* Proceedings of the First International Symposium. Reprinted here by permission of World Scientific Publishing Company, 1998.

comprehensive information about morphology, nanostructure, molecular and atomic organization for a broad range of materials. In recent attempts to apply AFM to study I_E aqueous solutions, well-defined granular structures were observed. A tentative analysis of the data is discussed.

1 Introduction

Atomic Force Microscopy (AFM) is a revolutionary technology that provides three-dimensional information about structures on micron to atomic scale. AFM is widely used for evaluation of sample composition, local mechanical and adhesive properties of heterogeneous materials. The method is based on the measurement of the attractive or repulsive forces between an AFM probe tip and a sample. In its most basic, contact mode, AFM measures topography of a surface by dragging the probe, consisting of a cantilever with a sharp tip at the end, across the sample (Figure 1). The cantilever deflection during scanning is monitored with a laser beam focused on the back of the cantilever. The beam is reflected off the back of the cantilever onto a photodiode detector. In the constant force operation, the cantilever deflection is kept constant by adjusting the vertical position of the sample with a piezo-scanner. These vertical adjustments are reproduced in height images, which describe the sample topography. This method, while quite successful in many applications, has a drawback of creating very strong friction forces which can cause serious damage to more delicate and softer samples. A recently introduced TappingMode™ technique overcomes this problem by oscillating the tip holding cantilever while scanning the surface of a sample. The method creates very short contact between tip and sample, and almost completely eliminates lateral forces. A reduction in amplitude of oscillation, as the cantilever contacts the sample surface, is used to identify and measure surface features (Figures 2 and 3). TappingMode AFM allows high resolution measurements of soft or fragile samples that are easily damaged and/or loosely held to their substrate in

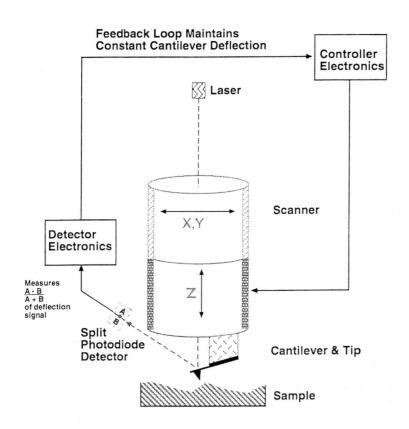

FIGURE 1 Contact Mode AFM.

In contact mode AFM, a probe tip attached to the end of the cantilever is dragged across the surface of the sample. The image is created based on a change in cantilever deflection which is continuously monitored with a photodiode detector. [From *Digital Instruments Scanning Probe Microscopy Training Notebook*].

both air and liquid environments. Etched silicon probes used in TappingMode AFM have a sharp tip with a diameter of 10-20 nm. In the low-force operation (carried out with the appropriate choice of instrumental parameters) the tip-sample contact area is even smaller than the tip diameter, allowing lateral resolution of 2-3 nm. This technique has found a wide range of applications, including studies of silicon wafer surfaces, metals and insulators, polymers, and biological samples

201

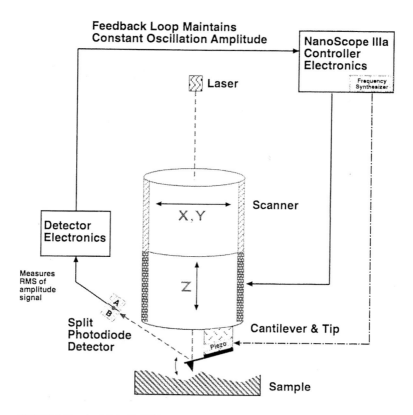

FIGURE 2 Tapping Mode™ AFM.

In TappingMode AFM, a probe tip attached to the end of cantilever is oscillated and "taps" on the sample surface during scanning. The image is created based on a change in amplitude of oscillation. [From *Digital Instruments Scanning Probe Microscopy Training Notebook*].

Self-organization of organic amphiphatic compounds, substances that contain both hydrophilic and hydrophobic functional groups, is a common phenomenon in aqueous solutions. The structure of such supramolecular assemblies was recently successfully studied by AFM[1-3]. The high resolution AFM images obtained, of amphiphathic adsorbates on graphite and mica, revealed their morphology and led to a structural model in which the supramolecular structures are formed by the fusing of spherical miscelles.

Stable associations of water molecules, called I_E™ Crystals, were developed by Lo[4,5] several years ago. It has been established that I_E Crystal aqueous

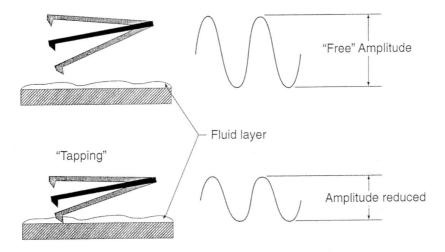

FIGURE 3 Tapping Mode cantilever oscillation amplitude.
A reduction in amplitude of oscillation is reduced when the tip contacts a sample surface. [From
Digital Instruments TappingMode™ Imaging; Applications and Technology].

solutions have distinctive physical and chemical properties[4,5], as well as exert strong stimulating activity on various biological systems[6-8]. In order to explain the unusual properties of these solutions, it is necessary to characterize the structure of I_E crystals. The objective of this work was to examine the morphology of I_E crystal adsorbates on mica surface.

2 Materials and Methods

Drops of aqueous I_E crystal solutions V_E-34, D_S-240, and Y_S-55 provided by American Technologies Group (ATG) were placed on freshly cleaved atomic smooth mica substrate surface and left to air dry. Height and lateral force images of I_E adsorbates were recorded in TappingMode with Scanning probe microscopy "Nanoscope III" (Digital Instruments, Inc., Santa Barbara).

3   Results

The structures observed with AFM in all samples were well-defined and consisted of numerous grains (Figures 4-6). The smallest grains had a diameter of about 10-50 nm and height of 1-5 nm. Larger linear structures made up of fused grains with lengths of 100-500 nm (Figure 6) and 1-5 μm (Figure 5) were also identified in all samples.

I_E structures are soft and springy: when higher force is applied during AFM scanning they become more flat but compact (Figure 7a). When the force is decreased, they bounce back to the original height and shape (Figure 7b). However, very high force leads to scraping of the adsorbate from the mica substrate (8). The thickness of the adsorbate layer scratched away with high-force scanning was determined to be 25 nm.

Although additional research is required before definite conclusions about the dynamics of I_E self-assembling can be made, the above data indicates that I_E crystals are, in fact, ordered structures with granular substructure.

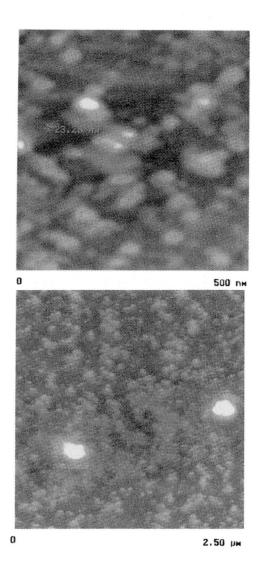

A

0   500 nm

B

0   2.50 μm

FIGURE 4 AFM height images of V_E-34 type I_E adsorbate on mica.
The contrast of the pictures covers height variations from 0.1 to 5 nm (A) and from 0.1 to 10 nm
(B). The scanned area was 500 x 500 nm (A) and 2.5 x 2.5 μm (B).

A

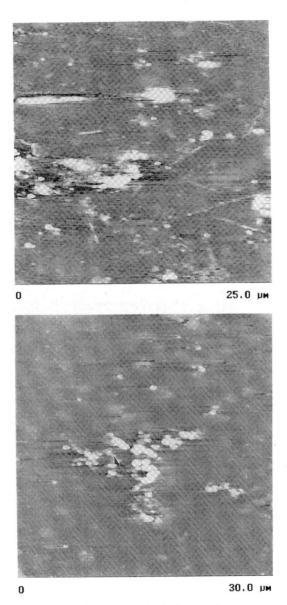

0   25.0 µм

B

0   30.0 µм

FIGURE 5 AFM height images of D_S-240 type I_E adsorbate on mica.
The contrast of the pictures covers height variations from 0.1 to 25 nm (A) and from 0.1 to 100
nm (B). The scanned area was 25 x 25 µm (A) and 30 x 30 µm (B).

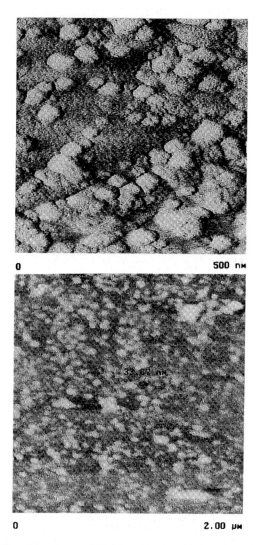

A

0   **500 nʍ**

B

0   **2.00 µʍ**

FIGURE 6 AFM lateral force image of V_E-34 type I_E (A) and height image of Y_S-55 type I_E (B) adsorbates on mica.

The contrast of the pictures is proportional to the lateral force variations in relative units (A) and it covers height variations in the 0.1-5 nm range (B). The scanned area was 500x500 nm (A) and 2x2 µm (B).

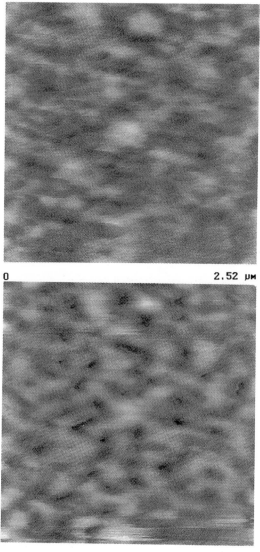

A

B

0   2.52 µм

FIGURE 7 AFM height images of D_S-240 type I_E adsorbate on mica.

The contrast of the pictures covers height variations from 0.1 to 4 nm (A) and from 0.1 to 10 nm (B).   The scanned area in both cases was 2.5 x 2.5 µm. The images were obtained in TappingMode by scanning with high (A) and low (B) force applied to the tip.

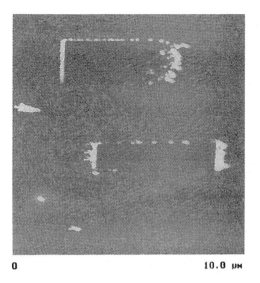

0   **10.0 μM**

FIGURE 8 AFM height image of V_E-34 type I_E adsorbate on mica.

The contrast of the picture covers height variation from 0.1 to 25 nm, the scanned area was 10 x 10 μm. Two areas with the scratched away adsorbate are shown (two "windows" in the central part of the image).

4   References

1. K. Cramer *et al.*, *New J. Chem.*, **20**, 5 (1996).
2. I. Tuzov *et al.*, *New J. Chem.*, **20**, 23 (1996).
3. I. Tuzov *et al.*, *New J. Chem.*, **20**, 37 (1996).
4. S.-Y. Lo, *Modern Phys. Lett.* B, **10** (19), 909 (1996).
5. S.-Y. Lo *et al.*, *Modern Phys. Lett.* B, **10** (19), 921 (1996).
6. A.P. Sinitsyn *et al.* in *The Proceedings of The First International Symposium on the Current Status of the I_E Crystal Technology*, (World Scientific, 1998).
7. L. Chistoserdova and M.E.Lidstrom in *The Proceedings of The First International Symposium on the Current Status of the I_E Crystal Technology*, (World Scientific, 1998).
8. B. Bonavida and X.H.Gan in *The Proceedings of The First International Symposium on the Current Status of the I_E Crystal Technology*, (World Scientific, 1998).

SUPPRESSION OF COKE FORMATION IN THE STEAM CRACKING OF ALKANES: ETHANE AND PROPANE

K. Y. GRACE CHAN, FIKRET INAL and SELIM SENKAN

Originally published as *Physical, Chemical and Biological Properties of Stable Water Clusters,* Proceedings of the First International Symposium. Reprinted here by permission of World Scientific Publishing Company, 1998.

The effects of an H_2PtCl_6 additive on the rate of formation of coke deposits on quartz and Incoloy surfaces were investigated in the steam cracking of ethane and propane in a continuous flow thermogravimetric analyzer (TGA). The TGA operating conditions were: 1 atm pressure, 820-845°C temperature range, about 1.5 s reaction time, and a steam to hydrocarbon molar ratio of about 2. Specific coke formation rates consistently decreased in the presence of the additive, both for ethane and propane pyrolysis. For example, in ethane pyrolysis the specific coke formation rate on the quartz surface at 830°C decreased from 0.34 $\mu g/cm^2$-min in the absence of the additive to 0.089 $\mu g/cm^2$-min in the presence of additive, representing an improvement by a factor of about 4 in coking rates. On the Incoloy surface, coke formation decreased from 0.98 $\mu g/cm^2$-min to 0.38 $\mu g/cm^2$-min. For the case of propane pyrolysis at 830°C, coke formation rate decreased from 0.51 $\mu g/cm^2$-min to 0.33 $\mu g/cm^2$-min on the quartz surface and from 1.9 $\mu g/cm^2$-min to 1.0 $\mu g/cm^2$-min on the Incoloy surface.

1 Introduction

Ethylene is one of the most important building blocks of synthetic, organic chemistry[1] and it is used in the manufacture of polyethylene and other products. Ethylene production rate has steadily increased over the years from 29 million lbs in 1985 to 46.7 million lbs in 1995. The ethylene production today is based predominately on the steam cracking or pyrolysis of alkanes, such as ethane, propane and butane, as well as heavier feedstocks such as naphtha and gas oil[2].

The steam cracking of a feedstock is accomplished in the coils of a pyrolysis furnace followed by quenching of the gas in a heat exchanger[1] or the transfer line exchanger. Coke is an undersirable product of steam cracking. Due to its cumulative nature, coke deposits build up on reactor walls and influence reactor performance in a number of ways. First, due to coke deposition, the surface temperature of the coils increases, which adversely affects the service life of the coil and makes it impossible to obtain normal pyrolysis temperatures in the reactor. Secondly, pressure drops increase due to the reduction of the inner diameter of the coil upon coking. Third, coking may lead to corrosion of the coil due to carbonization. As a consequence of these factors, decoking of the reactor coils has to be carried out periodically, resulting in a loss of production and in an increase in manufacturing costs. Typically in ethane cracking, commercial reactors must be decoked every 20-60 days[3]. Previous laboratory experiments were conducted to study coke formation during the cracking and steam cracking of ethane and propane. Sundaram et al.[3] studied the thermal cracking of ethane in a nitrogen matrix within a temperature range of 750-870°C, in a mixed reactor. Major products reported were ethylene, methane, C_4H_6, and C_5+. The results indicated the gas phase decomposition to be the first order in ethane concentration with an apparent activation energy of 54.0 kcal/mol in agreement with previous studies in a tubular pilot reactor[4]. Similar results were reported more recently by Froment[5] for the steam cracking of ethane. Coke was deposited on an Inconel 600 coupon suspended inside the reactor to the arm of an electrobalance. The rate of formation of coke was found to be time dependent, starting initially at a faster rate and reaching an asymptotic value later in the run. The initial fast coke formation rate was attributed to catalytic wall effects. Once the coke layer is deposited on the coupon, the rate reaches its asymptotic value corresponding to coke deposition on coke. The estimated activation energy for coke formation, based on a kinetic analysis of a reaction model, was in the range of 28.3-49.9 kcal/mole. Gas composition measurements also indicated the rapid formation rate of CO early in the experiments, which leveled off to an asymptotic value following the coverage of the metal surface by coke. Initial CO production was proposed to be due to metal catalyzed oxidation of hydrocarbon moieties on reactor walls, and subsequent CO formation was attributed to the steam gasification of carbon. These studies also indicated that higher steam dilutions decrease coke formation rates.

The decomposition of propane in a nitrogen matrix was studied by Sunderam and Froment[6] in a mixed reactor in the temperature range of 720-870°C. Major products reported were ethylene, methane, and propene. The disappearance of propane was found to be the first order in propane concentration with an activation energy of 49.0 kcal/mol. This is in agreement with the results of Van Damme et al[7] and Froment[5] in the steam cracking of propane. The activation energy for coke formation was estimated to be 75.0 kcal/mole, again based on the kinetic analysis of a reaction model. Coke formation on Fe-Cr-Ni alloys in the steam pyrolysis of propane was also studied by Trimm et al.[8] using a microbalance reactor. These investigators reported an activation energy for coke formation of about 70 kcal/mole, consistent with the results of Sundaram and Froment[6].

Crynes and Crynes[9] also studied the formation of coke during the pyrolysis of light alkanes on Incoloy 800 coupons in a flow reactor. Temperature was maintained at 700°C by means of an electric furnace. They studied coking during the pyrolysis of methane, ethane, ethene, propane, propene, and isobutane. They found the following order for coking on the coupon: ethane<ethene< propene<propane<isobutane, with no coke deposition observed for methane under the experimental conditions. The effects of reactor surfaces on coke deposition rates during the pyrolysis of propane has been studied extensively by Renjun[10] in an electrobalance reactor at 850°C. The order of increasing coke deposition rates was found to be nickel> stainless>quartz. High coking rates were also observed early on in the experiments, which later reached an asymptotic value upon surface coverage by coke.

In related studies, Jackson *et al.*[11,12] studied coke formation on a series of Fe-Ni-Cr alloys as well as other materials in the steam cracking of propylene and hydrogen using a microbalance reactor. The effects of alloy composition on coke formation and gasification rates were studied.

At present, three mechanisms have been proposed to account for coke formation in hydrocarbon pyrolysis in industrial and laboratory reactors: (1) Coke formation via surface-catalyzed reactions in which, for example, metal carbides have been proposed to be intermediates[11-13]. The resulting coke is filamentous and contains 1-2 wt% metal; the metals are positioned primarily at the tips of the filaments. Filamentous coke has also been produced at low temperatures. This can be one of the coke formation mechanisms on metal reactors' surfaces. (2) Coke has also been proposed to form via polycyclic aromatic hydrocarbons (PAH) in the gas phase (e.g., Wang and Frenklach[14], and Gargurevich[15] studied chemical paths of coke in fuel-rich combustion), their nucleation and condensation into tar droplets followed by adsorption on surfaces where the tar proceeds to dehydrogenate into coke. This mechanism generally results in film or globular coke formation[16]. (3) Coke can also grow directly through the reactions of small gas phase species with sites on the coke surface. These species are likely to be acetylene or other olefins, butadiene, and free radicals such as methyl, ethyl, vinyl, phenyl or benzyl radicals. This mechanism should be favored by higher temperatures and with higher concentrations of acetylene in the gas phase (e.g., Marinov[17] discussed surface growth mechanisms of soot particles in combustion).

The development of coke inhibitors have paralleled the various coke formation mechanisms described. The techniques commonly used today to reduce coke formation include the pretreatment of feedstocks, changing the materials of construction of the reactor, altering the surface chemistry of the reactor, or the addition of coke inhibitors to the feedstock[10,18]. The development and use of additives appears to be the most effective and practical method. Coke inhibitors reported in the literature include salts of alkali metals or alkali-earth metals at parts per million (ppm) quantities, which are believed to promote coke gasification by steam. In addition, the use of organic polysiloxane compounds in ppm quantities have been shown to reduce the adhesion of coke to the coil walls. Sulfur compounds have also been used widely to suppress coke formation, especially early on in the pyrolysis process, by passivating metal surfaces[8,10]. Compounds containing tin, antimony, copper, phosphorous and chromium were also reported to have a beneficial effect in suppressing coke formation[10].

In this communication, we report on the effects of about 1 ppm H_2PtCl_6 additive in water on coke formation in the steam pyrolysis of ethane and propane. This was accomplished by comparing the amounts and rates of coke production on quartz and Incoloy surfaces both in the absence and presence of the additive.

2   Experimental Section

The experimental apparatus used to study the formation of coke during the steam cracking of ethane and propane is illustrated in Figure 1. The apparatus is a modified version of the setup used previously in the pyrolysis and oxidative pyrolysis of methane and methyl chloride[19]. The main component of the experimental system is a Cahn 131 thermogravimetric analyzer (TGA, Madison, WI) that has a detection sensitivity of 1 μg. The system has an electronic microbalance which continuously measures and records the mass loss or gain of a substrate material, or coupon, which is suspended from the balance by means of a 0.0127 cm diameter platinum hang-down wire. The furnace temperature profile and coupon mass data are acquired and stored by the data acquisition and control system. The data acquisition hardware consists of an IBM compatible PC and software provided by Cahn Systems. The software allows for the operation of the furnace for any temperature time history. Two coupons were used in the experiments; quartz (SiO_2) and Incoloy (Fe 46.6%, Ni 30.3%, Cr 20.5%, Mn 0.46%, Ti 0.57%, Cu 0.054%, Al 0.42%, C 0.065%, Si 0.60%, S 0.001%). The coupon dimensions were about 2 cm wide x 2 cm long x 0.1 cm thick.   The coupons were centrally located inside a 3.5 cm internal diameter x 32.5 cm long quartz reactor that was vertically placed inside a single zone electrical furnace. The heating elements inside the furnace span a distance of about 15 cm, thereby

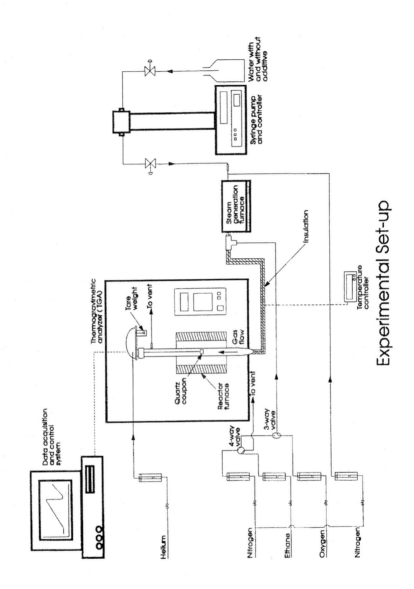

Figure 1 Sketch of the experimental facility.

allowing the establishment of a near isothermal central zone of about 2 cm in length, where the coupon was placed[19]. Deionized (DI) water or water containing 1 ppm H_2PtCl_6 additive (ATG, Monrovia, CA) was pumped using a high precision metering syringe pump (ISCO-2600 with a Series D Controller, Lincoln, NE), and was vaporized in an electric furnace maintained at $400^\circ C$. Nitrogen gas was introduced into the liquid at the upstream of the steam furnace as a gas carrier. The reactant gases consisting of ethane or propane, and some additional nitrogen carrier gas were then mixed with the steam and transported to the reactor through electrically heated lines. All gas flows were regulated by high accuracy rotameters (Matheson, Cucamonga, CA) that were calibrated before the experiments. The weighing components of the TGA were protected from the reaction products by passing helium purge gas through the chamber. The gases used were obtained from Matheson (Cucamonga, CA), unless otherwise indicated, and had the following stated purities: He: 99.99 %, C_2H_6: 99.9%, C_3H_8: 99.99%, N_2: 99.999%, and O_2: 99.9% (Liquid Air Co.).

All the experiments were conducted at an atm pressure of 1 for a 1 hour total reaction time. Before each run, the reactor was purged with N_2 for about 10 min and then decoked using 15% O_2 (balance N_2) mixture to ensure that the reactor walls and the coupon were coke free. This was accomplished by visually observing the appearance of the coupon through an observation hole in the furnace and by monitoring the weight of the coupon during the decoking process. If the appearance of the coupon was transparent and nonluminous (for the quartz coupon only), and its weight did not decrease with time, the coupon was assumed to be coke free. It should be noted that some coke remains on the hangdown wire even after the decoking process. This systematically increases the apparent weight of the coupon as measured by the TGA during one of the experiments. The reactor was again purged with N_2 for about 10 min, after which the hydrocarbon reactants and steam were introduced. The primary reason, for the nitrogen purge before and after the decoking experiments, was to minimize the accumulation of potentially explosive mixtures in the reactor. Each run was repeated at least five times to ensure reproducibility and to assess the range of experimental errors associated with the experiments.

3   Results and Discussion

There are several issues regarding the experimental conditions used and the analysis of experimental data that must be discussed first. Since the TGA had a sensitivity limit on a microgram level, it was necessary to determine the optimum gas flow rates that did not result in excessive fluid dynamic noise, yet allow the acquisition of reliable coking data over the range of concentrations and temperatures to be used during the experiments. Following the initial scoping studies, a total gas flow rate of about 2.5 cm^3/s, measured in STP, was determined to be suitable. Higher flow rates led to the establishment of undesirable flow patterns in the reactor that cause lateral movement of the hangdown wire and result in its contact with the baffle inside the reactor. Note that at 2.5 cm^3/s, the flow regime in the reactor would be laminar and corresponds to a nominal residence time of 15 s and about 1.5 s to cross the quartz coupon. This residence time was determined by taking into account the volume occupied by the baffle[20]. Overall reactant conversions, measured separately by gas chromatography at the exit of the reactor, were generally in the range 2-5%. However, because the quartz coupon occupied a small fraction of the reactor volume, it should be subjected to a nearly constant gas composition along the flow direction due to the differential conversion of the reactants within the 1.5 s reaction time. Consequently, one would expect uniform coke layer formation along the coupon if diffusion limitations were also absent. If diffusion limitations were present, the variation of the boundary layer thickness along the coupon would lead to non-uniform coke deposition. Coke formation appeared to be uniform along the coupon, as determined by SEM in previous studies[19], indicative of the absence of transport limitations under the experimental conditions investigated.

The following pre-reaction flow rates and temperature ranges were used: (1). Ethane Experiments: C_2H_6 0.714 cc/s, H_2O 1.45 cc/s, N_2 1.22 cc/s, temperature range 830-845°C; (2). Propane experiments: C_3H_8 0.75 cc/s, H_2O 1.48 cc/s, N_2 1.24 cc/s, temperature range 820-830°C. Coke formation rates were determined at these fixed gas compositions but over a range of temperatures both in the absence and presence of the additive. The temperature ranges studied varied for different mixtures because of differences in the onset of decomposition of C_2H_6 and C_3H_8. Consequently, all the experiments conducted did not correspond to identical residence times because of differences in gas velocities caused by different temperatures. In addition, changes in the number of moles caused by the reaction process would also alter residence times. These issues, however, should have a relatively small effect on the results presented here. For example, differences in reactor temperatures should introduce a variation in residence times no larger than about 2.3% between the lowest and highest temperature experiments, i.e., 100 x (840-820)/(820+273) = 2.3%. This uncertainty is well below the measurement errors with these types of experiments. Similarly, percent change in the total number of moles across the coupon would be extremely small due to small conversions involved and the presence of steam and nitrogen dilution.

Figure 2 is representative of the raw data obtained by the TGA using the quartz coupon for the steam pyrolysis of ethane. The results obtained using the propane feedstock and the Incoloy coupon were similar, thus will not be presented. The reproducibility of the experiments was excellent, well within 10% from one set to another, provided the first coking cycle is excluded. A close inspection of the individual experiments show that coking rates, i.e. the slope of the weight vs time lines, were generally initially higher, but level off to an approximately constant value. The latter rate, corrected for the baseline shift due to the loss or gain of coke on the hang-down wire after the decoking process, has been designated as the coke formation rate, R_{TGA}, in µg/min units. High initial coking rates were consistent with the results of other investigators [6, 7, 19, 21]. There can be several reasons for the high initial coking rates observed. First, the bare, carbon free, coupon surface may indeed have a higher propensity for coke formation than a coked surface. Second, the surface temperature of the bare coupon may be higher than the coked surface due to its lower emissivity and radiation effects. While a worthwhile endeavor, the study of the early coke formation rates was not the focus of this investigation.

An important issue that must also be addressed is the physical meaning of the weight change measured by the TGA. As evident from the experimental system previously described, the TGA simply measures the weight change experienced by the coupon. The weight change can be affected directly by molecular events, e.g. chemical reactions that result in the growth and/or destruction of molecular entities on the surface, or by macroscopic events, such as soot (tar particle collisions with the coupon). Clearly, TGA measurements cannot distinguish between these two type of mechanisms. Consequently, these lumped sets of events, as detected by TGA has been referred to as the coke formation process.

The specific coke formation rate (r_c, µg/cm^2-min) was then determined from the equation:

$$r_c = R_{TGA} / A, \tag{1}$$

where A is the surface area of the coupon. The specific coke formation rate can also be represented by the following phenomenological expression:

$$r_c = k_o exp(-E/RT)f(C) \ µg/cm^2\text{-min}, \tag{2}$$

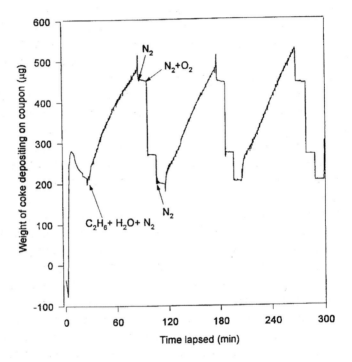

Figure 2 Representative raw data for ethane steam pyrolysis.

where k_o is the specific rate constant for coke formation, E is the apparent activation energy, and f(C) is a functional dependency of coke formation on the composition of the gas phase. This type of a rate expression has often been used to model coke formation kinetics (e.g., Froment[5], Sundaram and Froment[6], Tran and Senkan[19], Renjun[21]). As evident from the above expression, under differential conversions that should be observed along the coupons, f(C) would be nearly constant. The determination of f(C) was not the objective of this experiment.

In Figure 3, the weight of coke deposited on the quartz coupon are presented as a function of on-stream time for the steam pyrolysis of ethane at 830 and 845°C, to illustrate the effects of the additive. The specific coke formation rates, determined from the slopes of these lines by the least squares fit method and the surface area of the coupons, are presented in Table I. The amount of coke deposited on the coupon steadily increased with increasing time and reaction temperature; these results are totally consistent with previous studies [5, 19, 21]. What is important, however, is the significant and consistent reduction in coke deposition in the presence of the additive in the feedstream. For example, at 830°C, coke formation rate decreased from a high value of 0.34 $\mu g/cm^2$-min in the absence of the additive to a low value of 0.089 $\mu g/cm^2$-min, representing a 3.8 factor decrease in coke formation in the presence of the additive. Similarly, at 845°C, the coke formation rate decreased from 0.49 to 0.23 $\mu g/cm^2$-min, corresponding to a 2.2 factor improvement.

Significantly more coke formation was observed in the pyrolysis of C_3H_8 than C_2H_6 at the same reaction temperature (Table 1). The result is consistent with previous studies[9] and with the lower C-C bond dissociation energy of C_3H_8[22] . As evident from the results in Table I, the additive also significantly decreased the rate of coke deposition on the quartz coupon in propane pyrolysis. It is interesting to note that the effectiveness of the additive in suppressing coke formation decreased with increasing temperature. The result is consistent with a mechanism of coke suppression by the additive through the modification of surface reactions. Increasing temperatures increase the relative importance of gas-phase-induced coke formation. One would not expect to see a significant change in the coke suppression behavior of the additive if the mechanism of action was through the modification of gas phase reactions.

Coke formation during the steam pyrolysis of ethane

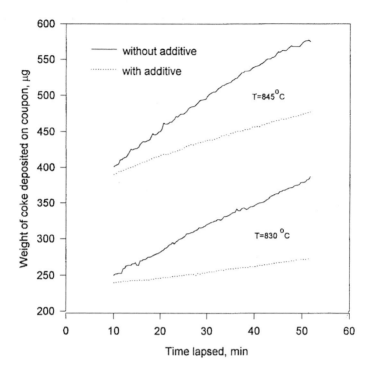

Figure 3 Effects of the additive on coke formation in the steam pyrolysis of ethane at 830° and 845°C.

Table I Specific Coke Formation Rate (r_c, $\mu g/cm^2$-min)

Quartz Surface				
Reactant	Temperature	$r_{c,n}$ (no additive)	$r_{c,a}$ (with additive)	$r_{c,n}/r_{c,a}$
Ethane	830°C	0.34	0.089	3.8
	840°C	-	0.16	-
	845°C	0.49	0.23	2.2
	E(kcal/mole)	59.	150.	
Propane	820°C	0.44	0.19	2.3
	825°C	-	0.27	-
	830°C	0.51	0.33	1.6
	E(kcal/mole)			
Incoloy Surface				
Ethane	830°C	0.98	0.38	2.6
	835°C	1.3	0.56	2.3
	840°C	1.6	0.88	1.9
	E (kcal/mole)	130.	200.	
Propane	830°C	1.5	0.58	2.5
	830°C	1.7	0.78	2.2
	830°C	1.9	1.03	1.9
	D (kcal/mole)	64.	140.	

Coke formation rates were also significantly higher on Incoloy surfaces than on quartz (Table 1). Results are consistent with previous studies [10]. In fact, for ethane pyrolysis, the experiments at 845°C had to be abandoned because of excessive coke formation. The coking rates on Incoloy surfaces also followed a pattern similar to the quartz surface. That is, the rate of coke formation was higher in propane pyrolysis compared to ethane. The additive consistently suppressed coke formation under all the conditions investigated, and the effectiveness of the additive diminished at higher temperatures.

The Arrhenius plots (Figure 4), for the specific coke formation rate (r_c) in the steam pyrolysis of C_2H_6 are presented in accordance with equation (2). For the quartz surface, the slope of these lines which correspond to apparent activation energies, were 59.0 and 150 kcal/mole, without and with the additive, respectively. Activation energies were 130 and 200 kcal/mole, respectively, for the Incoloy surfaces. The change in apparent activation energies suggests that the additive must have altered the rate limiting steps leading to the deposition and/or gasification of coke.

The activation energies determined were significantly high, which is indicative of the absence of transport limitations. If coke formation rates were limited by transport phenomena, the measurements would be less sensitive to temperature and the apparent activation energies would have been in the range 1-5 kcal/mole. An upper limit to coke formation rates was also determined using the wall collision frequency at the process conditions. The wall collision frequency based (diffusion limited) coke deposition rate was calculated using the following relationship [23] :

$$r_w = \frac{1}{4} C_{C2H6} \left(8RTM_{C2H6} / \pi\right)^{1/2} \; gm/cm^2\text{-min}, \tag{3}$$

where C_{C2H6} is the molar concentration of ethane, R the gas constant, T temperature, and M_{C2H6} the molecular weight of ethane. These calculations indicated that coke formation rates measured by TGA (r_c) were several orders of magnitude below the maximum limit set by the collision theory (r_w).

The apparent activation energy of 59.0 kcal/mole for coke formation on quartz surfaces is consistent with the results of Sundaram et al[3]. It is also considerably lower than the C-C bond dissociation energy of C_2H_6 (90 kcal/mole) and this is suggestive of the importance of free radical reactions leading to coke or coke

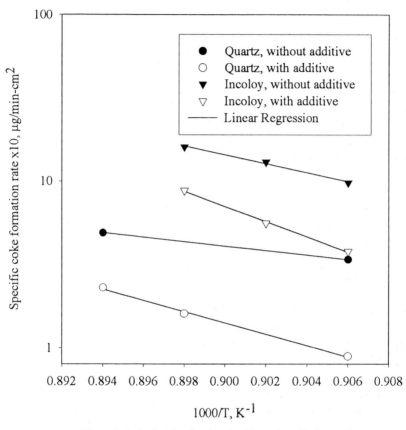

Figure 4 Arrhenius plots for the rate of formation of coke
in the steam pyrolysis of ethane on quartz and incoloy surfaces.

precursors in the gas phase. On the other hand, the activation energy of 149 kcal/mole is substantially higher than the C-C bond dissociation energy, and indicates autocatalysis as the mechanism for coke deposition[18]. Under autocatalytic conditions, the coke formation measured by the TGA would be the result of a complex sequence of chemical and physical events influenced by surfaces and cannot simply be related to the unimolecular decomposition rate of C_2H_6 in the gas phase. The high activation energies of 130 and 200 kcal/mole observed on Incoloy surfaces suggest the autocatalytic deposition of coke both in the absence and presence of the additive. Again, the observed differences in activation energies indicate changes in the rate determining steps, in the presence of the additive.

Arrhenius plots for the specific coke formation rates in the steam pyrolysis of C_3H_8 are presented in Figure 5. For the quartz surface, the apparent activation energies were 35 and 130 kcal/mole, in the absence and presence of the additive, respectively. Although these values are somewhat lower than those observed for ethane, they are still high and thus support that reaction kinetics, not transport limitations control coke formation rates in the experiments. The activation energy of 35 kcal/mole determined in our studies is in reasonable agreement with the 40-55 kcal/mole range estimated by Renjun et al.[21] based on the analysis of experimental data of propane pyrolysis in a nitrogen matrix. The activation energies for coke formation on Incoloy surfaces were 64 and 138 kcal/mole in the absence and presence of the additive, respectively. The former activation energy is consistent with the 71 kcal/mole value reported by Trimm et al.[8] over a different Fe-Cr-Ni alloy.

Based on bond dissociation energy considerations, i.e., gas phase reactions, propane is expected to undergo pyrolysis at lower temperatures, and should produce more coke and coke precursors than ethane at a given temperature. In addition, metal surfaces are known to catalyze hydrocarbon reactions, thus can promote surface coke formation[10] . The experimental results are consistent with these issues. The formation of gas phase coke or coke precursors involve the decomposition of the reactant followed by the polymerization of the decomposition products. Further molecular weight growth processes then lead to the formation of polycyclic aromatic hydrocarbons (PAH), tar, soot[14,17] and ultimately coke.

Alternately, coke formation can also proceed through surface reactions; however, our present day understanding of the fundamental elementary processes

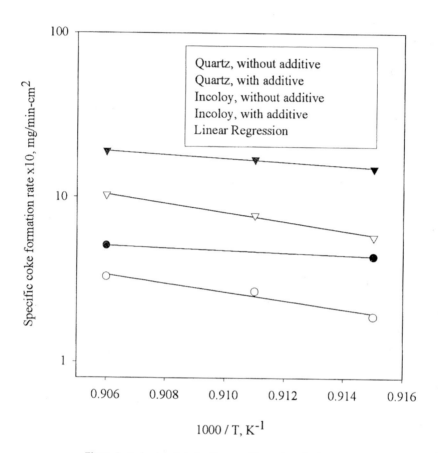

Figure 5   Arrhenius plots for the rate of formation of coke
in the steam pyrolysis of propane on quartz and incoloy surfaces.

leading to coke formation on surfaces is still quite primitive and inadequate to make definitive statements. Nevertheless, the results presented here and elsewhere clearly support the important role surface chemistry and physics play in promoting coke formation, as evidenced, for example, by higher coking rates observed on Incoloy surfaces compared to quartz. It is likely that both the gas phase and surface induced reactions contribute to coke formation in our experiments.

As previously discussed, coke formation rates decreased in the presence of the additive, although the apparent activation energies increased. These results coupled with reduced effectiveness of the additive with increasing temperature suggest that the primarily impact of the additive must be on the surface coke formation processes. The additive may preferentially adsorb on the surfaces and retard the adsorption of coke precursors, tar droplets or soot particles. In addition, the additive may chemically interfere with the surface reaction processes thus preventing the buildup of coke. Third, the additive may promote the surface gasification of coke and/or precursors.

Further research is warranted to better understand the mechanism by which the additive suppresses coke deposition and/or alters the reaction pathways leading to coke formation in the steam pyrolysis of alkanes. This will be necessary to establish optimal reactor design and operating conditions that will result in maximum ethylene production rates while minimizing the rates of formation of coke in production facilities.

4   Acknowledgements

This research was funded, in part, by the UCLA Center for Clean Technology and the American Technologies Group Inc. The authors also would like to thank Dr. Ivan Gargurevich for his help.

5   References

1. S. Matar and L.F. Hatch, *Chemistry of Petrochemical Processes* (Gulf Publishing Co., Texas, 1994).
2. A. K.K. Lee and A.M. Aitani, *Oil and Gas J.* **60** (1990).
3. K.M. Sundaram *et al, AICHE J.* **27**, 946 (1981).
4. G.F. Froment *et al, Ind. Eng. Che. Process Design Develop.* **15**, 495 (1976).
5. G.F. Froment, *Rev. Chem. Eng.* **6**, 293 (1990).
6. K.M. Sundaram and G.F. Froment , *Chem. Eng. Sci.* **34**, 635 (1979).

7. P.S. Van Damme *et al, AIChE J.*, **21**, 1065 (1975).

8. L. Trimm *et al, J. Chem. Tech. Biotech.* **31**, 311 (1981).

9. L.L. Crynes and B. L. Crynes, *Ind. Eng. Chem. Res.* **26**, 2139 (1987).

10. Z. Renjun, *Fundamentals of Pyrolysis in Petrochemistry and Technology* (CRC Press, Boca Raton , USA, 1993).

11. P.R.S. Jackson *et al, J. Mater. Sci.* **21**, 3125 (1986).

12. P.R.S. Jackson *et al, J. Mater. Sci.* **21**, 4376 (1986).

13. L.F. Albright and J.C. Marek *Ind. Eng. Chem. Res.* **27**, 755 (1988).

14. H. Wang and M. Frenklach, *J. Phys. Chem.* **98**, 11465 (1994).

15. I.A. Gargurevich, *Ph.D. Thesis, UCLA* (1997).

16. L. F. Albright and T.C. Tsai in *Pyrolysis: Theory and Industrial Practice*, ed. L.F. Albright (Academic Press, New York, 1983).

17. N.M. Marinov *et al, Combust. Sci. Tech.* **116**, 211 (1996).

18. K.G. Burns *et al, Hydrocarbon Processing* **83** (1991).

19. T. Tran and S. M. Senkan, *Ind. Eng. Chem. Res.* **33**, 32 (1994).

20. T. Tran, *MS Thesis (* UCLA, Chemical Engineering, 1992).

21 Z. Renjun *et al, Ind. Eng. Chem. Res.* **26**, 2528 (1987).

22. S.W. Benson *Thermochemical Kinetic*, (Wiley, New York 1976).

23. R.B. Bird *et al, Transport Phenomena*, (Wiley, New York 1960).

24. M.B. Colket and D.J. Seery in *Proceedings of the 25th Symposium* (The Combustion Institute, 1995).

25. J.A. Miller and C.F. Melius, *Combust. Flame* **91**, 697 (1992).

26. F. Mauss *et al, Combust. and Flame* **99**, 697 (1994).

27. C.F. McDonnell and B. D. Head in *Pyrolysis: Theory and Industrial Practice*, ed. L. F. Albright (Academic Press, New York, 1983).

28. D.L. Trimm in *Pyrolysis: Theory and Industrial Practice*, ed. L. F. Albright (Academic Press, New York, 1983).

USE OF I_E WATER FOR THE MITIGATION OF CALCIUM CARBONATE SCALING

SIMON A. PARSONS, GUILLIAUME SANCHEZ AND CLARE DIAPER

Originally published as *Physical, Chemical and Biological Properties of Stable Water Clusters,* Proceedings of the First International Symposium. Reprinted here by permission of World Scientific Publishing Company, 1998.

Duplicate recirculation loops simulating a real heat exchanger flow loop were used to study the effect of I_E water on calcium carbonate scale deposition. When the total amount of scale formed was greater than 250mg I_E water at a dose of 1000 ppm was found to reduce the amount of scale formed by up to 65%. However, when the total amount of scale formed was less than 200mg no effect or a reverse effect was noted. The effect of I_E water on the rate of precipitation of calcium carbonate was also investigated.

1. Introduction

The aim of this project was to test the efficacy of using I_E water for calcium carbonate scale control. The objective, of this preliminary study, was to investigate the effects of I_E water on calcium carbonate scaling on a heat exchanger surface.

Fouling of heat transfer equipment by inverse solubility salts, known as scaling or crystallization fouling, is a common process problem in domestic, commercial, and industrial applications. The primary agents causing scaling are the carbonates and sulphates of calcium and magnesium, although barium salts, silicate and phosphate scaling are significant, in certain areas and industries. Recent estimations of the overall cost of fouling to industry in the UK was in the range £8-1400 M. Costs due to water scaling constitute an important fraction of this total, which does not include the costs of scaling in domestic and trade water systems.

Mitigation methods include chemical treatment, particularly in cooling water systems; removal of active agents by ion exchange; and use of antifouling heat exchangers (e.g. fluidised beds, HEXTRAN inserts). These methods all involve increased capital and running costs, with varying degrees of environmental impact. The use of I_E water, where fouling mitigation is achieved with minimal maintenance and chemical/environmental costs, represents a very attractive option for systems subject to crystallization fouling.

Initial experiments examined calcium carbonate scale formation using I_E water on a heat exchanger test rig. The rig has been previously used to test magnetic treatment devices and is based on a standard design[1]. The rig consisted of test and control flow loops which allow direct comparison of treated and blank experiments conducted simultaneously. Objectives of this work were to establish reproducibility,

228

develop analysis protocols and compare fouling rates in the presence of I_E with existing crystallization fouling results.

2. Experimental Program

Two experimental protocols were used (i) scaling tests and (ii) precipitation experiments. The scaling tests were carried out in a recirculating heat exchanger test rig while the precipitation experiments were conducted in quiescent solutions.

2.1 Heat Exchanger Scaling Trials

The rig consisted of two identical flow loops for direct comparison between treated and untreated systems (Figure 1). The loop was designed to simulate a real heat exchanger flow loop. The experiment was conducted under conditions that expedited scaling, including a pH range of 7.5-8.0, a heated surface temperature of 65°C, and a flow velocity of 1.5 m/s. The fouling cell had flat plate design used previously at Cranfield. Figure 2 is a schematic diagram of the device and shows the heating plate A where scale developed.

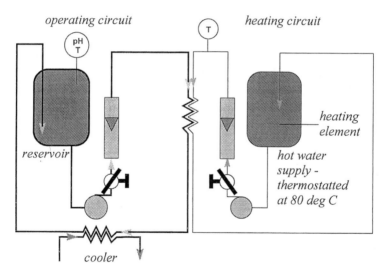

Figure 1   Recirculating heat exchanger test rig.

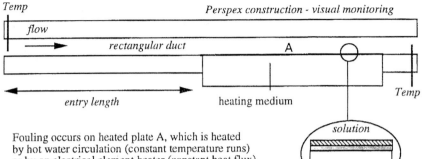

Fouling occurs on heated plate A, which is heated
by hot water circulation (constant temperature runs)
or by an electrical element heater (constant heat flux).
The plate is a thin steel sheet on top of a permanent
support, in which are fixed microfoil heat flux sensors.
The whole unit is thermally insulated.

Figure 2   Schematic diagram of fouling cell.

A series of experiments were completed with I_E water concentrations of 500,
1000 and 2000 ppm, Table 1. The rig was acid washed prior to each experiment by
circulating a HCl solution through the experimental loop. The rig was then
thoroughly rinsed with deionized water. $CaCl_2 \cdot 2H_2O$ and $NaHCO_3$ were added to 70
liters of deionized water in the feed tanks to provide a hardness of 250 ppm and an
alkalinity of 500 ppm. I_E water was added to the desired concentrations. The
solution was circulated through the loop for four days.

Table 1 I_E water dose.

Run	I_E water dose ppm Loop A	I_E water dose ppm Loop B
a	1000	0
b	0	1000
c	0	1000
d	0	500
e	0	2000
f	0	2000
g	0	1000
h	0	0
I	0	1000

Daily samples were collected from each circulation loop and then analyzed for dissolved solids, calcium, magnesium, iron, copper and zinc concentrations, particle size distributions, and pH. Alkalinity and hardness were adjusted daily by the addition of $CaCl_2 \cdot 2H_2O$ and $NaHCO_3$. Crystal morphology, of the solids formed on the heating plate was investigated using scanning electron microscopy (SEM). The amount of scale formed on the heating plate was measured by weighing and drying the plates at the start and the end of each experiment.

2.2 Precipitation Tests

In addition to scaling experiments the effect of I_E water on calcium carbonate precipitation was also investigated. A UV spectrophotometer, set at $\lambda = 302$ nm, was used to follow the precipitation reaction. I_E water at the desired concentration was injected into the UV cell.

Solutions of $CaCl_2$, $CaSO_4$ and Na_2CO_3 (Analar grade) were prepared using pure water provided by an Elga Optima 60 Laboratory Water Purifier (<15 mΩ). Concentrations of 8×10^{-3} mol/L were used for absorbance and SEM analysis. All solutions were kept in air-tight bottles at $20°C \pm 1°C$ prior to mixing.

The effects of I_E water on the formation of $CaCO_3$ crystals were determined quantitatively by absorbance measurement. Simultaneously, 1.5 ml of each reagent ($CaCl_2/Na_2CO_3$ and $CaSO_4/Na_2CO_3$) were injected into a spectrophotometer cell to ensure complete mixing. The cell was then placed in the spectrophotometer and absorbance was measured at wavelength of 302 nm [2,3]. An increase in absorbance values was attributed to the number and size of $CaCO_3$ particulates, and a decrease in sedimentation.

3. Results

3.1 Heat Exchanger Scaling

Initial experiments (a, b, and c) showed that I_E water reduced the total amount of scale formed on the heating plate (Figure 3). An I_E water dose of 1000 ppm produced a reduction in scale of up to 65%. However, subsequent to these results, dosing I_E water had no effect on the amount of scale formed, and in some cases, the amount of scale was increased. The explanation for this anomaly is thought to be related to the absolute amount of scale formed. In the latter experiments (d to i) the total amount of scale formed was less than ~ 250 mg (Figure 4). This reduction in the amount of scale formed in the circulation loops reduced the accuracy of % inhibition calculations. Blank experiments were run to confirm that the two loops were equivalent. The average error found was approximately 10%.

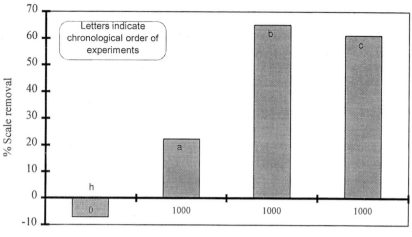

Figure 3 Summary of the scaling results a-c.

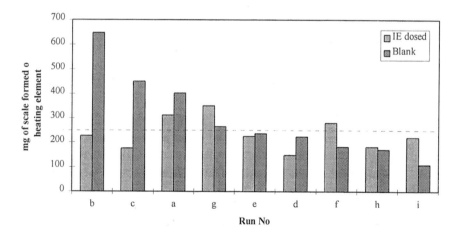

Figure 4 Summary of all the scaling experiments.

232

3.2 Crystallization Results

Calcium carbonate exists in at least five crystalline forms. The two polymorphs commonly found in nature are calcite and aragonite. Vaterite is a rarer metastable form which crystallizes at ordinary temperatures and pressure.

Calcite belongs to the trigonal crystal system and is commonly found exhibiting a rhombohedral shape in hand specimens and micro-crystalline deposits. The crystalline structure of calcite may be described as a cubic close packing with alternative Ca^{2+} and CO_3^{2-}. Aragonite belongs to the orthorhombic crystal system and is commonly found in acicular or needle like form. The crystallization of aragonite is favored by temperatures between 50°C and 80°C, pressure and the presence of zinc.

Changes, in both the crystal habit and the proportion of each form, were observed. We found no quantitative change in crystal habit in the course of our work. Qualitative observations revealed that I_E water produces deformations in the calcite form of calcium carbonate scale on the heat exchanger surface. Samples of scale were collected and analysed by SEM, and aragonite was found only in the untreated system. The results of the SEM trials are found in Table 2. Although microscopy gives good visual evidence of the effect of I_E water, the results are purely qualitative and can only be viewed as providing complimentary evidence to quantitative measurements.

Table 2 Crystalline structure of scale formed on heating elements.

I_E Dose and position on heating element		Blank		I_E Treated	
		% Calcite	% Aragonite	% Calcite	% Aragonite
500	Top	90	10	95	5
	Bottom	70	30	100	
1000	Top	100		100	
	Bottom	60	40	100	
2000	Top	100		100	
	Bottom	90	10	100	

| Blank | Treated |

| Blank | Treated |

Figure 5   Examples of SEM photos of the scale found on the heat exchanger surface.
The top images are at a dose of 500 ppm I_E water, the lower images are at a dose of 1000 ppm.

3.3 Precipitation Experiments

The sparse precipitation of soluble salts from solutions has been found to occur in three successive steps.

1. Nucleation

2. Crystal growth

3. Agglomeration and ripening

Experiments were carried out, to evaluate the influence of varying I_E water dose (500 - 1500 ppm), on calcium carbonate nucleation and precipitation.

Figure 6 compares the precipitation of calcium carbonate with calcium carbonate treated with 1250 ppm of I_E water. The curves show the formation and precipitation of calcium carbonate crystals.

Table 3   Summary of precipitation experiments.

Run Number	I_E Water dose (ppm)	T_{ind} (secs)	Absorbance value
1	0	350	0.07
2	500	300	0.06
3	750	200	0.06
4	1000	200	0.05
5	1250	100	0.05
6	1500	200	0.06

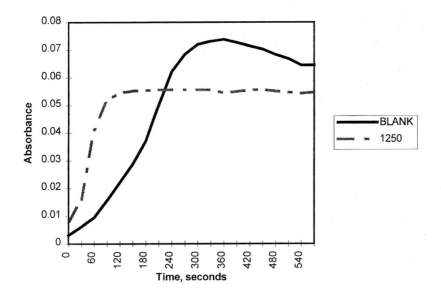

Figure 6   Change in absorbance with time curves for calcium carbonate precipitation blank and with I_E water at 1250 ppm.

A comparison of the absorbance values between treated and untreated solutions indicates that I_E water added to the reagents alone can reduce absorbance ($CaCO_3$ crystal formation) values. The influence on $CaCO_3$ precipitation is greatest at a dose of 1250 ppm. There is a clear difference between mean absorbance values for the treated and blank reagents with the growth in absorbance for the treated solutions always less than for the untreated. This reduction is attributed to the influence on $CaCO_3$ nucleation. Nucleation is increased in the presence of high concentrations of I_E water.

In an ideal experiment, the plot would show that the sample would precipitate until the sample becomes clear. The crystals would settle according to Stokes Law. The particles in the blank settle completely over time, but the treated system showed no evidence of settling even after a period of hours. This could be due to a decrease in the particle diameter, or a change in the relative density of the particle compared to the solution.

4. Conclusions

It is concluded from this study that I_E water influences $CaCO_3$ formation *under quiescent conditions* and that the mechanism possibly involves an interfacial effect. In addition, within certain experimental parameters, the influence of I_E water on $CaCO_3$ scaling was demonstrated.

4.1 Mechanism

Although there is insufficient, reproducible evidence to support the effect on scale formation, the results indicate that the principal action of I_E water is through formation of hydrophilic crystallites with modified surface charge instead of attached scales[4]. The implication is that colloidal stability is influenced by the application of the sample water. Growth on existing scale is thermodynamically favorable[5]. Therefore, to prevent scale or produce descaling, I_E water could act so as to alter the size and surface charge of growing crystallites, thereby increasing their tendency to remain entrained within the bulk of the solution[4]. However, this phenomenon is difficult to confirm for particles as small as crystallization nuclei.

5. References

1. D. Hasson and D. Bramson, *Ind. Eng. Chem. Process Des. Dev.* **24**, 588 (1985).
2. K. Higashitani *et al*, *J. Coll. Interface Sci.* **152,** 125 (1992).
3. K. Higashitani *et al*, *J. Coll. Interface Sci* **156**, 90 (1993).
4. J.L. Crolet and J. Ledion, *Techniques, Sciences, Methods - L'Eau* **83**, 435 (1988).
5. A.E. Nielsen, *Kinetics of Precipitation* (Pergamon Press, Oxford, UK, 1964).

SURFACE, SOLUTION AND LIQUID PROPERTIES OF I_E WATER

SHERRIL D. CHRISTIAN, JOHN F. SCAMEHORN,
AHMADALI TABATABAI

OLGA BERSON

Originally published as *Physical, Chemical and
Biological Properties of Stable Water Clusters,*
Proceedings of the First International Symposium.
Reprinted here by permission of
World Scientific Publishing Company, 1998.

Physical properties of I_E water were measured and compared with those of purified by distillation and/or deionization water. The densities, viscosities, and conductivities of I_E water and purified water were essentially identical. However, initial tests demonstrated that I_E water, either distilled or prepared without distillation, has surface properties and foaming behavior that differ from ordinary water. Some I_E water solutions (undistilled samples) demonstrated reduction in surface tension as much as 17% compared to pure water and promoted formation of larger volumes of more stable foam. Further research is suggested to explore potential uses of I_E water in combination with surface active agents in commercial applications.

1 Introduction

Surface-active agents (surfactants) are among the most widely-used products of the chemical industry that have application in detergents, pharmaceuticals, motor oils, biotechnology, printing, etc. Surfactants usually greatly reduce the surface tension, although some applications of surfactants do not involve large surface tension effects. Surface tension, the amount of work required to create a unit area of surface, is one of the key characteristics of surface phenomena.

Surfactants are organic compounds consisting of two parts: hydrophilic (water-loving) and hydrophobic (water-hating). This characteristic molecular structure is responsible for concentration of the surfactant at the surface and resulting reduction of the surface tension of water due to less work required to create unit area of water-air interface. When used in detergent formulations, surfactants improve the wetting ability of water, help to loosen and remove soil, emulsify and solubilize soils in the wash solution.

A new form of water, described as "containing ice formed under electric field (I_E)", has been discovered by the American Technologies Group (ATG) of Monrovia, CA. ATG suggested that this form of water has properties which make it far more advantageous than normal water for a variety of applications, including detergency. Surfactant Associates, Inc. (SA), a company with extensive experience in studies using surfactants in detergency and other processes, was asked to measure specific parameters of the I_E water and solutions made up using it as a solvent and to compare those to properties of normal water and aqueous solutions.

SA performed a number of experiments which we believe elucidate the differences in fundamental properties of I_E water (compared to ordinary water) and its effects in modifying the behavior of aqueous surfactant solutions. In these tests, blank experiments were carried out using water purified by SA as well as the distilled/deionized water ordinarily used by ATG in preparing I_E water. The results reported here are preliminary in the sense that they cover a range of properties that need to be measured for numerous systems before it will be possible to conclude that I_E water clusters are responsible for the effects observed.

2 Experimental Methods

A variety of experimental methods are regularly used in our laboratories for studying the properties of aqueous solutions of surfactants. These include: the Ross-Miles foam test (supplemented by a foam stability method for use with smaller volumes of solutions); the du Noüy ring and Wilhelmy balance methods for measuring surface tensions; direct gravimetric methods for measuring liquid and solution densities; the Ostwald viscometer for measurement of viscosity; electrical conductivity measurements using a resistance bridge (null) method; a highly-precise total vapor pressure method developed by Professor Edwin E. Tucker of the University of Oklahoma Chemistry Department; and methods for measuring solubility and solubilization of organic or inorganic compounds in aqueous micellar solutions. So far, methods in each of these categories, except the last (solubility and solubilization), have been used to measure the properties of I_E water and solutions made with I_E water and other added components. Additional work is underway to determine the effects of I_E water on solubility and solubilization, as well as the utility of foam-fractionation as a method for removing surface active components (including organic impurities and possibly I_E clusters).

Sonication was used as a method of pre-treating some samples before measurements. Effects of sonication on surface tension was noted and will be discussed.

I_E aqueous solutions were prepared using ATG's proprietary technology and are referred to as undistilled I_E samples. Some I_E solutions were distilled, and the distillates, referred to as distilled I_E samples, were tested. A relative concentration of I_E crystals in the aqueous solutions was determined by measuring UV absorbance at 195 nm. The higher absorbance, the higher the relative concentration of I_E crystals in the solution. The concentration of I_E crystals decreased in the following order: Undistilled (1)> Undistilled (2) >Distilled (1) = Distilled (2), where the numbers identify different batches of the I_E solutions.

3 Experimental Results

3.1 Surface Tension

Surface tension of I_E water and its solutions is a key to the interpretation of many effects caused by the presence of I_E water clusters. The ability of I_E water to cause foaming, its apparent effects on detergency, and the possibility that I_E clusters are surface active themselves or promote surface activity of naturally-surface active compounds, need to be investigated. Although all of the studies described here need to be extended and repeated, some of the results indicate that the surface tensions of solutions containing I_E water vary with time, particularly for samples that have been sonicated for several minutes prior to making the surface tension measurements. The tendency of I_E water to foam can also be modified by pre-foaming, followed by removal of some of the foam. In other words, some surface active components can be removed by foaming.

Surface tension of I_E water, purified water and their solutions, with or without sonication or pre-foaming, was measured (Tables 1-4 and Figure 1). Control water samples, labeled SA Water and ATG Water, were purified by distillation and

240

deionization by, respectively, Surfactant Associates and by American Technologies Group. In a number of systems, sonication was used to disperse the chemical substances responsible for forming films at the liquid/air interface (Table 3); foaming was also used to remove surface active materials (Table 2).

Table 1 Surface Tension Measurements of Purified Water and I_E Water.

Sample	Average Surface Tension (Standard Deviation), dyne/cm	Temperature, °C
Controls (purified water)		
SA Water	71.9 (0.1)	25.0
ATG Water	71.6 (0.4)	25.0
I_E water		
Distilled (1)	72.0	25.0
Distilled (2)	71.4 (0.1)	27.5
Undistilled (1)	59.6 (1.0)	25.0
Undistilled (2)	70.3 (0.3)	25.4

A KRUSS digital tensiometer, model K10T, was used for these measurements. Temperature was controlled using a Brinkmann MGW/LAUDA (RC3) Cooling Unit. Each measurement was repeated 3-5 times, except for the Distilled (1) sample, where only one measurement was made.

Table 2 Effect of Foam Removal on Surface Tension.

I_E Sample	Average Surface Tension (standard deviation), dyne/cm
Prior to foam removal	59.8 (0.8)
After foam removal	63.9 (0.7)

A KRUSS digital tensiometer, model K10T, was used for these measurements. Temperature was controlled using a Brinkmann MGW/LAUDA (RC3) Cooling Unit. Each measurement was repeated at least 5 times.

Table 3 Effect of Sonication on Surface Tension of I_E and Water Solutions.

Sample	Time of sonication, min.	Time elapsed after sonication, seconds	Surface Tension, (standard deviation) dyne/cm	Temperature, °C
Control ATG Water	10	10 min.	71.5	27.5
I_E water Undistilled (1)	7	10 min.	61.0 (0.9)	25.2
Distilled (1)	8	10 min.	71.4 (0.1)	25.2
Undistilled (1)	2	70	64.5	26.1
		150	63.8	26.1
		360	62.6	26.1
		600	60.5	26.1
		900	60.6	26.1
Undistilled (1)	15	90	61.6	26.1
		240	60.9	26.1
		390	60.9	26.1
		540	60.5	26.1
Undistilled (1)	2	60	63.3	25.5
		180	61.6	25.5
		420	60.1	25.5
		5 hours	62.8	25.2
Undistilled (2)	2	90	70.3	25.5
		240	69.9	25.5
		420	69.2	25.5
		600	69.4	25.5
		5 hours	64.6	25.2

A KRUSS digital tensiometer, model K10T, was used for these measurements. Temperature was controlled using a Brinkmann MGW/LAUDA (RC3) Cooling Unit. Standard deviations are shown for measurements that were repeated 2-3 times.

Table 4   Surface Tensions of Solutions Prepared with Sodium Dodecyl Sulfate (SDS)   Surfactant and a Commercial Detergent (CD) provided by ATG.

Solvent	Surfactant type	Surface Tension, (Standard Deviation) dyne/cm	Temperature, °C
SA water	SDS	39.9	25.0
ATG water	SDS	39.9	25.0
Distilled (1)	SDS	39.9	25.0
Solvents were mixed with CD 2 days prior to measurements			
ATG water	CD	32.4 (0.1)	25.2
Distilled (1)	CD	31.2 (0.1)	25.4
Undistilled (1)	CD	30.8 (0.2)	25.4
Solvents were mixed with CD immediately before measurements			
ATG water	CD	32.8 (0.1)	25.4
Distilled (1)	CD	32.3 (0.1)	25.4
Undistilled (1)	CD	33.3 (0.3)	25.4

A KRUSS digital tensiometer, model K10T was used for these measurements. Temperature was controlled using a Brinkmann MGW/LAUDA (RC3) Cooling Unit. SDS solution was prepared by dissolving 1.6 g of SDS per liter of a solvent (SA or ATG control water, or I_E water). CD solution was prepared by mixing 0.04 ml of CD with 50 ml of solvent (SA or ATG control water, or I_E water). All measurements were repeated at least 3 times.

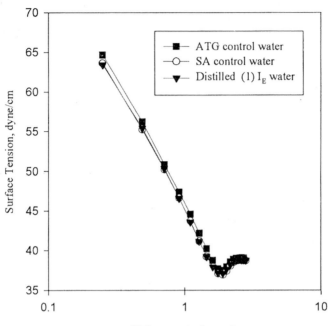

Figure 1 Surface Tension of Solution of Sodium Dodecylsulfate (SDS) in ATG or SA control water or Distilled (1) I_E Water as a Function of SDS Concentration in the Solution.

A Cahn Dynamic Contact Angle Analyzer (model DCA-322) was used to carry out these measurements. A predetermined amount of stock SDS surfactant was added incrementally to control or I_E water, and the surface tension of the obtained solution was measured. The concentration of SDS in the stock solution was 24 mM.

3.2 Vapor Pressure

Vapor pressures were measured at 25°C for control water and for I_E samples. The values for all of the samples were equal within ± 0.03 torr, the approximate maximum uncertainty in absolute vapor pressure, allowing for errors in calibration, temperature uncertainty, and incomplete removal of dissolved air and/or impurities. These results are in good agreement with reported values for the vapor pressure of water at 25 °C (Table 5).

Table 5   Vapor Pressure of Control and I_E Water.

Sample	Average Vapor Pressure (Standard Deviation), Torr	Temperature, °C
Control ATG Water	23.795 (0.001)	25
I_E Water Undistilled (1)	23.770 (0.005)	25
Undistilled (2)	23.744 (0.003)	25
Distilled (1)	23.750 (0.008)	25

All measurements were repeated 4 times.

3.3 Bulk Liquid Properties

Density, viscosity (Table 6), and conductivity (Figure 2) of control water as well as two types of I_E water were measured. No significant differences in the values of the parameters measured were observed. Evaporation of samples to dryness (at approximately 140° C) did not yield a measurable residue for 10 g samples of either water control or distilled I_E water samples. On the other hand, residuals of about 2 to 4 mg were obtained when 10 ml of an undistilled I_E water sample was evaporated.

Table 6 Density and Viscosity Measurements of Control and I_E Water.

Sample	Viscosity, cp	Density, g/ml
Control		
SA Water	nd	0.991
ATG Water	0.91	0.995
I_E Water		
Distilled (1)	0.90	0.991
Undistilled (1)	0.92	0.991
Undistilled (2)	0.94	0.990

Viscosity was measured with Ostwald viscometer.

nd -- the parameter was not determined.

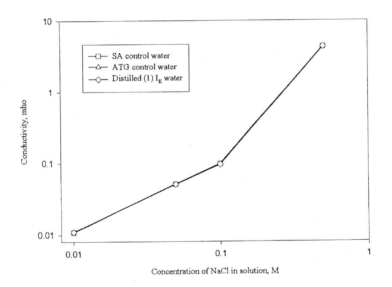

Concentration of NaCl in solution, M

Figure 2 Conductivity Measurements of SA and ATG Control Water and Distilled I_E Water. An Orion Research Conductivity Meter-101 was used in this study.

3.4 The Foaming of I_E Water

The volume of the foam layer formed in a sample of control or I_E water after 20 s of vigorous shaking (up and down) in a 50 ml burette was measured (Table 7). In all of the foaming experiments, with control and distilled I_E water, most of the foam disappeared fairly rapidly, while in the case of undistilled I_E water more foam was formed and it persisted for longer time. Preliminary experiments were carried out to show the feasibility of removing foam from I_E water samples to concentrate surface active component(s) of the system. It was observed that the surface tension is raised following removal of foam, indicating that some surface active material had been removed (Table 2).

Table 7 Foaming of Control and I_E Water.

ATG Control Water		Distilled (1) I_E Water		Undistilled (1) I_E Water	
Time after end of shaking, s	Foam volume, ml	Time after end of shaking, s	Foam volume, ml	Time after end of shaking, s	Foam volume, ml
0	0.1	0	0.3	0	1.5
		35	0.1	20	0.5
		60	0.005	30	0.4
				50	0.35
				70	0.35
				90	0.3
				360	0.3
				600	0.3
				1200	0.25

A 50 ml burette filled with 20 ml of ATG control water or Distilled (1) I_E water or Undistilled (1) I_E water was shaken vigorously for 20 seconds. The volume of foam was measured at time intervals.

4 Discussion of Surface Tension, Foaming, and Adsorption at the Water-Vapor Interface

Before discussing differences in surface tensions and foaming characteristics of the individual samples of I_E water, as compared with the water control samples, we will comment on the significance of surface tension as a method for determining the presence and surface concentration of components dissolved in water. It is possible for trace amounts of slightly soluble impurities (usually organic compounds) to lower surface tensions considerably, producing nearly a monolayer of organic compounds at the boundary between the bulk liquid and the vapor. The Gibbs adsorption equation can be used to determine the surface (excess) concentration of such solutes if they are present in the bulk at known concentrations.

When a water sample contains dissolved impurities that possess both hydrophilic and hydrophobic chemical groups (e.g., neutral compounds like alkylated phenols, naphthols, and ethers), the surface tension can be lowered considerably from the expected value of about 72 dyne/cm at 25°C. This effect is particularly pronounced for compounds that have quite low solubilities in water. Such compounds, at very low concentrations, will act somewhat like the commercial surfactants in their ability to decrease the surface tension of water. Their solubility is much more limited than that of the commonly used surfactants, so they cannot perform as well as these compounds in detergency or the formation of relatively stable foams and emulsions. It is certainly an important question whether any of the surface tension and foaming effects studied here can be attributed to impurities present in I_E water. On the other hand, if I_E water is able to change the surface activity of compounds that are useful in detergency, that would be an important observation in relation to the potential use of I_E water in a wide variety of cleaning processes and in forming aqueous colloids (emulsions, foams, dispersions, etc.). We do not consider that the question of the role of I_E water in modifying the properties of aqueous surfactant solutions has yet been answered, but several additional studies of systems involving both surfactants and I_E water still should be performed to answer this question.

The question of the importance of I_E water in promoting foaming also needs to be examined in greater detail. Most observers, on handling samples of I_E water in glass containers, seem to believe that this water is more viscous than ordinary water, although our quantitative measurements of bulk viscosity do not confirm

248

this. On the other hand, there is little doubt that the I_E water samples do foam, although most of the foam disappears quickly.

It is well known in the chemical engineering literature that foaming (by a process called foam-fractionation) is an important method for collecting surface active materials dissolved in water. Simple foam fractionators can be set up in the laboratory to recover the surface active compounds, and although we have not yet had time to do these experiments, it would be advantageous in our opinion to develop programs to collect and determine the concentration of the materials responsible for foaming and depression of surface tension. To be sure, if the I_E samples contain surface-active organic impurities, one result will be that these will become highly concentrated in the removed foam. On the other hand, if the collected foaming materials are highly enriched in the I_E water (as determined by physical and structural methods), foaming could be a valuable method for obtaining I_E clusters in highly-concentrated form.

5 Conclusions and Suggestions for Further Development

Initial results indicate that I_E water, either distilled or prepared without distillation, has surface properties and foaming behavior that differ from ordinary water. Sonication is a method that changes surface properties of some samples, in several cases, causing a decrease in the apparent concentration of the agent(s) responsible for the surface tension effects. Removal of foam also reduces the concentration of surface active materials (at least temporarily), although with time, the surface tension of the I_E water does change part way back to its initial value before foaming.

Synergistic effects of I_E clusters and detergents have not been systematically studied. Experiments to determine the properties of mixtures of various commercial detergents (including some that are pure individual compounds) need to be planned for the future. The feasibility of concentrating I_E water by foaming and reusing the concentrate in subsequent detergency studies needs to be investigated.

The possibility that detergent action can be enhanced by I_E water clusters needs to be examined in detail. Either by foaming or other methods, attempts should be made to obtain I_E water in highly concentrated form. If the clusters are surface active, the effect needs to be put on a quantitative basis. The foam concentrate should be analyzed carefully to determine the content of organics as well as the quantity and structure of I_E water clusters. This concentrate could be used in a variety of ways, including substituting it for some of the components in heavy duty or specialty household cleaning formulations. Moreover, the effect of the I_E water in stabilizing foams, emulsions, and suspensions of solids in aqueous (or other) systems needs to be evaluated. Finally, the possibility that I_E water may adsorb at a variety of surfaces or interfaces and modify film properties should be explored. To summarize, the potential use of I_E water in combination with well-characterized surface active agents might lead to important commercial applications.

EXPERIMENTAL STUDY OF SATURATED POOL BOILING HEAT TRANSFER OF I_E WATER

CHUNSING WANG

Originally published as *Physical, Chemical and Biological Properties of Stable Water Clusters,* Proceedings of the First International Symposium. Reprinted here by permission of World Scientific Publishing Company, 1998.

Pool boiling, of saturated I_E water clusters, at one atmosphere was investigated. In the experiments, a vertical copper surface with a mirror surface was used. The wall heat flux and superheat were determined with the help of thermocouples embedded in the test block. The still photographs were taken during the experiments. The nucleate boiling, critical and film boiling heat fluxes as function of wall superheat patterns for I_E water are compared with these for water. It is concluded that I_E water changes bubble formation, flow pattern above heating surface, and enhances boiling heat transfer as compared to plain water.

1. INTRODUCTION

Boiling is a phase heat transfer process that involves more than a knowledge of the usual heat transfer modes: conduction, convection and radiation. It continues to attract attention because it allows engineers to remove a tremendous amount of heat from small spaces. Rocket engines, superconductors, jet aircraft engines, electronic devices and nuclear reactors all produce a large amount of heat that has to be removed efficiently by means of a new boiling technology. A precise evaluation of the boiling process is very important for component cooling, in these high density energy systems.

The wall superheat is the temperature difference between the heater surface and the ambient liquid. As the surface temperature is increased, until a certain thermal condition is met, the incipient nucleation occurs. The vapor bubbles begin to form on the cavities of the boiling surface. This is called the discrete bubble regime or partial nucleate boiling regime. In this regime, the frequency and number density of the bubbles increase when surface superheat is increased, thereby resulting in a higher heat flux. As wall heat flux or superheat increases further, the frequency of bubble release and the number density of active cavities also increase. At a certain bubble release frequency, the distance between rising bubbles is equal to, or less than, one bubble diameter and the vapor bubbles merge to form columns.

As the superheat increases further, the number of vapor columns on the surface increases. The bubbles on top of the vapor columns begin to merge with bubbles of neighboring vapor columns to form bigger vapor structures called vapor mushrooms. Vapor appears to jet away from the heating surface. Thus massive vapor mushrooms[1] and columns can be seen near the heating surface. This is called fully developed nucleate boiling. Then, the maximum heat flux occurs at a peak and is called the critical heat flux or maximum heat flux. The critical heat flux occurs either because of the limit on vapor removal rate or vapor generation rate on the surface.

After the critical heat flux, the surface heat flux is decreased with increasing surface superheat. This is called transition boiling regime. Transition boiling is believed to be a mixed model of nucleate and film boiling. Liquid-solid as well as vapor-solid contacts must therefore exist and have indeed been observed in experiments. Surface heat flux reaches a minimum as surface temperature is further increased. This is called minimum film boiling condition.

When surface temperature becomes higher than a minimum boiling condition temperature, the surface heat flux is increased with surface temperature and it is known as the film boiling regime. The heat transfer coefficient in film boiling is much lower than in nucleate boiling, hence is generally considered to be inefficient. In the design of heat exchangers, film boiling is usually avoided.

Wang and Dhir[2] investigated the active nucleation sites on a heating surface. They found that the condition for gas/vapor entrapment from preexisting nuclei can be stated as

$$\phi > \varphi_{min} \tag{1}$$

where φ_{min} is the minimum cavity side angle of a spherical, conical or sinusoidal cavity. The minimum superheat corresponds with the minimum diameter of curvature which equals the diameter of the cavity mouth. The corresponding expression for incipient superheat is obtained as

$$\Delta T = \frac{4\sigma T_{sat}}{\rho_v h_{fg} D_c} K_{max} \tag{2}$$

where ΔT, σ, T_{sat}, ρ_v, h_{fg} and D_c are correspondingly wall superheat, liquid surface tension, saturated temperature, vapor density, latent heat and minimum diameter of a cavity. For a spherical cavity, the K_{max} is expressed as

$$K_{max} = 1 \text{ for } \phi \le 90^{\circ} \text{ and } K_{max} = \sin \phi \text{ for } \phi > 90^{\circ} \tag{3}$$

The cumulative number density of active nucleation sites for a contact angle ϕ can be expressed by surface cavity size distribution as

$$N_a = \frac{1-\cos\phi}{1-\cos\varphi} \cdot N_{as}(\varphi) \qquad (4)$$

where $N_{as}(\varphi)$ is surface cavity density with a cavity mouth angle less than φ and φ is any reference cavity side angle.

In the isolated bubble regime, transient conduction into liquid adjacent to the wall is probably the most important mechanism for heat removal from the wall. After bubble inception, the superheated liquid layer is pushed outward and mixes with bulk liquid. The bubble acts like a pump in removing hot liquid from the surface and replacing it with cold liquid. This mechanism was originally proposed by Forster and Grief[3]. Mikic and Rohsenow[4] were the first to formalize the derivation of functional dependence of partial boiling heat flux on wall superheat. Assuming that the contribution of evaporation to total heat removal rate was small they obtained an expression for the partial nucleate boiling heat flux as

$$q = \frac{K_o^2}{2}\sqrt{\pi \cdot k_l \cdot \rho \cdot C_{pl} \cdot f}\, D_d^2 N_a \Delta T + (1 - \frac{K_o^2}{4} N_a \pi D_d^2) h_{nc} \Delta T \qquad (5)$$

In this equation, the parameter K_o is reflective of the area of influence of a bubble, and a value of 2 is assigned to it. The bubble diameter of bubble departure and frequency, f, is obtained from the following correlation:

$$fD_d = 0.6 \left[\frac{\sigma \cdot g(\rho_l - \rho_g)}{\rho_l^2} \right]^{1/4} \qquad (6)$$

For the natural convection heat transfer coefficient, any of the correlation available in the literature could be used.

According to Gaertner[1], most evaporation occurs at the periphery of vapor stems in the fully developed nucleate boiling regime. Energy of the phase change is supplied by the superheated liquid layer in which the stems are implanted. A time and area average model for fully developed boiling has been proposed by Dhir and Liaw[5], who assumed that vapor stems provide a stationary interface. Energy from the wall is conducted into the liquid layer and utilized in evaporation at the

the wall is conducted into the liquid layer and utilized in evaporation at the stationary liquid-vapor interface. The heat transfer rate into the thermal layer and the temperature distribution in the thermal layer is obtained by solving a two-dimensional steady state conduction equation. The geometry of the vapor stem adjacent to the wall is related to the contact angle and hence surface wettability can be quantitatively related to heat transfer. Employing experimentally observed void fractions and assuming nucleation site density as function of heat flux, the investigators were able to predict nucleate boiling heat flux and critical heat flux for different contact angles.

The phenomenon of film boiling is very similar in nature to film condensation. The correlations of the Nusselt number for laminar film condensation can be used for laminar film boiling with liquid properties replaced by vapor properties and adjustments made in multiplying constants.

During the 1970s and 1980s significant advances were achieved in the development of enhanced boiling surface. The enhanced surface consists of two basic types, as described by Webb[6], which are "structured" surface and "porous coated" surface. These types of enhanced surface are capable of providing a threefold to fivefold improvement in boiling heat transfer[7]. However, despite initial claims to the contrary, the use of these commercial surfaces does not appear to eliminate the superheat excursion encountered in the boiling of highly-wetting liquids. You et al.[8] reduced the incipient superheat by epoxying (UV-cured) several layers of fine alumina particles (0.3 to 3 micron diameter) onto an alumina heater.

The addition of certain amounts of surfactants in a aqueous solution has been known to significantly enhance the boiling heat transfer of water. The mechanism is still not understood.

In a given heating surface and system pressure, the boiling heat flux depends on the liquid and vapor properties as discussed above. There is little difference in thermodynamic properties between bulk water and a water cluster which Lo et al.[9] described and called I_E crystal. The purpose of this study is to show if I_E water changes the boiling phenomenon due to its unique cluster structure. Since most of the thermodynamic properties of I_E water are not available, the mechanism of the enhancement of boiling heat transfer of I_E water is not explained.

2. EXPERIMENTAL SETUP AND PROCEDURES

2.1 Apparatus and Preliminary Work

The apparatus used in this study was intended to measure heat flux and wall superheat in all regimes of boiling (i.e., nucleate, transition and film boiling). The apparatus also allowed observation of the boiling process from front and side.

254

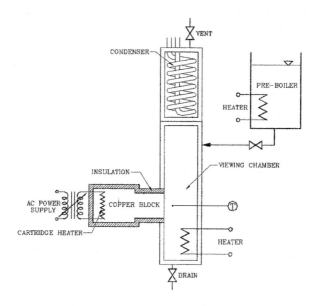

Figure 1 : Schematic diagram of primary experimental apparatus

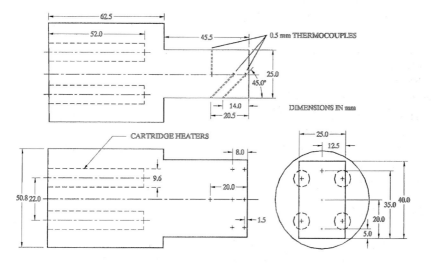

Figure 2 : Location of thermocouples in the test block

255

Experiments were conducted using deionized water (herein after referred to as water) and I_E Crystal aqueous solution (herein after referred to as I_E water) to study saturated pooling boiling at atmospheric pressure. The schematic diagram of the primary experimental apparatus is found in Figure 1. The test section was mounted on one side of the viewing chamber and polycarbonate sheets were placed on the remaining three sides. The rectangular heating surface was 25 mm wide and 40 mm high, and was machined from one end of a pure solid copper cylinder. The other end of the block was drilled to fit four cartridge heaters, rated at 400W each.

Figure 2 shows the dimensions of the test section and the locations of the various thermocouples. The test block projected into the viewing chamber. Since boiling on only the test surface was desired, the remaining heated areas were isolated from the test chamber. Seven K-type thermocouples were positioned along the vertical axis of the rectangular boiling surface at three locations: 5, 20, and 35 mm from the leading edge, respectively. At the edge of the first two locations, thermopiles were embedded normal to the surface at 1.5 and 8 mm from the surface. The central location, which was at 20 mm from the bottom, has extra thermopiles at 20 mm from the surface. The test surface was a mirror finish surface condition.

The chamber's windows were made of polycarbonate and were 6.4 mm thick. A Sony camcorder with a 50 mm macro lens was mounted near the chamber's window, to photograph the front view of the bubbles and vapor jet from the surface. During the boiling test, the boiling process was continuously recorded by the camcorder.

2.2 Experimental procedure

I_E water was prepared from highly purified water with a resistivity of 18 $M\Omega \cdot cm$ and the total amount of dissolved solids was less than 10 ppb by a special proprietary process.

Prior to the experiment, the test liquids were (water or I_E water) deaerated by vigorous boiling in a separate reservoir. Thereafter the test section was preheated and the chamber was filled with the test liquid from the reservoir. The power to the cartridge heaters was controlled with a transformer. Tests were considered to be in a steady state when the temperatures along the central test section did not deviate the linear distribution over 0.2K. The wall superheat was obtained by extrapolating the known temperature profile under steady state conditions. During the transient heating transition boiling, the test section was heated by gradually increasing the input power until the critical heat flux was reached. Then, the power was reduced to avoid overheating of the test block. In the test, the temperatures were recorded

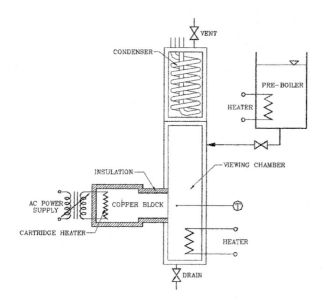

Figure 1 : Schematic diagram of primary experimental apparatus

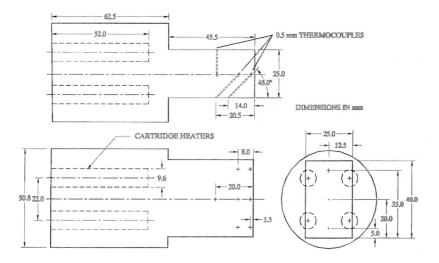

Figure 2 : Location of thermocouples in the test block

257

Experiments were conducted using deionized water (herein after referred to as water) and I_E Crystal aqueous solution (herein after referred to as I_E water) to study saturated pooling boiling at atmospheric pressure. The schematic diagram of the primary experimental apparatus is found in Figure 1. The test section was mounted on one side of the viewing chamber and polycarbonate sheets were placed on the remaining three sides. The rectangular heating surface was 25 mm wide and 40 mm high, and was machined from one end of a pure solid copper cylinder. The other end of the block was drilled to fit four cartridge heaters, rated at 400W each.

Figure 2 shows the dimensions of the test section and the locations of the various thermocouples. The test block projected into the viewing chamber. Since boiling on only the test surface was desired, the remaining heated areas were isolated from the test chamber. Seven K-type thermocouples were positioned along the vertical axis of the rectangular boiling surface at three locations: 5, 20, and 35 mm from the leading edge, respectively. At the edge of the first two locations, thermopiles were embedded normal to the surface at 1.5 and 8 mm from the surface. The central location, which was at 20 mm from the bottom, has extra thermopiles at 20 mm from the surface. The test surface was a mirror finish surface condition.

The chamber's windows were made of polycarbonate and were 6.4 mm thick. A Sony camcorder with a 50 mm macro lens was mounted near the chamber's window, to photograph the front view of the bubbles and vapor jet from the surface. During the boiling test, the boiling process was continuously recorded by the camcorder.

2.2 Experimental procedure

I_E water was prepared from highly purified water with a resistivity of 18 $M\Omega \cdot cm$ and the total amount of dissolved solids was less than 10 ppb by a special proprietary process.

Prior to the experiment, the test liquids were (water or I_E water) deaerated by vigorous boiling in a separate reservoir. Thereafter the test section was preheated and the chamber was filled with the test liquid from the reservoir. The power to the cartridge heaters was controlled with a transformer. Tests were considered to be in a steady state when the temperatures along the central test section did not deviate the linear distribution over 0.2K. The wall superheat was obtained by extrapolating the known temperature profile under steady state conditions. During the transient heating transition boiling, the test section was heated by gradually increasing the input power until the critical heat flux was reached. Then, the power was reduced to avoid overheating of the test block. In the test, the temperatures were recorded with a Data Acquisition System at 10Hz. The heat fluxes in steady or transient state were deduced from the recorded temperature.

In steady state tests, surface heat fluxes are readily calculable using the spatial temperature distribution recorded from thermocouples. One-dimensional heat flow was found to exist inside the test block up to 20 mm from the boiling surface. The heat flux is proportional to the negative of the temperature gradient:

$$q = -k\frac{dT}{dx} \tag{7}$$

The surface temperature was obtained by simply extrapolating the temperature profile to the surface. The q versus ΔT relation for transient runs was reduced from the temperature versus time data by solving one dimensional conduction equation. One-dimensional heat conduction equation is written as

$$T_t = kT_{xx} \tag{8}$$

Two boundary conditions are applied at x=1.5 and 20.0 mm from the boiling surface. The initial condition and boundary conditions are expressed as

$$T(x,0) = ax + b$$
$$T(x = 1.5mm, t) = g_1(t)$$
$$T(x = 20.0mm, t) = g_2(t)$$

The one dimensional conduction equation is solved numerically. The Crank-Nicolson formula with a weighting factor of $\frac{1}{2}$ is used in time discretization to assure unconditional stability. Peaceman-Rachford's ADI scheme is used in spatial splitting, as it is accurate to second order in both time and space. The surface temperature and heat flux are obtained by using Gregory-Newton forward extrapolation formula.

The uncertainty in wall superheat for nucleate and film boiling was estimated to be ±0.3K. For partial nucleate boiling and film boiling, the uncertainty in heat flux was calculated to be approximately 0.5 W/cm^2. Uncertainty in fully developed nucleate boiling heat flux was only about 1% because of high heat flux and low wall superheat. During the transition boiling, the uncertainty of temperature was not only found in x but also in z direction. Therefore, uncertainty in wall superheat was estimated to be ±1.2K and heat flux was bounded by two times the film and nucleate boiling values.

During the data reduction, the time elapsed was stamped on data sheets of wall superheat and heat flux. Based on the time stamped, the still pictures corresponding to the wall superheat and heat flux were captured from camcorder.

3.RESULTS AND DISCUSSION

3.1 Wall Superheat and Heat flux

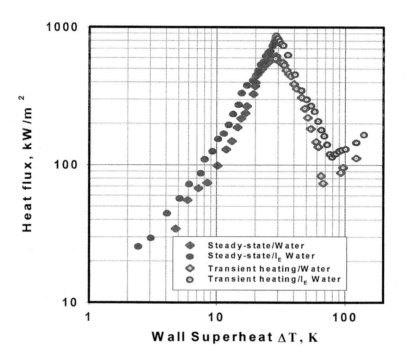

Figure 3 :Comparison of boiling curve between I_E water and water

During saturated pool boiling of water and I_E water, data were taken for wall superheat and heat flux. Figure 3 shows the obtained boiling curves under a mirror copper surface with a 90° contact angle. The reported data are for the mid-plane of the test surface. The nucleate boiling data were taken under steady state conditions, whereas the transition and film boiling data were obtained under transient conditions. The transition and film boiling heat fluxes were obtained from the thermocouple data by solving transient one dimensional conduction equations. In the partially nucleate boiling region where heat fluxes were under 150 kW/m^2, the heat flux for a given superheat of I$_E$ water was higher than that of water. For a given heat flux, the superheat of I$_E$ water was up to 3.5K, lower than that of water. In fully nucleate boiling region, where heat flux was above 150 kW/m^2, it was also shown that the heat flux with a given superheat of water clusters is higher than that of water. The maximum heat fluxes for I$_E$ water and water were 870 and 602 kW/m^2, respectively. In the transition region, where superheat was between 28 and 170 K, the heat flux curve of I$_E$ water was always higher than that of water. In the film boiling region where superheat is over 170K, the heat flux curve of I$_E$ water was higher than that of water

3.2 Bubble formation /Partially Nucleate Boiling

Figure 4 shows the comparison of bubble formation from the front view in the partial nucleate boiling between I$_E$ water and water. In this region, the bubbles leaving the heating surface were single separated bubbles. When the wall superheat attained 6K, the boiling incipient occurred for both test liquids. However, there were more bubbles formed in the heating surface of I$_E$ water than that of water. Naturally, the heat flux of I$_E$ water was higher than that of water. When the wall superheat increased to 8.1K, the heating surface of I$_E$ water was almost covered by bubbles, but the bubble formation of the heating surface with water was only similar to that of I$_E$ water at wall superheat of 6.0K. When the heating surface increased to 10.2K, the heating surface with I$_E$ water was totally covered by bubbles and the heat flux was up to 154 kW/m^2. At the same wall superheat, the heat flux of the heating surface with water was only 99 kW/m^2. The following table compares the heat flux of water and the heat flux of I$_E$ water at the same wall superheat. The enhanced boiling heat transfer with I$_E$ water is between 30.9 and 55.6 %.

Table 1: Comparison of heat flux in partial nucleate boiling region

	Water	I$_E$ water	Increasing heat flux
Superheat, ΔT (K)	Heat flux, q kW/m^2	Heat flux, q kW/m^2	%
6.0	55	72	30.9
8.1	71	110	54.9
10.2	99	154	55.6

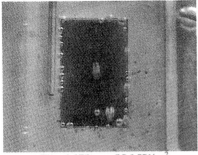

$\Delta T = 6.0K, \ q{=}55 \ kW/m^2$
Fig. 4-1a Water

$\Delta T = 6.0K, \ q{=}72 \ kW/m^2$
Fig. 4-1b I_E water

$\Delta T = 8.1K, \ q{=}71 \ kW/m^2$
Fig. 4-2a Water

$\Delta T = 8.1K, \ q{=}110 \ kW/m^2$
Fig. 4-2b I_E water

$\Delta T = 10.2K, \ q{=}99 \ kW/m^2$
Fig. 4-3a Water

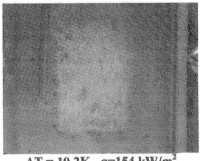

$\Delta T = 10.2K, \ q{=}154 \ kW/m^2$
Fig. 4-3b I_E water

Figure 4 : Comparison of bubble formation in partially nucleate boiling

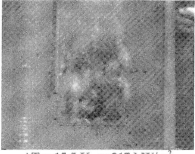

$\Delta T = 15.5$ K, q=217 kW/m^2
Fig. 5-1a Water

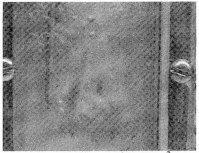

$\Delta T = 15.7$K q=333kW/m^2
Fig. 5-1b I_E water

$\Delta T = 19.3$K q=328 kW/m^2
Fig. 5-2a Water

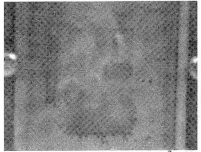

$\Delta T = 19.1$K q=410kW/m^2
Fig. 5-2b I_E water

$\Delta T = 22.4$K q=499 kW/m^2
Fig.5-3a Water

$\Delta T = 22.0$K q=535kW/m^2
Fig. 5-3b I_E water

Figure 5 Comparison of vapor stem in fully nucleate boiling

263

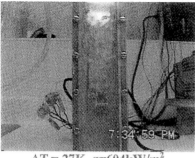

$\Delta T = 27K, q=604kW/m^2$

Fig. 6a Water critical heat flux

$\Delta T = 27K \quad q=733kW/m^2$

Fig.6b I_E water
fully developed nucleate boiling

3.3 Stem Formation/Fully Nucleate Boiling

Figure 5 shows the comparison of bubble formation from front view in the fully nucleate boiling between I_E water and water. In this region, the bubbles leaving the heating surface were continuous and acted as a steam jet. For all three different wall superheats, the wall heat flux of I_E water was higher than the heat flux of water. The comparison of Figures 5-1b and 5-2a indicates that the wall superheat of the heating surface with I_E water was 2.6K less than that with water as the same heat flux, of approximately 330 kW/m^2. Also, the steam jet of the heating surface with I_E water was uniformly distributed over the surface. The steam formation on the heating surface with water was more mushroom shaped (Figure 5-2a). The flow pattern difference between I_E water and water may be caused by the thermal conductivity of I_E water changing during boiling agitation. The following table compares the heat flux of water and the heat flux of I_E water at the same wall superheat. The enhanced boiling heat transfer with I_E water is between 7.2 and 53.4 %.

Table 2: Comparison of heat flux in fully nucleate boiling region

	Water	I_E water	Increasing heat flux
Superheat, ΔT (K)	Heat flux, q kW/m^2	Heat flux, q kW/m^2	%
15.5/15.7	217	333	53.4
19.3/19.1	328	410	25.0
22.4/22.0	499	535	7.2

$\Delta T = 122K \quad q=112kW/m^2$

Fig. 7a Water film boiling

$\Delta T = 122K \quad q=145kW/m^2$

Fig. 7b I_E water film boiling

3.4 Maximum Heat Flux and Film Boiling

Figure 6a shows the front view of the heating surface with water at the critical heat flux of 604 kW/m^2 with wall superheat of 27K. At the same wall superheat (Figure 6b) shows the front view of the heating surface with I_E water at a heat flux of 733 kW/m^2. At the high heat flux, the surface is obscured by the steam mushroom formation. Above the heating surface, the flow pattern of heat flux with I_E water was different from the flow pattern of heat flux with water. The former was like bubble jets while the latter was like steam slugs.

Figures 7a and 7b show the front view of the heating surface with water and I_E water at wall superheat 122K during film boiling region. The films were formed at the heating surface with water and with I_E water. The heating surface with water was covered with a clear film; however, the heating surface with I_E water was covered with a film topped with tiny bubbles. The flow pattern above the heating surface was also different. Huge bubble slugs were continuously generated from the heating surface with water, but steam bubbles were formed above the heating surface with I_E water. The heat flux of the heating surface with I_E water was 19% higher than that with water at the same wall superheat. Since the phenomenon of film condensation on immersed plates is very similar in nature to film boiling, it is implied that enhanced film condensation can also be obtained.

4. SUMMARY AND CONCLUSIONS

1. In a nucleate boiling region, I_E water enhances the boiling heat transfer up to 56%.

2. The critical heat flux with I_E water is enhanced by 39%.
3. In a film boiling region, I_E water enhances the boiling heat transfer by 19%.
4. More bubbles are formed on a heating surface with I_E water than on a heating surface with water in nucleate boiling regime.
5. Flow pattern, above the heating surface with I_E water, is more like bubble clusters and flow pattern above the heating surface with water is more like a slug or a slug annular in film boiling regime.

5. REFERENCES

1. R.F. Gaertner, *J. Heat Transfer*, **87**, 17-29 (1965).
2. C. Wang and V.K. Dhir, *J. Heat Transfer*, **115**, 670-679 (1993).
3. D.E. Forster and R. Greif, 1959, *Heat Transfer to a Boiling Liquid-Mechanism and Correlation, ASME J. Heat Transfer*, **81**, 43-53.
4. B.B. Mikic and W.M. Rohesenow, *ASME J. Heat Transfer*, **91**, 245-250 (1969).
5. V.K. Dhir and S.P. Liaw, *ASME J. Heat Transfer*, **111**, 739-746 (1986).
6. Webb, R.L., *Heat Transfer Engineering*, **2**, *No.4-4*, 46-69 (1981).
7. K. Nishikawa, *Proceedings ASME/JSME Thermal Engineering Joint Conference, JSME, Tokyo, Japan*, **3**, 11-20 (1983).
8. S.M. You, et al., *Proceedings, IEEE/ASME ITERM III, IEEE Catalog Number 92CH3096-5, New York*, 66-73 (1992).
9. S.Y. Lo, et al., *Modern Physics Letters B*, **10**, *No. 19*, 921-930 (1996).

EFFECT OF I_E CRYSTAL WATER ON ENZYME ACTIVITY

LUDMILA CHISTOSERDOVA, MARY E. LIDSTROM

Originally published as *Physical, Chemical and Biological Properties of Stable Water Clusters,*
Proceedings of the First International Symposium. Reprinted here by permission of
World Scientific Publishing Company, 1998.

Activities of seven commercial enzyme preparations used in the laundry detergent industry (three
proteases, two alpha amylases, one cellulase and one lipase) were compared using four
preparations of I_E crystal water (D_S-20, D_S-50, D_S-93 and D_S-320). The only enzyme for which
significant stimulation was observed was the cellulase (Celluzyme), which was stimulated up to
60% by D_S-50. Some enzymes showed significant inhibition with specific preparations of I_E
crystal water. Our conclusion is that these preparations of I_E crystal water are not generally
stimulatory to enzyme activity under the conditions used for the enzyme assays, but that
moderate stimulation of cellulase apparently occurs with one of the preparations.

1   Introduction

Enzymes are the catalysts for cellular reactions. They usually increase reaction
rates by at least a million fold and sometimes up to a factor of 10 to 12. Enzymes
are active only when they have folded into the proper three-dimensional structure,
which is determined by the sequence of the amino acid monomers and folding
pathways.

A large global market exists for enzymes in commercial applications, which
include food additives, detergents, production of small molecules such as alcohol
and glucose, a variety of pharmaceutical applications, textile industry, etc.
Therefore, stimulation of enzymatic activity with an additive has an obvious
commercial benefit.

Stable I_E™ water clusters (I_E water) were described recently by Lo[1] and Lo *et
al.*[2]. Preliminary studies have revealed the biological activity of various I_E
preparations *in vivo* and *in vitro*[3]. The purpose of this study was to look at the
effect of different concentrations of D_S type preparation of I_E water on the activity
of commercial enzymes used in the laundry detergent industry.

2   Methods

The tested enzymes represent five different commercially important classes:
proteases (Alcalase, Esperase and Savinase.), α-amylases (Duramyl, Termamyl),
cellulases (Celluzyme), and lipases (Lipolase). Additionally Soy Bean Lipoxidase
(Sigma, St. Louis) was tested. The concentration of I_E water in activity assays was

from 50 to 90 percent.

2.1 Protease Assay, Continuous (Alcalase, Esperase, Savinase)

The protease assay is based on measuring the formation of a colored compound as a result of the reaction of primary amino groups with a chromogen, trinitrobenzoic acid. Absorbency was measured at 420 nm. The assays were run at room temperature.

Reaction mixture contained in a final volume of 1 ml:
190 µl of 0.5 M Tris-HCl buffer pH8.5,
500 µl of 0.5% dimethylcaseine,
300 µl of 0.1% trinitrobenzoic acid,
10 µl of appropriately diluted enzyme.

2.2 Alpha Amylase Assay, Continuous (Duramyl, Termamyl)

The alpha amylase assay is based on determination of the release of a colored compound, 4-nitrophenol from a chromogenic alpha amylase substrate, 4-nitrophenyl-a-D-maltopentaoside. Absorbency was measured at 405 nm. The assays were run at room temperature.

Reaction mixture contained in a final volume of 1 ml:
970 µl of 50 mM K-Phosphate buffer pH7.0,
10 µl of 27 mM 4-nitrophenyl-a-D-maltopentaoside,
10 µl of a-glucosidase (Sigma), (5000U/ml)*,
10 µl of appropriately diluted enzyme.

* The addition of α-glucosidase to the assay mixture was not necessary, which might be due to contamination of the enzyme preparations with α-glucosidase.

2.3 Cellulase Assay, Discontinuous (Celluzyme)

The cellulase assay is based on determination of reducing capacity of low molecular weight glucose oligomers originating from carboxymethylcellulose in the ferricyanide reaction, by reversed colorimetry.

Reaction mixture contained in a total volume of 0.5 ml:
365 µl of 50 mM K-Phosphate buffer pH7.0,
125 µl of 0.75% carboxymethylcellulose,
10 µl of appropriately diluted enzyme.

268

The mixture was incubated at 40°C for 10 to 60 min. 250 µl of Stop Reagent (0.125 M Na_3PO_4 x 12 H_2O, pH12) was added to stop the reaction. 250 µl of Ferry Reagent (0.16% $K3Fe(CN)_6$ in 1.4% Na_3PO_4) was added, and tubes incubated at 100°C for 10 min.

Absorbance was measured at 420 nm against individual blanks. The blanks were prepared as follows. Reaction mixture was prepared as above, and the Stop Reagent was added immediately. Then blanks were incubated at 40°C along with the samples.

2.4 Lipase Assay, Continuous (Lipolase)

The lipase assay is based on the hydrolysis of tributirin resulting in a pH change.

The reactions were performed in a total volume of 50 ml at room temperature with constant stirring. Measurements of pH were performed using an Orion Research microprocessor pH/ millivolt meter 811.

The reaction mixture contained:

39 ml of H_2O,

10 ml of Emulsifier,

1 ml of tributirin.

The pH was adjusted to 7.0 using 0.1 N NaOH. Then 10 µl of appropriately diluted enzyme was added. Immediately after the addition of enzyme, pH measurements were followed every 5 seconds for about 1 minute. Based on these time points, pH curves were built, and the linear segment of each curve was used for calculating the activity.

The emulsifier was prepared as follows:

NaCl, KH_2PO_4 and glycerol were dissolved in H_2O to the final concentration of, respectively, 1.7%, 0.04% and 54%. Under vigorous stirring, Gum Arabic was sprinkled into the solution to the final concentration of 0.6%.

2.5 Lipoxidase Assay, Continuous

The method is based on following an increase in absorbance at 234 nm (Sigma). The assays were run at room temperature.

The reaction mixture contained in a final volume of 1 ml:

90 µl of 1M Tris-HCl buffer pH8.5;

900 µl of Substrate,

10 µl of appropriately diluted enzyme.

269

Substrate was a 0.03% solution of linoleic acid, first emulsified with an equal volume of 100% ethanol, and then diluted with water to an appropriate volume with constant stirring.

3   Results and Discussion

Activities of seven commercial enzyme preparations used in the laundry detergent industry (three proteases, two alpha amylases, one cellulase and one lipase) were compared using four preparations of I_E crystal water (D_S-20, D_S-50, D_S-93 and D_S-320). For all seven enzymes, double distilled water was used for control measurements. In addition, a purified preparation of lipoxidase purchased from Sigma chemical company was tested in the same set of water preparations under two conditions, using optimal and non-optimal pH.

With the exception of the cellulase assay, which was discontinuous, enzyme activities were measured in continuous assays providing minimal assay error. All measurements were done at least in triplicate, and standard deviation was calculated for the average values obtained.

The effects of crystal water preparations on enzyme activities were as presented in Tables 1 and 2.

No pronounced effect was observed on the proteases (Alcalase, Esperase and Savinase). A slight inhibitory effect of D_S-50, D_S-93 and D_S-320 on Alcalase (in the range of 5-10%) was observed.

No pronounced effect was observed on alpha amylases (Duramyl and Termamyl). A slight inhibitory effect (in the range of 10%) on Duramyl by D_S-320 was observed.

D_S-20 caused slight stimulation of cellulase (Celluzyme) activity (in the range of 10-35%), while D_S-50 caused more pronounced stimulation of Celluzyme activity (in the range of 35-60%). The error for this assay is rather high, as a continuous cellulase assay is not available. Therefore, the range observed for this stimulatory effect was fairly wide.

No pronounced stimulatory effect was observed for lipase (Lipolase), while an inhibitory effect was observed with D_S-320 (up to 35%). Since the substrate for this reaction is highly hydrophobic, the apparent inhibitory effect may be due to changed substrate availability rather than altered enzyme activity.

In the case of purified lipoxidase (Sigma), a pronounced inhibitory effect of D_S-320 was observed for both optimal and non-optimal assay conditions, and it was more pronounced under optimal pH conditions (up to 74%). Under non-optimal

Table 1. Activities of commercial enzyme preparations in I_E crystal water compared to activities in double-distilled water (as percent of activity in double-distilled water)

Type of I_E	Type of Enzyme						
	Alcalase	Esperase	Savinase	Duramyl	Termamyl	Celluzyme	Lipolase
Control	100 +/-5	100 +/-3	100 +/-5	100 +/-6	100 +/-7	100 +/-5	100 +/-5
D_S-20	94 +/-12	86 +/-3	100 +/-7	97 +/-5	99 +/-12	122 +/-13	103 +/-7
D_S-50	88 +/-3	104 +/-5	108 +/-9	93 +/-7	105 +/-9	148 +/-13	87 +/-6
D_S-93	86 +/-7	93 +/-9	105 +/-8	91 +/-7	98 +/-7	100 +/-10	90 +/-4
D_S-320	88 +/-8	105 +/-12	98 +/-4	84 +/-4	112 +/-5	113 +/-14	65 +/-3

Table 2. Activity of purified lipoxidase (Sigma) in I_E crystal water compared to activity in double-distilled water (in percent)

Type of I_E water	pH 8.5 (optimal)	pH7.0 (non-optimal)
Control	100 +/- 5	100 +/-5
D_S -20	96 +/-3	75 +/-10
D_S -50	100 +/-7	80 +/-8
D_S -93	89 +/-14	84 +/-6
D_S -320	28 +/-2	77 +/-7

conditions, preparations D_S-20, D_S-50 and D_S-93 were also slightly inhibitory (in the range of 10 - 35%). As with lipase activity, the inhibitory effect on lipoxidase may be due to the hydrophobic nature of the substrate.

These results suggest that I_E water does not exert a general effect on enzymatic activity. This is an encouraging result for potential medical applications, because it may be possible to selectively increase activity of certain enzymes, while not affecting others. The results also indicate that activity of certain commercial enzymes, e.g. cellulases, can be stimulated with I_E preparations.

This preliminary study does not allow us to comment on mechanisms responsible for the described effects of I_E waters on the tested enzymes. However, it is unlikely that I_E structures have a direct effect on the active site of an enzyme, due to size constraints. The size of enzymes is on the order of 10 to 30 nanometers, which is comparable to the size of the smallest I_E structures[4]. The size of an enzyme active site is about an order of magnitude smaller. Enzyme molecules or their substrates (or both) might be absorbing on I_E structures, which might explain the observed phenomenon as a concentration effect. However, a more detailed study is required to confirm or to refute this hypothesis.

4   References

1.   S.-Y. Lo, *Modern Phys. Lett.* B, 10 (19), 909 (1996).
2.   S.-Y. Lo *et al.*, *Modern Phys. Lett.* B, 10 (19), 921 (1996).
3.   A.P. Sinitsyn *et al.*, *Microbiology J.*, In preparation.
4.   O. Berson, S.-Y. Lo, *Personal communication.*

EFFECT OF I_E SOLUTIONS
ON ENZYMES AND MICROBIAL CELLS

ARKADY P SINITSYN

OLGA BERSON, SHUI YIN LO

Originally published as *Physical, Chemical and
Biological Properties of Stable Water Clusters,*
Proceedings of the First International Symposium.
Reprinted here by permission of
World Scientific Publishing Company, 1998.

The effects of five I_E^{TM} water preparations (D_S, A_{CE}, S_S, I_M, C_S) of various concentrations on aerobic fungi and aerobic bacteria were investigated *in vivo,* by substituting I_E water for distilled water in culture media. It was established that the bioactivity of I_E waters depends on the type of I_E preparation, its concentration, and the type of microorganism used for fermentation. As much as 100% increase in maximum enzymatic activity and up to 30 hours decrease in fermentation time was observed in some microorganisms when culture media were prepared with certain types of I_E water. However, no effect or even inhibition of enzymatic activity by I_E was seen in some microorganism/I_E combinations. An optimal I_E preparation was identified for each microorganism for further scale-up experiments. The fungal colonies grown on agar plates in the presence and in the absence of I_E water demonstrated distinct morphological differences and thus, these findings indicate a significant bioactivity of I_E waters. The rate of methane production by a methanogenic consortium increased about 2 times over control when stimulated by Ds-50 I_E water. The effects of different types of I_E waters on cellulase activities (FPA, CMCase, β-glucanase, β-glucosidase), xylanase, α-amylase, glucoamylase and lipoxigenase activities were investigated *in vitro,* by substituting I_E water for 50-100% of distilled water in the enzymatic reaction mixtures. The most significant stimulating effect of certain I_E preparations (up to 80 %) was detected in the case of cellulases. Increase in enzymatic activity (15-70 %) was observed in the other enzymes following their stimulation with I_E waters.

1 Introduction

Microorganisms are generally divided in four major groups: bacteria, fungi (molds, yeasts, and mushrooms), algae, and protozoa. All of these organisms are single cell or clusters of cells of the same type. Microbial biotechnology, or industrial microbiology, deals with processes involving microorganisms, both naturally existing and genetically engineered. Pharmaceutical, Agricultural, Food, Chemical, and Environmental Industries widely use microbial products and processes (Figures 1, 2).

One of the important groups of industrial products are enzymes, globular catalytic proteins, highly specific in the reaction they catalyze. There is considerable evidence that a definite three-dimensional configuration is essential for the enzyme to work properly. The so called, lock-and-key model, postulates that the enzyme has a specific site, the "lock", which is a geometrical compliment of the substrate, "key", and that only substrates with the proper complementary shape can bind to the enzyme so that catalysis occurs.

There are thousands of enzymes presently known, however, the proteases, enzymes that hydrolyze peptide bonds in proteins, and the α-amylases, enzymes which hydrolyse starch, dominate the present commercial enzyme market. These enzymes are widely used in the laundry, dry cleaning, food, textile, paper, pharmaceutical, and other industrial applications to name a few.

Another group of enzymes with a large potential for industrial application are the cellulases, enzymes involved in hydrolysis of cellulose. The production of glucose from cellulose containing wood based materials and agricultural wastes is not yet profitable but is being intensively studied world-wide. Glucose, produced by hydrolysis of cellulose, can be fermented to produce ethanol and other chemical intermediates. Although the cellulase enzyme can be produced efficiently, the relatively low activity of the enzyme means that it must be used in large quantities to achieve adequate cellulose hydrolysis.

The activity of an enzyme defines its ability to catalyze a reaction. The higher the activity of an enzyme, the faster the reaction it catalyzes will go and/or smaller amount of the enzyme will be required to catalyze the same reaction.

Recently Lo[1] and Lo et al.[2] reported on distinct physical and chemical properties of stable I_E™ water clusters (I_E water). Water is one of the most essential substances for living. Approximately 70% of a bacterial cell mass is water, while cells of higher organisms are as much as 90% water (Neidhardt et al.[3]). It is important, therefore, to study the biological activity of I_E water.

Major industries which make wide use of industrial microbiology:

- **Pharmaceutical**
  Production of:
    - antibiotics
    - hormones
    - vaccines
    - blood-clotting factors
- **Agricultural**
    - Manufacturing of pharmaceuticals for veterinary medicine
    - Plant genetic engineering
    - Cultivation of leguminous plants
- **Food**
  Production of:
    - dairy products
    - pickles
    - fructose and citric acid added to carbonated drinks
    - vitamins
    - wine, beer, spirits
- **Chemical**
  Manufacturing of:
    - alcohols
    - solvents
    - organic acids
- **Environmental protection**
    - biodegradation of pollutants
    - biosorption of pollutants

Figure 1   Industries that rely on microbiological processes.

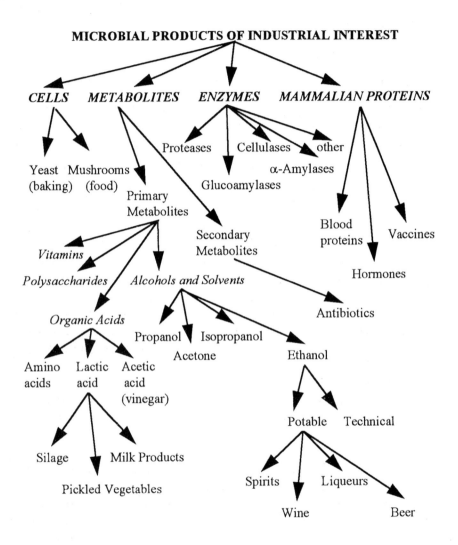

MICROBIAL PRODUCTS OF INDUSTRIAL INTEREST

CELLS   METABOLITES   ENZYMES   MAMMALIAN PROTEINS

Proteases   Cellulases   other

Yeast   Mushrooms   α-Amylases
(baking)   (food)   Glucoamylases
                    Primary
                    Metabolites

Vitamins   Secondary   Blood
                             Metabolites   proteins   Vaccines

Polysaccharides   *Alcohols and Solvents*   Hormones

Organic Acids   Antibiotics

                    Propanol   Isopropanol
                    Acetone   Ethanol
Amino   Lactic   Acetic
acids   acid   acid
                  (vinegar)   Potable   Technical

Silage   Milk Products
                                        Spirits   Liqueurs
        Pickled Vegetables
                                            Wine   Beer

Figure 2 Important products of biotechnology

276

The objectives of this research were to investigate the bioactivity of I_E waters in aerobic and anaerobic bacteria and aerobic fungi (*in vivo* experiments) and to study the influence of I_E waters on activities of various bacterial and fungal enzymes (*in vitro* experiments).

2   Materials and Methods

2.1 Microbial Strains and Growth Conditions for In Vivo Experiments

Fungal strains FS11, FS22, FS33, and AA, and bacterial strains BL and PS were used for *in vivo* and *in vitro* experiments. All fungal and bacterial strains were initially grown on agar slants prepared with the appropriate growth media without I_E water added. Some amount of cells from the plates were suspended in a small amount of the growth medium with no I_E water to prepare an inoculum. The prepared inoculum was then added into the liquid production medium, prepared with different types of I_E waters or with distilled water as a control. The content of I_E waters in the cultivation media was about 100%.

The cultivations of FS11, FS22, and FS33 strains were carried out for 160-180 hr. in shaking glass flasks. At time intervals, samples were removed for assay of xylanase activity and CMCase activity, activity toward soluble carboxymethyl cellulose. All measurements were carried out in triplicate.

The BL, PS and AA strains were cultivated for 72-144 h. At different time intervals, samples were withdrawn for assay of α-amylase activity (BL and PS strains) and glucoamylase activity (AA strain). All measurements were repeated three times.

To demonstrate the *in vivo* bioactivity of I_E waters, agar nutrition medium was prepared with D_S-20 and D_S-94 I_E waters and with distilled water as a control. The prepared agar plates were seeded with AA strain from an agar slant (prepared with distilled water) and incubated at room temperature to obtain single colonies.

An effect of D_S-50 I_E solution on the activity of three anaerobic methanogenic consortia [from preacidification stage and methanogenic stage of pilot two-stage methanogenic reactor, and from industrial methanotank for utilization of municipal wastes] were studied. Experiments were carried out in lab-scale bioreactors (2.8 L plastic methanotanks), and were duplicated for each sample of methanogenic consortium.

The components of nutritional medium were dissolved either in distilled water (control) or in $I_E D_S$-50 water. Methanotanks were filled by 90% with the obtained media and inoculated with 10 % v/v of one of the three types of active biomass. The overall content of $I_E D_S$-50 water in methanotanks, therefore, was 90%. The cultivation was carried out in a batch-mode. Acetic acid was used as the substrate for methanogenic bacteria. It was added to the nutritional medium at the beginning of the cultivation, to give the initial concentration of 3 g/L.

CH_4 was measured in off-gas of the methanotanks by a gas chromatography (GC Type LHM 8 MD-3, Moscow Experimental Chromatography Plant, Russia) and the rate of CH_4 production was determined. The ratio of the methane production rate to dry weight of methanogenic consortium biomass was calculated. This ratio was used as a measure of the activity of methanogenic consortium.

2.2 Enzyme Preparations for In Vitro Experiments

Super ACE Blends (#1 and #2), crude liquid industrial preparations of cellulase and xylanase, were extracted from FS11 fungal strain. The crude dry preparation #3.29.1 of cellulase and xylanase was produced from FS22 fungal strain. The crude dry preparation F60-4 UF-FD #213.3 of cellulase and xylanase was prepared from the FS33 fungal strain. The crude industrial dry preparation AA G18x of glucoamylase was obtained from the AA fungal strain. The crude industrial dry preparations PS G3x of α-amylase and protease were produced from the bacterial PS strain. The crude industrial dry preparation BaL: G18x of α-amylase was made from the BL bacterial strain. The crude industrial dry preparation AA G10x of lipoxigenase was processed from the AA fungal strain.

2.3 Assays of Cellulase Activities

Cellulases are enzymes which split β-1,4-glucosidic bonds in cellulose. Most cellulases are made up of at least three different activities (several endo-β-1,4,-glucanases, cellobiohydrolases and a cellobiase). Another activity that is associated with cellulase and has an important role in hydrolytic breakdown of lignocellulosic biomass to single sugars is xylanase (breaks xylan).

The activities of cellulases towards soluble substrates were studied using IUPAC recommended standard carboxylmethylcellulase (CMCase), β-glucanase, β-glucosidase and xylanase activity assays as described elsewhere[4,5]. CMCase activity was measured as cellulase activity towards soluble carboxymethyl cellulose. β-glucanase activity was assayed as cellulase activity towards soluble barley β-glucan. Xylanase activity was measured as activity towards soluble birch wood xylan. Activity of β-glucosidase activity was measured as an initial rate of p-nitrophenol production from soluble p-nitrophenyl-β-D-glucoside (pNPG). The activity of cellulase towards insoluble cellulose was analysed with filter paper assay (FPA). FPA reflects total saccharification cellulase activity in filter paper hydrolysis (initial rate of reducing sugar production).

The I_E waters were used to dilute cellulase preparations by 500-30,000 times and to prepare 0.1-0.2 M acetic, pH 5.0, buffer. The stock solutions of soluble substrates (CMC, β-glucan, Xylan, pNPG) were prepared with distilled water. The insoluble filter paper substrate was suspended in I_E-based acetic buffer solution. The resulting content of I_E waters in filter paper assay was about 100% and it was 95% in β-glucosidase activity assay. Final I_E concentrations in CMCase, β-glucanase, and xylanase activity assays were about 50%. All experiments were carried out in triplicate in plastic vessels. Control assays were performed the same way, but with no I_E water in the reaction mixtures.

2.4 Assays of Glucoamylase, Lipoxigenase, α-Amylase, and Protease Activities

Glucoamylase is the exo-depolymerase, which hydrolyzes starch by non-random cleavage of α-1,4-glucosidic bonds from the terminal side of the polymeric molecule of starch. Glucoamylase activity was determined as an initial rate of glucose production from soluble corn starch at 30°C, pH 4.7.

Soluble starch was dissolved in I_E D_S-20 or D_S-94 water, boiled for 10 min., and then cooled to 20°C. The obtained solution was diluted with acetic buffer (pH 4.7), prepared with I_E D_S-20 or D_S-94, to give 1.5% w/v final concentration of starch. 10mL of this starch solution was mixed with 5mL of AsAw G18x α-amylase preparation, and incubated for 10 min. at 30°C. After the reaction was stopped, glucose concentration was determined.

α-amylase is the endo-depolymerase, which hydrolyzes starch by random cleavage of internal α-1,4-glucosidic bonds. α-amylase activity of PrSu G3x preparation was determined at pH 6.0 and 30°C and that of BaL G18x at pH 7.5 and 90°C as described below.

Soluble starch was dissolved in I_E D_S-20 or D_S-94 water, boiled for 10 min. and cooled to 20°C. The obtained solution was then diluted with phosphate buffer, to a pH of 6.0 or 7.5, prepared with I_E D_S-20 or D_S-94, to give 1.5% w/v final concentration of starch. 10mL of this starch solution was mixed with 5mL of PrSu G3x or BaL G18x α-amylase preparation, and incubated for 10 min. at the proper temperature. After the reaction was stopped, reducing sugars concentration was determined, and activity of the enzyme was calculated as an initial rate of reducing sugars production.

Protease is the enzyme, which catalyzes hydrolysis of peptide bonds in polypeptides and proteins. Protease activity toward casein was determined spectrophotometrically at 670nm.

Casein was dissolved in phosphate buffer (pH 8.5), prepared with I_E D_S-20 or D_S-94, to produce 2% w/v solution. 2mL of the obtained solution was mixed with PrSu G3x protease preparation and incubated for 15 min. at 55°C. The remaining (at the end of the reaction) substrate was precipitated with 4mL of 5% trichloroacetic acid (TCAA) and filtrated. A 1mL sample was withdrawn from the filtered solution and mixed with 5mL of 0.5M Na_2CO_3 and 1mL of Folin Reagent. The optical density was measured against an appropriate blank at 670nm.

Lipoxigenase (lipoxidase) activity was determined spectrophotometrically at 234nm. A mixture of linoleic, linolenic and arachidonic fatty acids was used as a substrate. Substrate stock solutions were prepared by adding 0.25 mL of the fatty acids mixture drop by drop to 5mL of universal buffer with a pH of 6 for fungal lipoxigenase or pH 9 for soybean lipoxidase, prepared in both cases with I_E water D_S-20 or D_S-94. The obtained solutions were homogenized by hand mixing and then they were diluted with the appropriate buffer to bring the volume to 50mL. Immediately before activity determination, the stock substrate solution was diluted 3.5 times with the buffer solution, with an appropriate pH. 10 mL of the diluted substrate solution was then mixed with 1mL of AsAw G10x lipoxigenase preparation or soybean lipoxidase preparation (Sigma), and the mixture was incubated for 10 min. at 16°C. Optical density (234nm) was measured against appropriate blank at the end of the reaction.

The content of I_E waters in the reaction mixtures of glucoamylase, lipoxigenase, α-amylase and protease activity assays was about 100%. The same enzyme preparations, buffers and substrates were used for control assays, but without any I_E water added to the reaction mixture. All experiments were triplicated and they were carried out in plastic vessels. Magnetic stirring was not used to prevent any influence of magnetic field on charged I_E structures.

2.5 I_E Waters Used in the Study

Five types of I_E waters were used: D_S, A_{CE}, S_S, I_M, C_S. Four concentrations of D_S I_E water were studied: D_S-20, D_S-50, D_S-94, and D_S-310 (the larger the number in the code, the higher I_E concentration). Two concentrations of C_S (C_S-18 and C_S-80) and I_M (I_M-25 and I_M-70) I_E solutions were examined. Three concentrations of S_S

(S_S-16, S_S-32, S_S-46) and one concentration of A_{CE} (A_{CE}-20) I_E solutions were used in the study.

All I_E water solutions were prepared by the same method, but using different substances (C_S -- cellulose; I_M -- isomaltose; S_S -- sophorose; A_{CE} -- cellulase; D_S -- proprietary solution) to initiate the process of I_E crystals' formation. First, very dilute solutions (10^{-13} M) of the above substances in ultra pure water (less than 10 ppb total dissolved solids, resistance of $18M\Omega$) were prepared by consequent dilution and mixing by shaking. The obtained solutions contained low levels of I_E crystals. They were further concentrated to produce I_E solutions of various concentrations [1,2].

3 Results and Discussion

3.1 In Vivo Experiments

3.1.1 Effect of I_E Waters on Fungal Strains, Producers of Cellulases and Xylanases

Fungal strains FS11, FS22 and FS33, producers of cellulases and xylanases, were used in this study. *In vivo* bioactivity of I_E waters was assessed by the influence of I_E waters on the level of maximum CMCase and xylanase activities observed in the course of fermentation in shaking flasks, and by the effect of I_E waters on the cultivation time required to attain the maximum CMCase or xylanase activities.

Table 1 illustrates *in vivo* bioactivity of various I_E waters in aerobic fungal strains FS11, FS22, and FS33 as compared to distilled water controls. A positive bioactivity toward FS11 strain was observed for all I_E waters tested except for C_S-18. The majority of I_E waters, with the exception for D_S-20, S_S-46, A_{CE}-20, and I_M-25, positively stimulated the FS33 strain. However, no effect or inhibiting activity of all I_E waters, aside from S_S-16 and A_{CE}-20, on FS22 strain, were observed.

3.1.2 Effect of I_E Waters on the Bacterial Strains BL and PS and the Fungal Strain AA

The effect of D_S type of I_E water at two concentrations (D_S-20 and D_S-94) on BL and PS bacterial strains, producers of α-amylase, and AA fungal strain, producer of glucoamylase, was investigated. The content of I_E waters in the fermentation media was about 100%. During the cultivation, samples of cultures were withdrawn and α-amylase activity (BL, PS strains) and glucoamylase activity (AA strain) were assayed. The results are shown in Table 2.

Table 1 Effect of I_E waters on the aerobic fungal strains, producers of cellulases and xylanases

Fungal strains	Type of I_E water	Effect of I_E waters on maximum enzymatic activity observed during fermentation		Effect of I_E waters on cultivation time required to attain maximum enzymatic activity	
		CMCase	Xylanase	CMCase	Xylanase
FS11	D_S-20	++	+	++	0
	D_S-50	++	++	++	0
	D_S-94	++	+	++	0
	D_S-310	+	+	0	+
	A_{CE}-20	+	-	-	0
	S_S-16	++	0	0	0
	S_S-32	+	+	0	0
	S_S-46	++	++	-	++
	I_M-25	-	++	+	++
	I_M-70	+	+	-	-
	C_S-18	0	-	0	0
	C_S-80	+	+	0	+
FS22	D_S-20	0	0	0	0
	D_S-50	0	0	0	0
	D_S-94	0	0	0	0
	D_S-310	0	0	0	0
	A_{CE}-20	+	+	0	0
	S_S-16	+	0	++	0
	S_S-46	0	0	0	0
	I_M-25	-	0	0	0
	I_M-70	+	0	0	-
FS33	D_S-20	0	0	0	0
	D_S-50	0	+	0	+
	D_S-94	++	+	+	+
	D_S-310	0	0	+	0
	A_{CE}-20	++	+	++	+
	S_S-16	+	+	0	0
	S_S-46	+	0	- -	-
	I_M-25	-	+	-	-
	I_M-70	++	++	+	0
	C_S-18	+	0	-	0
	C_S-80	-	++	+	++

(++) - increase of the parameter by more than 50% versus control

(+) - increase of the parameter by 5-50% versus control

(0) - insignificant, less than 5% change in the parameter as compared to control

(-) - decrease of the parameter by 5-25% compared to control

(- -) - decrease of the parameter by 25-50% versus control

Table 2 Effect of D_S-20 and D_S-94 I_E waters on α-amylase production by the BL and PS bacterial strains and glucoamylase production by the AA fungal strain.

Cultivation time, hr.	Change in enzymatic activity in samples prepared with D_S-20 versus controls , %			Change in enzymatic activity in samples prepared with D_S-94 versus controls , %		
	BL strain (α-amylase)	PS strain (α-amylase)	AA strain (gluco-amylase)	BL strain (α-amylase)	PS strain (α-amylase)	AA strain (gluco-amylase)
72	10	-6	ND	3	-10	ND
96	42	-9	ND	4	6	ND
120	51	-21	ND	-3	-17	ND
168	ND	ND	-11	ND	ND	-25

ND - parameter was not determined.

The positive numbers indicate increase and the negative numbers show decrease in the enzymatic activity.

D_S-20 I_E water stimulated a significant increase of α-amylase activity in the BL strain (up to 50% versus control), but it slightly inhibited α-amylase production in the PS strain (up to 20%) and glucoamylase production in the AA fungal strain (up to 10%). D_S-94 I_E water was neutral or inhibitory for all strains tested.

3.1.3 Effect of Diluted (D_S-20) and Concentrated (D_S-94) I_E Waters on Morphology and Density of Fungal Colonies Grown on Agar Plates.

Agar solid growth media were prepared with D_S-20, D_S-94 and distilled water as a control. The prepared agar plates were seeded with the AA fungal strain and incubated at room temperature.

Apparent morphological differences between colonies grown on agar plates with D_S I_E waters and distilled water were observed. The addition of D_S-20 I_E water to the growth media produced more colored pigment colonies with more spores. On the contrary, colonies detected on agar plate prepared with D_S-94 were transparent, without any pigment, and with very low sporulation.

3.1.4 Effect of D_S-50 I_E Water on Consortia of Anaerobic Methanogenic Microorganisms

Consortium of anaerobic microorganisms is widely used in large scale for digestion and utilization of organic wastes and for production of "bio-gas" (70% of CH_4 and 30% of CO_2 mixture). The effects of D_S-50 I_E water on three methanogenic consortia were studied: a consortium from the preacidification stage, of pilot two-stage methanogenic reactor; a consortium from the methanogenic stage of the same reactor, and a consortium from industrial methanotank for utilization of municipal wastes.

The addition of D_S-50 to the growth medium of the consortium from the methanogenic stage of pilot scale reactor led to a significant increase (1.7 times over control) of methane production. The other two consortia were not stimulated by D_S-50. Although a further detailed study is required, a conclusion can be made about the possibility of using I_E in an industrial setting for boosting the efficiency of municipal waste digestion.

3.2 In Vitro Experiments

3.2.1 Effect of I_E Waters on Cellulase and Xylanase Activities

The effects of various types and concentrations of I_E waters on the activity of fungal cellulases and xylanases were studied. Since cellulases are made up of at least three different activities, assays for carboxylmethylcellulase (CMCase), β-glucanase, and β-glucosidase activities were carried out. Overall activity of cellulases towards insoluble cellulose was analysed with filter paper assay (FPA). The obtained results are shown in Table 3.

Based on the analysis of Table 3, a conclusion can be drawn about a prominent stimulating effect of the tested D_S, A_{CE}-20, S_S-46, and C_S-18 I_E waters on cellulase and xylanase activities in the FS11, FS22, and FS33 fungal strains. On the other hand, S_S-16, S_S-32, I_M-25, I_M-70, and C_S-80 I_E water preparations have a neutral or slightly inhibiting effect on cellulase and xylanase activities in the studied fungal strains.

3.2.1 Effect of I_E Waters on Glucoamylase, Lipoxigenase, α-Amylase, and Protease Activities

The effects of various types and concentrations of I_E waters on the activity of fungal glucoamylase and lipoxigenase, and bacterial α-amylase and protease were studied

Table 3 Effect of I_E waters on cellulase and xylanase activities

Fungal enzyme blends	Type of I_E water	Enzymatic activities assayed				
		FPA (overall cellulase)	CMCase	β-Glucanase	Xylanase	β-Glucosidase
Super Ace Blend #2, FS11 strain	D_S-20	+	+	+	+	++
	D_S-50	+	+	+	++	++
	D_S-94	+	+	+	++	ND
	D_S-310	+	+	++	+++	ND
	A_{CE}-20	+	++	++	+	ND
	S_S-16	0	-	-	-	-
	S_S-32	+	-	-	+	0
	S_S-46	+	+	++	+	++
	I_M-25	0	-	-	-	0
	I_M-70	+	-	-	0	0
	C_S-18	+	+	++	+	+
	C_S-80	+	-	-	+	++
Super Ace Blend #1, FS11 strain	D_S-20	+	++	+	+	+
	D_S-50	+	++	+	+	+
	D_S-94	+	+++	+	++	0
Blend #3.29.1, FS22 strain	D_S-20	+	+	++	+	+
	D_S-50	+	+	++	++	+
	D_S-94	+	+	+	++	0
Blend #213.1, FS33 strain	D_S-20	0	++	+++	+	0
	D_S-50	0	+	++	+	+
	D_S-94	0	+	++	+	-

(+++) - over 50% enzymatic activity increase over control

(++) - 25 to 50% enzymatic activity increase over control

(+) - 5 to 25% enzymatic activity increase over control

(0) - insignificant, less than 5% change in the activity as compared to control

(-) - 5 to 25% activity decrease compare to control

(ND) - activity was not determined

Table 4 Effect of I_E waters on glucoamylase, lipoxigenase, α-amylase, and protease activities

Type of I_E water	Enzymatic activities assayed			
	Glucoamylase (fungal preparation AA G18x)	Lipoxigenase (fungal preparation AA G18x)	α-Amylase (bacterial preparation PS G3x)	Protease (bacterial preparation PS G3x)
D_S-20	0	+	0	-
D_S-50	ND	ND	ND	ND
D_S-94	0	+++	0	+
D_S-310	-	ND	-	+
A_{CE}-20	-	ND	-	+
S_S-16	0	ND	-	+
S_S-32	0	ND	-	+
S_S-46	0	ND	0	0
I_M-25	-	ND	-	-
I_M-70	0	ND	-	0
C_S-18	0	ND	0	+
C_S-80	0	ND	0	0

(+++) - over 50% enzymatic activity increase over control

(++) - 25 to 50% enzymatic activity increase over control

(+) - 5 to 25% enzymatic activity increase over control

(0) - insignificant, less than 5% change in the activity as compared to control

(-) - 5 to 25% activity decrease compare to control

(ND) - activity was not determined

in vitro. The content of I_E waters in the reaction mixtures was about 100%. The obtained results are shown in Table 4.

Data presented in Table 4 demonstrate neutral or slightly negative effect of tested I_E waters on glucoamylase and α-amylase activities. A slight stimulation of protease activity (up to 25% over control) was observed with D_S-94, D_S-310, A_{CE}-20, S_S-16, S_S-32, and C_S-18 I_E preparations, while the other I_E waters were slightly inhibiting. Fungal lipoxigenase was strongly stimulated (up to 120% over control) with D_S-94 I_E sample, and only slightly (about 10% increase over control) with D_S-20.

The *in vivo* and *in vitro* data presented above strongly suggest a possibility for development of customised I_E waters for each particular microorganism and enzyme. Such I_E preparations can be used in enzyme manufacturing processes instead of water to increase yields and activities of the produced enzymes. Similarly, a customized I_E preparation can be mixed with a purified enzyme to maximize its activity and to reduce its consumption in an application.

4   References

1. S.-Y. Lo, *Modern Phys. Lett.* B, 10 (19), 909 (1996).
2. S.-Y. Lo *et al.*, *Modern Phys. Lett.* B, 10 (19), 921 (1996).
3. F.C. Neidhardt *et al.* in *Physiology of the Bacterial Cell: A Molecular Approach*, ed. F.C. Neidhardt (Sinauer Associates, Inc., Massachusetts, 1990).
4. K.R. Sharrock, *J. Biochem. Biophys. Methods*, 17, 81 (1988).
5. T.K. Ghose, *Pure & Appl. Chem.,*59(2), 257 (1987).

ANOMALOUS STATE OF ICE

SHUI-YIN LO*

Originally Published in Modern Physics
Letters B, Vol. 10, No. 19 (1996) 909-919

Anomalous state of ice, which is a novel stable structures made from water molecules, can be induced to form under the action of ions in very dilute solutions, perhaps from a similar physical mechanism that forms ice VI. These stable structures change the UV transmission characteristic of water. Different structures formed from different ions are shown to have similar UV transmission characteristics. These structures can be filtered, concentrated and photographed using a transmission electron-microscope. A dipole–dipole interaction model is constructed to suggest an explanation of the elongated shape of these structures.

1. Introduction

It is well known that water molecules form stable rigid structures: for example, ice VI at room temperature and at high pressure (> 7 kB).[1] Generally, such a high pressure does not occur naturally on Earth. However, we wish to point out that such a high pressure could exist between an ion and its nearby water molecules due to the electrostatic attraction between the charge of an ion and the electric dipole moments of a water molecule. Anomalous state of ice which are stable rigid structures of water molecules similar to ice VI can be grown in water at room temperature and normal pressure provided that suitable dilution of ions in water is performed.

2. Growing Structures Around Ions in Very Dilute Solution

Positively or negatively charged ions in aqueous solutions attract water molecules which have electric dipole moments p that can be expressed as $p = \eta e d = 2.45$ debyes, with $e =$ charge of electron, $d =$ size of water molecule $= 0.278$ nm and $\eta =$ scale factor $= 0.1837$. The electric potential energy, U, experienced by a water molecule at a distance r from the ion is $U = -p \cdot E$ where E is the electric field

*Visiting Associate, Department of Chemistry, California Institute of Technology, Pasadena, CA 91107, USA.

exerted by the ion on the water molecule and is given by

$$E = -\frac{e}{[4\pi\varepsilon r^2]\hat{\mathbf{r}}} \qquad (2.1)$$

with ε = dielectric constant of water = 80. The pressure, P, experienced by the water molecule is equal to the energy density:

$$P \approx \frac{U}{d^3} = \frac{\eta e^2}{4\pi\varepsilon r d^2} . \qquad (2.2)$$

The pressure is inversely proportional to the square of the distance between the ion and water molecule which is a characteristic of coulomb force. The pressure is smaller by a factor of ε as compared with vacuum because of the dielectric property of water. Numerically, it is $P = 0.61$ kB/s^2, where $s = r/d$ is the distance scaled in units of water molecule size. However if the next layer of water molecules around an ion are packed in a regular, spherical symmetric rigid fashion, the pressure experienced by the water molecule immediately outside this layer will be boosted by a factor of $\varepsilon = 80$. This is because the electric field determined from Gauss law $\oint \mathbf{E} \cdot d\mathbf{s} = Q/\varepsilon_0$ is given by the total charge Q enclosed by a closed surface; and the surface is chosen to include the ion and the next layer of water molecules completely. The polarized positive and negative charge of any water molecule is all inside the same closed surface and they cancel out one another. The total charge Q is that of the ion and does not contain polarization from water molecules. So the pressure exerted by an ion on the sth layer of orderly arranged water molecules is in fact boosted to $P = 71.8$ kB/s^2. For the second layer ($s = 2$) of water molecules around an ion, the pressure is 18 kB and the pressure decreases to 8 kB when $s = 3$. If one checks on the phase diagram of water, water turns to ice VI at room temperature at pressure around 7 kB.

With a large pressure arising from a regular structure, one may expect that the water molecules surrounding an ion will turn into ice VI. It is, however, not the ordinary ice VI where the unit cell has a translational invariance. One expects that the crystalline structured water surrounding the ion would have special symmetry due to the spherical symmetrical nature of pressure. There is no study on what properties a spherical symmetric ice crystal should have. The unit cell probably is not rectangular. For lack of a better reliable alternative, it is assumed that the spherical symmetric icy structures surrounding ions have similar properties as that of ordinary ice VI and ice VII. We will call it I_E structure indicating that it is an icy structure formed under the effect of an electric field.

The I_E structure formed around ions is influenced by the movement of ions in water. When two similar charged ions come close together, the pressure on water molecules between them decreases and the I_E structure previously formed will melt. As the ions move away from each other, the pressure builds, and the I_E structure starts to grow again. Let the destruction rate of the I_E structure due to collision be R_D and the growth rate of the I_E structure be R_G. The destruction rate is given by the inverse of collision time t_c: $R_D = 1/t_c$. When ions move in a random fashion in a solution, the collision time is $t_c = k_i^2 \Delta t$, where k_i is the average number of water molecules between two ions and Δt is the collision time between an ion and water molecule. The growth rate R_G is the growth speed v_g of the I_E structure divided by the size of the structure a_c. Therefore the condition for the existence of stable I_E structures in a very dilute solution is: growth rate R_G greater than destruction rate R_D or

$$k_i \gg \left[\frac{a_c}{v_g \Delta t} \right]^{1/2}. \tag{2.3}$$

The growth speed v_g of ordinary ice is well-known to be a function of super-cooling temperature.[1] It ranges from 10^{-4} cm/sec to 10 cm/sec depending on how far ($10^{-2}\,°C$ to $10°C$) the temperature is from the phase transition point at $0°C$. In our case the growth of I_E structures comes from the deviation in pressure rather than in temperature from the phase transition point. Let us take the fast growth rate $v_g = 3$ cm/sec, $a_c \sim 3d$ and $\Delta t \sim 10^{-12}$ sec, then the average number of water molecules between ions k_i has to be greater than 167. Or the ratio of density of ions n_i to that of water molecules has to be smaller than $n_i/n_0 < 2.2 \times 10^{-7}$ which is about 10^{-5} molar concentration and a very dilute solution indeed before there are stable I_E structures.

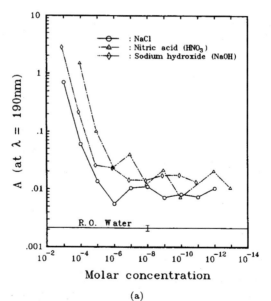

(a)

Fig. 1. (a) UV absorbance (A) measurement at wavelength $\lambda = 190$ nm for three very dilute solutions: NaCl, NaOH, HNO3 at different molar concentrations. The control sample is pure water (RO water, bottom line). (b) UV transmission measurement in the interval of wavelength from $\lambda = 190$ nm to 250 nm for very dilute solutions of NaCl with molar concentrations of 10^{-5} (Y3), 10^{-6} (Y4), ...10^{-12} (Y10) from top to bottom. (c) UV transmission measurement for very dilute solutions of HNO3 with N2 (molar concentration 1.15×10^{-5} M) and N6 (2.1×10^{-11} M), and NaOH with Na2 (1.32×10^{-3} M) and Na10 (1.32×10^{-11} M).

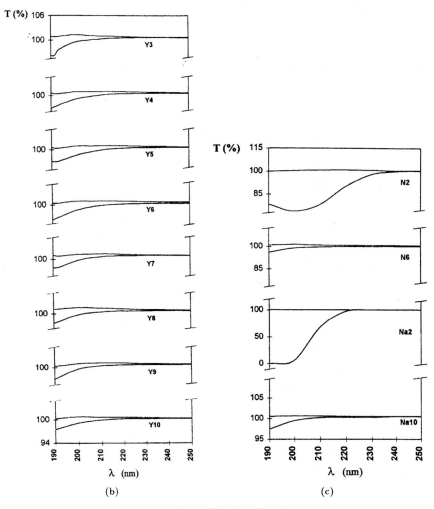

Fig. 1. (*Continued*)

3. UV Transmission Measurement

Evidence for I_E structures shows up easily in UV transmission measurement. The standard method for preparing a very dilute solution is to dissolve a small amount of salt (NaCl), acid (HNO_3), or base (NaOH) in pure water, then dilute it one part to ten parts of pure water.[2] Shake the solution and dilute again one part to ten parts of pure water. Repeat this many times. The solution is measured for UV transmission via a dual beam Perkin–Elmer Lambda 2S machine with a standard reference cell filled with pure water. The absorbance readings from Lambda 2S, which also include effects from scattering as well as absorption of UV light, are

291

displayed in Fig. 1(a) for four solutions: sodium chloride NaCl, sodium hydroxide NaOH, and nitric acid HNO_3 and pure water with molar concentration ranging from 10^{-3} to 10^{-13}. There is clearly a drop of absorbance as molar concentration decrease. Then starting at molar concentration 10^{-5} to 10^{-7} they all fluctuate in the order of 10^{-2}, regardless of their origin. We show selectively a few UV transmission measurements for these types of solutions in the range of wave length $\lambda = 190$ nm to 250 nm in Figs. 1(b) and (c). There is no qualitative difference in the spectrum for various very dilute solutions ($< 10^{-7}$ M) made up from different salts, acids, or base. The UV transmission characteristic of these very dilute solutions is significantly different from the dilute solution when $n_i/n_0 > 10^{-7}$ or molar concentration $> 10^{-5}$. It is important in the experimental procedure that we carefully wash the quartz cell to get rid of any I_E structures each time a measurement is made. A clean quartz cell with pure water is verified by a flat UV transmission flat curve from the Lambda 2 machine. This is done each time prior to the next measurement.

We interpret these results as follows: As solutions become very dilute, I_E structures are formed from water molecules around ions. These water molecules are formed under strong electric field, which is 2×10^6 V/m at three water molecules distance from ions. Hence water molecules in I_E structures are expected to maintain the alignment of their dipole moments. The effective dipole moment of I_E structure is negative towards a positive ion side and positive on the side opposite from the ion. Furthermore, the electric field has spherical symmetry. This condition is quite different from ice VI formed under high pressure which has translational invariance. Unit cell of ice VI is tetragonal and can be repeated in all directions indefinitely. No one so far has constructed a crystal with a spherical symmetry. Hence not much is known about a spherical symmetric crystal or any non-translational invariant unit cell.

The I_E structures are first formed around ions in the solution and do not occur anywhere else. We could generate these structures by breaking them up with shaking. The spherical symmetric I_E structures will break up into many small pieces. These small pieces have electric dipole moment which generate a strong electric field at the poles to attract nearby water molecules to form a bigger piece. These bigger pieces are magnet like except they have an electrical dipole and not a magnetic dipole. They exist independent of ions. They can be broken into smaller pieces and grow bigger. Therefore, as the solution is diluted further from molar concentration 10^{-7} to 10^{-13}, I_E structures remain undiminished by dilution many many times. Since shaking, breaking and then growing of I_E are random, we do see a random spread of UV absorbance around 10^{-2} at $\lambda = 190$ nm for various very dilute solutions as shown in Fig. 1(a). There are great similarity among very dilute solutions of HNO_3, NaOH, and NaCl with different molar concentration and having I_E structures. In Fig. 1(c), the dilute solution N2 of HNO_3 (1.15×10^{-5} M) looks very different from both of the dilute solution NaOH (2.5×10^{-5} M) and the very dilute solution nitric acid (2.1×10^{-11} M) because UV transmission of N2 is still a characteristic of nitric acid.

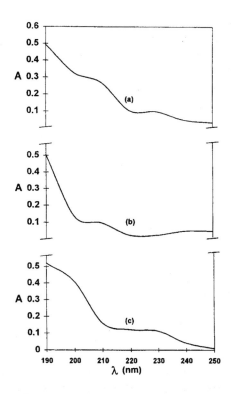

Fig. 2. The UV absorbance for a concentrate I_E structured water (a) before low pressure distillation, (b) evaporated solution and (c) residue solution.

In order to further test the idea of I_E structure, we search for a way to increase the I_E structures in the very dilute solution. In our dipole model, I_E structures created by ions cannot be big. The electric dipoles of the I_E structures on the right hand side of a positively charged ion have the induced charges in the order of negative, positive, negative, positive etc. with polarization vector pointing to the left while the electric dipoles of I_E structure on the left hand side of a positive-charged ion will have exactly the opposite polarization. Hence, the total electric dipole around an ion will tend to cancel out. Less and less I_E structure can grow away from the ion because of diminishing electric field. However for very dilute solutions with mostly I_E structures and very little ions (say $n_i/n_0 < 10^{-11}$), we introduce some dielectric material which does not ionize but has an uneven electronic distribution outside. Then I_E structures can grow outside the dielectric material with polarization lining up on both sides of the molecules. The electric dipole moments of the total I_E structure add up and there is no diminishing of the electric field at the boundary of the I_E structures. So I_E structures can easily grow bigger. For this to occur, we have experimented by introducing an dielectric material with high boiling point ($\sim 350°C$) slowly in the very dilute solution to about several parts per million. And we see a much stronger UV absorbance as well as many more rod-like structures in the electron microscope pictures.

Since the dielectric material having a high boiling point (350°C) and does not evaporate with water, we have used a low pressure rotary evaporator and boil the solution at 67°C. The evaporated and condensed solution has similar UV transmission characteristic as shown in Fig. 2. This strongly suggests the increase of the UV absorbance is due to an increase in I_E structures and not due to impurity such as the dielectric material that we add.

4. Electron Microscope Pictures of I_E Structures

The direct evidence for existence of these stable I_E structures comes from pictures taken with the electron microscope. The very dilute solution with I_E structures is filtered through a 0.1 μm filter paper and then is sputter coated with carbon. The carbon coated filter paper is dissolved in boiling chloroform for twenty minutes. Water and I_E structure will be dissolved away and only carbon skeletons remain. Hitachi transmission microscope H600A is used to take the pictures. The X-ray emitted by the striking electron beam is also examined. If there is any impurity such as solid salt or biological entity, a characteristic X-ray of their constituent atoms by atomic excitation will be emitted. No such characteristic X-rays are seen. Hence it is concluded that the skeleton pictures are not from impurities in the water or biological specimen such as bacteria or virus. The pictures are consistent with the hypothesis that the I_E structures are made up of water molecules alone. Some of the typical pictures are shown in Fig. 3.[3] They are from very dilute solutions of sodium chloride with small and large amount of UV absorbance. For control, we also treat pure water (reverse osmosis water from Millipore machine) the same way; we see none of these structures. Since these structures are of micron size, they can be observed by ordinary optical microscope with some patience also.

5. Dipole–Dipole Interaction Square Lattice Model

In order to understanding the rod-like structures as seen by the electron microscope, we propose the following mechanism. After the I_E structures are created, broken and then grow to larger size, they have larger electric dipole moments. The electrostatic forces between any two adjacent pieces is huge. They either join each other head to tail or side by side. If they lie side by side, their electric dipole moment will be opposite each other to obtain the lowest energy states. The circular sizes of the order of 100 nm seen inside the rod-like structures are assumed to be electric dipoles. Let us assume they are of equal size and have the same amount of electric dipole moment p. The interaction between any two dipoles i and j is given by dipole–dipole interaction.

$$U_{ij} = \frac{\mathbf{p}_i \cdot \mathbf{p}_j - (\mathbf{p}_i \cdot \hat{\mathbf{n}})(\mathbf{p}_j \cdot \hat{\mathbf{n}})}{r_{ij}^3} \tag{5.1}$$

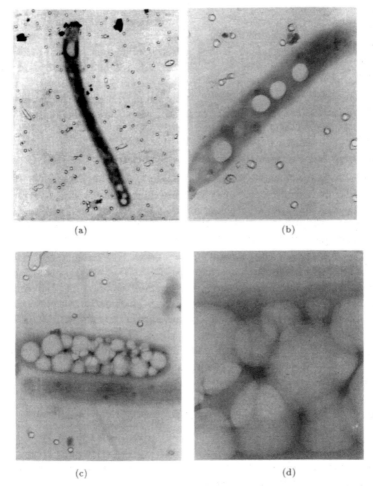

(a)   (b)

(c)   (d)

Fig. 3. Transmission electron microscope photographs of I_E structures. (a) & (b) From NaCl (10^{-11} M) solution with UV absorbance $A = 0.0132$ at $\lambda = 190$ nm, small circles are from filter hole of 0.1 μm for all photographs. Magnification $\times 10,000$ for (a) and $\times 25,000$ for (b). (c) From concentrated NaCl solution with more I_E structures obtained from adding small amount of dielectric material, the UV absorbance being $A = 0.795$ at $\lambda = 190$ nm. Magnification $\times 20,000$. (d) A magnification of $\times 80,000$ of the middle part of the I_E structure in (c). (e) Photographs of I_E structures obtained in the way as that of (c). (f) A magnification of $\times 80,000$ of the middle part of the upper I_E structures in (e).

where r_{ij} is the distance between dipole p_i and p_j and $\hat{n}$ is the unit vector of r_{ij}. The total interaction energy of N dipoles is

$$U = \sum_{i,j}^{N} U_{ij} \,. \tag{5.2}$$

295

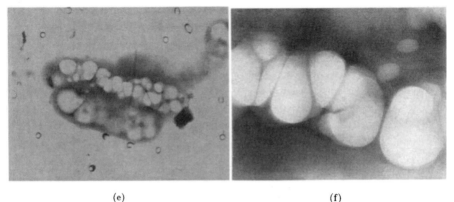

(e)   (f)

Fig. 3. (*Continued*)

For a two dimensional model where each dipole sits on a square lattice where each
lattice spacing is a, it is easy to obtain an analytical solution for the nearest neighboring approximation:

$$U^{(0)} = [-3nl + 2n + l]u_0 \qquad (5.3)$$

where $u_0 = p^2/a^3$ and $nl = N$. The N dipoles are arranged in n row and l column,
where each row of the dipole has the dipole moment pointing in the same direction
along the lattice point. The dipole moments of the next row has just the opposite
direction. The dipole moments in our model are restricted to point only two ways. If
we include the next set of neighboring dipoles which have the strongest interaction,
the additional interaction energy is

$$U^{(1)} = \left[\left(-\frac{1}{4} + \frac{\sqrt{2}}{4}\right)nl + \left(\frac{1}{2} - \frac{\sqrt{2}}{4}\right)n - \frac{\sqrt{2}}{4}l + \frac{\sqrt{2}}{4}\right]u_0. \qquad (5.4)$$

It is possible to find the configuration with the minimum interaction energy $U = U^{(0)} + U^{(1)}$. The shape is rod-like with the ratio r of length l to width w to be

$$r = \frac{l}{n} = \frac{(5/2) - (\sqrt{2}/4)}{1 - (\sqrt{2}/4)} \approx 3.3. \qquad (5.5)$$

It is an elongated object as indicated by electron microscope pictures. This is
displayed in Fig. 4. The experimental values of the ratio r peaks sharply at the
theoretical minimum of 3.3 with a spread from 1 to 14.

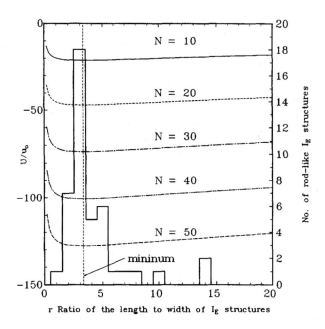

Fig. 4. Dipole–dipole interaction energy of rod-like I_E structure in dimensionless unit U/u_0 versus the ratio r of its length to width. N is the number of dipoles in each rod-like I_E structure. The histogram are numbers of rod-like structures from electron microscope pictures with a given ratio r.

6. Summary

There are considerable experiments in the field of biology, biochemistry and pharmacology indicating that ultra low doses have significant effects on living organisms.[4] Our experiments here show that ultra small amounts of acid, base or salt can induce a stable rigid I_E structures in water itself. These I_E structures have different UV transmission characteristics from pure water. Transmission electron microscope pictures are consistent with the idea that these I_E structures are made up of electric dipoles. Further physical properties of I_E structures will be presented in a separate paper.

Acknowledgment

I wish to thank Professor T. H. Chan of McGill University, Professor Alfred Wong of UCLA, Professor D. Tsui of Princeton University and Professor Sunney Chan of Caltech for suggestive and critical comments. David Gann's support is gratefully acknowledged.

References

1. N. Fletcher, *The Chemical Physics of Ice* (Cambridge University Press, 1970), Fig. 5.4.
2. We use water produced by Millipore RO Plus system that guarantee purity of water to less than several parts per billion of impurity.
3. Similar I_E structures are also seen using Atomic Force Microscope directly. They have also been studied successfully *in situ* by laser autocorrelation method to be published.
4. In *Ultra Low Doses*, edited by C. Doutremepuich, Taylor & Francis, London, Washington D.C. (1991).

Dr. SHUI-YIN LO

EDUCATION

Ph.D., Physics, University of Chicago, Chicago, Illinois, USA, 1966

B.S., Highest Distinction in the Department of Physics, University of Illinois, Urbana, Illinois, USA, 1962

PROFESSIONAL BACKGROUND

Director, Quantum Health Research Institute, 2005- present
Professor of Research in Chinese Medicine, American University of Complementary Medicine, Los Angeles, 2003-present
Founder, and Chairman of World Life Physics Association, 2006
Visiting Faculty Member Department of Physics, California Institute of Technology, Pasadena, CA USA, 1994 to 1998
CEO, Institute for Boson Studies, Pasadena, CA USA, 1987-1992
Senior Lecturer (1977-1986), Tenured Lecturer (1975-1977), Fixed Term Lecturer (1972-1975), University of Melbourne, Victoria, Australia
University Fellow, University of Glasgow, Glasgow, UK, 1969-1972
Research Fellow, Rutherford High Energy Laboratory, Chilton, UK, 1966-1969

SHORT-TERM VISITING SCHOLAR

Institute for Theoretical Physics, Academy of Science, Beijing, China, 1986
Stanford Accelerated Center, California, USA, 1985
Department of Physics, McGill University, Montreal, Canada, 1983
Department of Physics, National University of Singapore, Singapore, 1981-1982
Institute of High Energy Physics, Being, China, 1979-1980
Institute of Theoretical Physics, State University of New York at Stonybrook, New York, USA, 1978
Institute of Theoretical Physics, Berlin University, West Berlin, Germany, 1977

Niels Bohr Institute, Copenhagen, Denmark Department of Physics, University of Prince Edward Island, Charlottetown, P.E.I., Canada

HONOR:

Fellow of Australian Institute of Physics
Marquis Who's Who in the World, 1999 – present
Marquis Who's Who in America, 1996 – present
Marquis Who's Who in Science and Engineering, 1994 – present
Phi Beta Kappa, Sigma Xi, Fellow of Australian Physical Society

TEACHING EXPERIENCE:

Graduate Level Quantum Field Theory, Particle Physics, Mathematical Physics, and General Relativity
Advised four Ph.D. and six M.S. students of physics
Undergraduate Level First year: General Physics
Advanced year: Quantum Mechanics, Electromagnetic Theory, Classical Mechanics, Thermodynamics, Advanced Quantum Mechanics, Advanced Electricity and Magnetism, Statistical Mechanics, Particle Physics
First year organizer: For three years, organized all laboratory and tutorial materials for over one thousand first year physics students

SCIENTIFIC PUBLICATIONS

Lo, S.Y., Cai, X., Liu, B.H., and Matheys, J.P., Partition Temperature and $e + e$ - Annihilation, Europhysics Lett. V6: 19-23, 1988

Li, Yang-Guo, and Lo, S.Y., Proton Nucleus Collision, Long Range Correlation and Pion Condensation, High Energy Phys. and Nucl. Phys., VII 717-719, 1987

Li, Yang-Guo, and Lo, S.Y., Long-Range Correlation Single-Particle Spectrum and Pion Condensation, in Proton-Nuclear Scattering , Nuovo Cim. 98: 539-549, 1987

Lo, S.Y., Massless Model for Multi Particle Production and Pion Condensation, Phys. Lett. B186: 416 420, 1987

Lo, S.Y., and Schreiber, A., Coherent Pions as the Origin of Excessive Soft Photons in Hard Collisions, Phys. Lett. B181: 475, 1986

Lam, C.S., and Lo, S.Y., Induced Production of Bosons and its Application to Centauro Events, Intern. J. Mod. Phys. VI: 451, 1986

Lam, C.S., and Lo, S.Y., Mechanism for Coherent Production of Pions from the Decay of Resonances, Phys. Rev. D33: 1336-1343, 1986

Li, Yang-Guo, and Lo, S.Y., The Influence of D-Wave on High Energy p-D Elastic Scattering, Physica Energie Fort is et Physica Nucleolar 8: 497-501, 1984

Li, Yang-Guo, and Lo, S.Y., Particle Ratios at pp at Ultra-High Energies, Aust. J. Phys. 225-262, 1984

Lam, C.S., and Lo, S.Y., Mechanism for Bunching of Bosons in High Energy Collisions, Phys. Rev. 52: 1184-1187, 1984

Chew, C.K., Liang, T.Y., and Lo, S.Y., Particle Ratios at pp Collider, Phys. Rev. D20: 1003-1006, 1983

Lo, S.Y., and Li, Yang-Guo, Transverse Momentum Spectrum of Inclusive Reaction in Geometrical Picture, Phys. Rev. D28: 2756-2761, 1983

Lo, S.Y., and Li, Yang-Guo, A Unified Approach to Elastic Scattering and Inclusive Spectrum in Geometrical Picture, Nuovo Cim. Lett. D39: 33-37, 1984

Lai, C.H., and Lo, S.Y., and Phua, K.K., Possible Existence of Further Dip Structure on p and Kp Elastic Collisions, Phys. Rev. D27: 2214-2215, 1983

Lai, C.H., Lo, S.Y., and Phua, K.K., Determination of the Pion Form Factor at Larger Momentum Transfer Squared, Phys. Lett. B 122: 177-180, 1983

Lai, C.S., and Lo, S.Y., Alternative Formulation of the Interaction of Electromagnetic Radiation and Matter, Phys. Lett. 87A: 5-8, 1981

Desmond, P., and Lo, S.Y., Possible Tests of Meson as a Gauge Particle, Journal of Phys. G8: 319-332 , 1982

Lo, S.Y., and Chao, Wei-Gin, Nuovo Cim. 63A: 204-216, 1981

Lo, S.Y., Li, Y.I., and Lui, Y.P., Operator Formalism Geometrical Picture and Double Charge Exchange, Journal of High Energy Phys. and Nucl. Phys., China, 5: 653-663, 1981

Chang, Cha-Hsi, and Lo, S.Y., Structure of Multiparticles in Quark Jets, Nuovo Cim. V31: 157-162, 1981

Malone, M.M., and Lo, S.Y., Operator Form of Droplet Model and Neutral Current, Nuovo Cim. 57A: 320-333, 1980

Lo, S.Y., Desmond, P., and Kovac, E., General Self Dual Non-Abelian Plane Wave, Phys. Lett. 90B: 419-421, 1980

Chew, C.J., Lo, H.D., Lo, S.Y., and Phua, K.K., Particle Ratios-Quarks and Chao-Yang Statistics, J. Phys. G6: 17-24, 1980

Clarke, D.J., and Lo, S.Y., Spin Structure of Proton-Proton Scattering in the Current-Current Interaction Pacture, Phys. Lett. 87B: 379-382, 1979

Kovacs, E., and Lo, S.Y., Self-Dual Propagating Wave Solutions in Yang-Mills Guage Theory, Phys. Rev. D19: 3649-3653, 1979
Lo, S.Y., and Melia, F., Static Quark Potential, Nuovo Cim. 50A: 90-96, 1979
Kovacs, E., and Lo, S.Y., Index Summery of Classical Yang-Mills Fields, Phys. Rev. D19: 2966 2973, 1979

Clarke, D., and Lo, S.Y., The Appearance of the Second Dip in pp Scattering, Phys. Rev. D20: 193-201, 1979

Box, M.A., Lo, S.Y., McKeller, B.H.J., and Reich, M., The Application of the Rayleigh-Gans Approximation to Scattering by Polydisperson, Quarterly J. of the Royal Meteor Soc. 104: 959-969, 1978

Chew, C.D., Lo, S.Y., and Phua, K.K., Suppression Factor in the Decays of the ψ Family, Phys. Rev. 18: 2495, 1978

Kellett, B.H., Joshi, G.C., and Lo, S.Y., Factorization in the Central Region of Inclusive Reactions, Nuovo Cim. 47A:281-286, 1978

Melia, F., and Lo, S.Y., Linear Planar Wave Solutions of the Yang-Mills Theory, Phys. Rev. 77B: 71-72, 1978

Lo, S.Y., and Chang, C.Y., Classification of Weakly Interacting Particles, Lett. Nuovo Cim. 22: 567-572, 1978

Kellett, B.H., Joshi, G.C., and Lo, S.Y., Factorization in Inclusive Reactions II, Nuovo Cim. 41A: 351-358, 1977

Box, M.A., Lo, S.Y., Kellett, B.H., Joshi, G.C., and Lo, S.Y., Factorization in Inclusive Reactions, Nuovo Cim. 41A: 331-350, 1977

McKellar, B.H.J., and Reich, M.H., Atmospheric Turbidity and the Circular Solar Radiations, Applied Optics 16: 341-344, 1977

Malone, M.M., and Lo., S.Y., Quark Fragmentation Models, Nuovo Cim. 46: 455-467, 1978

Malone, M.M., and Lo, S.Y., Minimal Rule and Fragmentation Model, Phys. Rev. D16: 2184-2195, 1977

Lo, S.Y., Low, H.B., Phua, K.K., and Chan, S.C., The Implication of Chou-Yang Model in π Elastic Scattering, Phys. Rev. D17: 802-805, 1978

Lo, S.Y., A Classical Solution, Lett. Nuovo Cim. 44A:187-190, 1978

Lo, S.Y., and Lai, C.S., Study of Energy Dependence in Geometrical Models, J. Phys, G3: 465-472, 1976

Lo, S.Y., Joshi, G.C., and Kellett, B., Quark Gluon Model for Total Cross Section, Lett. Nuovo Cim. 17: 535, 1976

Lo, S.Y., and Thulborn, E., Hadron Form Factors, Phys. Rev. D16: 2251-2255, 1976

Lo, S.Y., Possible Origin of Zwig's Rule, Lett. Nuovo Cim. 17: 405-413, 1976

Box, M.A., and Lo, S.Y., Approximate Determination of Aerosol Size Distribution, Applied Meteorology 15: 1068-1076, 1976

Lo, S.Y., Fragmentation of Pion Near Phase Space Boundary, Nuovo Cim. 34A: 89-98, 1976

Lo, S.Y., On the New Quantum Number in Nieh-Wu-Yang's Theory, Phys. Rev. D13: 184, 1976

Lo, S.Y., Possible Selection Rules for the Decays of J,ψ and ϑ Phys. Rev. D11: 1358-1361, 1975

Lo, S.Y., Constraints of Disfavored Fragmentation, Phys. Rev. D11: 1358-1361, 1975

Lo, S.Y., Are Annihilations Processes Statistical? Nuovo Cim. V12: 542-544, 1975

Lo, S.Y., Phua, K.K., and Low, H.B., An independent Determination of SU(3) Couplings from Inclusive Reactions, Nuovo Cim. 30A: 221, 1975

Lo, S.Y., and Clarke, D., The Shift of Peaks and Dips of Elastic Scattering in Chou-Yang Model, Phys. Rev. D10: 1519-1526, 1974

Lo, S.Y., and Joshi, G., Factorization in Two Body Scattering, Nucl. Phys. 93: 405-415, 1975

Lo, S.Y., The Minimal Rule of Hadron Scattering, Lett. Nuovo Cim. 10:41-46, 1974

Lo, S.Y., and Noble, D., Study of K+p Inclusive Reaction at 10 Ge V/C, Nuovo Cim. 22A: 137-156, 1974

Lo, S.Y., Lai, C.S., and Noble, D., Gentle Fragmentation of Hadrons, Phys. Rev. D8: 1598-1602, 1973

Lo, S.Y., and Lai, C.S., Possible Consequences of Quark Model in Fragmentation Processes, Aust. J. Phys. 26: 291-299, 1972

Lo, S.Y., Selection Rules for Hadron Scattering, Lett. Nuovo Cim. V4: 262-266, 1972

Lo, S.Y., and Thompson, G.D., High Energy pp Scattering, Current-Current Interaction and Droplet Model, Lett. Nuovo Cim. V3: 223-226, 1972

Lo, S.Y., and Phua, K.K., Selection Rules for Inclusive Reactions, Phys. Lett. 38B: 415-418, 1972

Lo, S.Y., and Reid, A.W., πN Scattering in the Operator Droplet Model, Nucl. Phys. B36: 493-511, 1972

Lo, S.Y., The Forbidden Emission of Soft Pions at Asymptotic Energy, Lett. Nuovo Cim. V2: 1091-1095, 1971

Lo, S.Y., and Lai, C.S., Sum Rule for e -e + Annihilation and U(3) x U(3) Symmetry Breaking, J. Phys. A: 859-861, 1971

Lo, S.Y., and Lai, C.S., Symmetry Breaking Parameters under U(3) x U(3) and η-X mixing, Nuovo Cim. 4A: 198, 1971

Lo, S.Y., and Lai, C.S., Symmetry Breaking Under U(3) x U(3), Nuovo Cim. 4: 1037-1043, 1970

Lo, S.Y., The Factorization of Multipion Production, Lett. Nuovo Cim. 3: 555-558, 1970

Lo, S.Y., Chou-Yang Model, Current-Current Interaction and Nucleon-Nucleon Scattering, Nucl. Phys. B7: 286-300, 1970

Lo, S.Y., Zeros in the Droplet Model, Lett. Nuovo Cim. 2:124-126, 1969

Lo, S.Y., The Shape of Mesons, Nucl. Phys. 9B: 10-16, 1969

Lo, S.Y., The Neutron Form Factor, Phys. Lett. 27B: 308, 1968

Lo, S.Y., Field-Current Identity, Universality and K/13 Decay, Nucl. Phys. B7: 68-78

Lo, S.Y., Meson Production from Electron-Positron Annihilation, Phys. Rev. 148: 1431-1436

Lo, S.Y., and Freund, P.G.O., M(12) Prediction for PP Scattering, Phys. Rev. 140: B927-B928

Lo, S.Y., and Freund, P.G.O., Baryon-Antibaryon Scattering in the M(12) Symmetry Scheme, Phys. Rev. 140: B95-B96, 1965

Lo, S.Y., Sum Rules for Nonleptonic Weak Gamma-Ray of Baryons, Nuovo Cim. 37: 753-755, 1965

Review Papers:
Lo, S.Y., On the Accuracy of One Part in 10^{12} in Particle in Fields 2, Edited by Capri, A.Z. and Kamal, A.N., Plenum Press, 1983

Invited Papers:
Lo, S.Y., Paser, Pion Condensation and Centauro Events, Proceeding of International Symposium on Comic Ray Superhigh Energy

Interactions, Oct. 29-Nov. 3, 1986, Beijing, China, I-26 to I-51

Papers Presented at Conferences:
Leverton, P., and Lo, S.Y., A Determination of Proton Form Factor up to q2=200 GeV2/c2, paper submitted to XXII International Conference on High Energy Physics, Leipzig, DDR, 1984

Lam, C.S., and Lo, S.Y., Induced Transitions of Pions and Unusual Charge Distribution, paper submitted to XXII International Conference on High Energy Physics, Leipzig, DDR, 1984

Lam, C.S., and Lo, S.Y., Induced Production of Bosons and its Application to Centauro Events, paper submitted to XXII International Conference on High Energy Physics, Leipzig, DDR, 1984

Li, Yang-Guo, and Lo, S.Y., Nucleus Elastic Scattering at Energies up to 10_4 TeV, paper presented at Asia-Pacific Physics Conference, Singapore, June 12-18, 1983

Li, Yang-Guo, and Lo, S.Y., The Role Multiple Scattering in Inclusive Reactions, paper delivered at Asia-Pacific Physics Conference, Singapore, June 12-18, 1983

Lo, S.Y., Propagating Waves in Yang-Mills Guage Theory, Proceedings of International Conference of Particle Physics, Guanzhou, China, 1125-1130, 1980

Lo, S.Y., Clarke, K.J., and Malone, M.M., Spin Structure and Dip Development in Elastic Proton-Proton Scattering, University of Melbourne preprint, UM-P-79/49, Proceedings of International Conference of Particle Physics, Guanzhou, China pp 813-831, 1980

Lo, S.Y., Stringent Limit on Direct Coupling of Electron and Hadron, Proceedings of the 6th AINSE Nuclear Physics Conference, Abstract only, 1976

Lo, S.Y., Fragmentation Processes at High Energy, Fifth AINSE Nuclear Physics Conference, Australian National University, Canberra, Paper 43, Abstract only, 1974

Lo, S.Y., Geometrical Picture of Hadron Scattering, Proceedings of 1978 International Meeting of Frontiers of Physics, Singapore, Edited by Phua, K.K., *et al*, pp 939-970, 1978

Lo, S.Y., Classical Chromodynamics (CCD) A Derivation of Heavy Quark Bound States, Proceedings. of 1978 International Meeting on Frontier of Physics, Singapore, Edited by Phua, K.K., *et al*, 971-976,

1978 Lo, S.Y., Remarks on Bounds, Multiplicities and Energy

Dependence, Proceedings of Colloquium on High Multiplicities, pp I59, Edited by Krzywicke, A., *et al*, Laboratorie de Physique Ecole Polytechnique, Paris, 1970

Preprints and Unpublished Works:

Lo, S.Y., and Lai, C.S., Feynman's Path Integral Formalism, Dirac Equation and Nonintegratable Phase Factor, University of Melbourne Preprint UM-P-81/73

Malone, M.M., and Lo, S.Y., Development of Dips and Peaks in Elastic Scattering at Isabelle Energies, University of Melbourne Preprint UM-P-79/27

Lo, S.Y., Media, F., Warner, R.C., and Joshi, G.C., Derivation of the Heavy Quark Bound States from Classical Chromodynamics, University of Melbourne Preprint, UM-P-78/77

Lo, S.Y., Low, H.D., Phua, K.K., and Chan, S.C., Is the Asymptotic Value of the Ratio $\sigma T (\pi p)/ \sigma (pp)=2/3$ Sacred?

Box, M.A., Lo, S.Y., and MacKellar, B.H.M., Aerosol Parameter Determination from Turbidity Measurements using the Anomalous Diffraction Approximation, UM-P-76/3

Box, M.A., and Lo, S.Y., Tables of Turbidity Parameters for a Haze-H Aerosol, University of Melbourne Preprint UM-P-75/26

Lo, S.Y., Stringent Limit on Direct Coupling of Electron and Hadron, University of Melbourne Preprint UM-P-75/1

Lo, S.Y., A Model for Diffractive Excitation Processes, Rutherford Laboratory Preprint, RPP/A55,RPP/A 57, 1968

Lo, S.Y., The Path Approximation in Strong Interaction, Rutherford Laboratory Preprint RPP/A, 1966

Lo, S.Y., Electron as a Probe of Weak Interaction, Rutherford Laboratory Preprint RPP/14, 1966

Lo, S.Y., The Hypothesis of Spin-Unitary Sine, Independence in Hadron Scattering and Reactions Processes, EFINS 66-67, 1966 Thomas, E.A., and Lo, S.Y., Scalar Mesons as Higgs Particles, UM-P-83/19
PUBLICATIONS ON THE BASER PROJECT:

Tsao, C.C., Lobo, J.D., Okurmura, M., and Lo, S.Y., Generation of Charged Droplets by Field Ionization of Liquid He, submitted for publication

Lo, S.Y., Lobo, J.D., Blumberg, S., Dibble, T.S., Xu, Z., Tsao, C.C., and Okumura, M., Generation of Energetic He Atom Beams by a Pulsed Positive Corona Discharge, J. Appl. Phys. 81, Vol. 81: 5896-5904, 1997

Lo, S.Y., Highly Charged Superfluid Helium Cluster Beam, Int'l. J. Mod. Phys. B, Vol. 10: 713-727, 1996

Lo, S.Y., and Ruan, Tu-nam, Production of Coherent Bosons by Multiphoton Ionization Processes, submitted for publication

Lo, S.Y., and Ruan, Tu-nam, Enhancement of Nuclear Fusion Rate Among Coherent Bosons, submitted for publication

Lo, S.Y., and Ruan, Tu-nam, Quantum Stimulated Raman Scattering, accepted for publication in Communication in Theoretical Physics

Lo, S.Y., Enhancement of Nuclear Fusion in a Strongly Coupled Cold Plasma, Mod. Phys. Lett. B V16: 1207-1211, 1989

Publication on stable water clusters (I_E)Projects and Medial physics: Shui-yin Lo and Wenchong Li: Onsager's Formula, Conductivity, and Possible New Phase Transition, Modern Physics letters B, V .13(1999) 885-893
Shui-yin Lo, Anomalous state of Ice, Modern Physics Lett B, V 10(1996) 909-919
Shui-yin Lo, A. Lo, W.C. Li, Li T.H., Li H. H., and Xu Geng, Physical properties of water with I_E structures, Modern Physics Lett. B, v 10(1996) 921-930
Shui-yin Lo and B Bonavida: Proceedings of First Int. Sypm. Of Physical, Chemical, and Biological Properties of Stable Water (I_E) Clusters (World Scientific 1998)---Book
Shui-yin Lo and W. C. Li and S. H. Huang, Water clusters in Life, Medical Hypotheses (2000)v 54(6),948-953
Shui-yin Lo and W. C. Li, Nanostructures in very dilute aqueous solutions, Russian Mendelev Journal of Chemistry 541.6:54 145.3,p41-48
Shui-yin Lo, Stories of I_E crystal, color picture books, 100 pages, un-published
Shui-yin Lo, Biophysics Basis for Acupuncture and Health, Dragon Press, 2004, 285 pages.
Shui-yin Lo, Meridians in acupuncture and infrared imaging, Medical Hypotheses (2001) v58, 72-76
Shui-yin Lo, Left and Right symmetry in acupuncture, Acupuncture Today, June, 2003
Shui-yin Lo, Diabetic and Infrared Imaging, Acupuncture Today, to be published in November, 2003
Shui Yin Lo, Evidence for Exponential decay behavior in Pain Relief by Acupuncture, Medical Acupuncture, 2007
Shui Yin Lo, Evidence and mechanism of external qi in Chinese Medicine, to be published in Medical Acupuncture

Articles in Acupuncture Today

Can Emotion Be Quantified A*ugust, 2009 (Vol. 10, Issue 08)*
Molecular Basis of Meridians *April, 2009 (Vol. 10, Issue 04)*
Evidence of Instant Effect of External *Qi November, 2008 (Vol. 09, Issue 11)*
Acupoints for Thyroid Disorders *August, 2008 (Vol. 09, Issue 08)*
Customized Diagnosis, Instant Verification and Personalized Modality *April, 2008 (Vol. 09, Issue 04)*
Perfect Symmetry, Perfect Health *January, 2008 (Vol. 09, Issue 01)*
Warming Up and Cooling Down Simultaneously by External *Qi November, 2007 (Vol. 08, Issue 11)*
A Sign of Serious Disease: Heating Up the Body With External *Qi September, 2007 (Vol. 08, Issue 09)*
Oscillating Nature of Recovery From Serious Sickness
  July, 2007 (Vol. 08, Issue 07)
Predictive Power of Meridian Theory
  May, 2007 (Vol. 08, Issue 05)
Improve Your Brain With *Qi*
  March, 2007 (Vol. 08, Issue 03)
How Many Different Kinds of Lower Back Pain Are There?
  January, 2007 (Vol. 08, Issue 01)
Are You Ready for the Bird Flu Yourself?
  November, 2006 (Vol. 07, Issue 11)
How Soon Does Acupuncture Begin to Work?
  September, 2006 (Vol. 07, Issue 09)
Breast Cancer, Breast Abnormalities, and Infrared Imaging
  November, 2005 (Vol. 06, Issue 11)
Infrared Evidence for External *Qi*
  July, 2005 (Vol. 06, Issue 07)
Cancer, Acupuncture, and Infrared Imaging
  May, 2005 (Vol. 06, Issue 05)
How Does Moxibustion Work Scientifically?
  February, 2005 (Vol. 06, Issue 02)
What Is *Qi*? Can We See *Qi*?
  September, 2004 (Vol. 05, Issue 09)

What Are Acupoints? Can We See Them?
  May, 2004 (Vol. 05, Issue 05)
What Are Meridians? Can We See Them?
  March, 2004 (Vol. 05, Issue 03)
Old Pain, New Pain, Hot Pain and Cold Pain
  January, 2004 (Vol. 05, Issue 01)
Diabetes and Acupuncture
  November, 2003 (Vol. 04, Issue 11)
How Does Infrared Imaging Help Acupuncture?
  June, 2003 (Vol. 04, Issue 06)

Conference Contributions:
Lo, S.Y., Nuclear Fusion in a Strongly Coupled Cold Plasma, Bull.
Am. Phys. Soc. V34 No. 9 2162, 1989

Lo, S.Y., Enhancement of Nuclear Fusion from Coherent Deuterons,
Bull. Am. Phys. Soc. V34, No. 8 1811, 1989

Institute of Boson Studies Progress Reports
1991, IBS-91-1 to IBS-91-7, seven issues
1990, IBS-90-1 to IBS-90-12, twelve issues
1989, IBS-89-1 to IBS-89-12, twelve issues
1988, IBS-88-1 to IBS-88-12, twelve issues
1987, IBS-87-9 to IBS-87-12, four issues

BOOKS:

Lo, Shui-yin , Biophysics basis for acupuncture and health (Dragon eye press) 2004

LO, Ip, J.S., Lo, S.Y., Wong, C.Y., Joy of the Search for Knowledge, A Tribute to Professor Dan Tsui, 1999

Lo, S.Y., Bonavida, B., First International Symposium of on the Current Status of the Physical, Chemical, and Biological Properties of Stable Water (I_E) Cluster, edited by being published by World Scientific Publishing Co., Inc., 1997

Lo, S.Y., Scientific Studies of Chinese Character, by Guo Ming Newspaper Publishing Co., Beijing, China, in Chinese, 1987

Lo, S.Y., Geometrical Picture of Hadron Scattering, World Scientific Publishing Co., Singapore, 1986

Lo, S.Y., Unification in Physics, 400 typed pages, manuscript completed

PATENTS

Invented by Shui-Yin Lo: Three provisional US patents on medical devices and infrared imaging ,2001

Title	Application No.	Filing Date
A Method for Generating Nuclear Fusion Through High Pressure	US Patent 661,759	
Macroscopic Apparatus	US Patent 645,919	
Compact Vacuum Distillation Method	US Patent 638,608	
A Descalant Comprising Structure Liquid Solid	US Patent 587-880	
Compact Vacuum Distillation Device	US Patent 530,789	
		June 11, 1996
		May 14, 1996
Macroscopic Apparatus	US Patent 320,216	April 26, 1996
Forming Charges in a Fluid and Generation of a Charged Beam	US Patent 177,669	January 18, 1996
Emission Control Device (Air Intake System Device)	US Patent 941,778	
Method & Apparatus for Generating Nuclear Fusion Energy by Coherent Bosons	US Patent 801,804	September 20, 1995
Emission Control System	US Patent 554,279	
Method and Apparatus for Forming a Coherent Beam of Bosons with Mass	US Patent 4,875,213	
Forming Charges in Liquid and Generation of Charged Cluster	US Patent 338,706 US Patent 537,444	October 11, 1994

Enhanced Fusion Decay of Deuterium	US Patent 338,706	January 4, 1994
Method and Apparatus for Generating Energy	US Patent 337,020	September 9, 1992
Particle Accelerator	US Patent	
	US Patent 542,587	December 1, 1991
Creating Coherent Charged Bosons	US Patent 340,951	August 8, 1990
Nuclear Fusion Process	US Patent 338,707	
	US Patent 421,601	June 12, 1990
Production of Coherent Deuterons	US Patent 338,705	April 12, 1990
	US CIP 340,051	April 22, 1989
	US CIP 366, 890	May 4, 1989
Method and Apparatus Utilizing Decay of Coherent Bosons Plasma	US Patent 338,706	June 25, 1990
	US Patent 340,951	
Methods and Apparatus for Forming Coherent Clusters	US Patent 169/648	April 20, 1989
	PCT AU 89/00108	
Method and Apparatus for Cooling Electrons, Ions or Plasma	US Patent 103,631	April 13, 1989
	PCT AU88/00383	
Accelerator for Coherent Bosons	US Patent 4,926,436	October 16, 1989
Method and Apparatus for Producing Nuclear Energy	US Patent 203,678	April 14, 1988
	US Patent 338,706	
	US Patent 340,950	April 18, 1989
	US Patent 461,014	June 15, 1989

Electrical Conductor	US Patent 4,995,699	April 13, 1989 October 16, 1989
		March 18, 1988 March 17, 1989
Generating a Coherent Beam of Bosons	US Patent 035,734	October 1, 1987 September 30, 1988
	PCT AU 86/00212	October 4, 1990
	US CIP 343,176	June 7, 1988 April 11, 1989 April 20, 1989 January 4, 1990